Logic & Memory Experiments Using TTL Integrated Circuits—

Book 2

by

Peter R. Rony and David G. Larsen

Also Published as

Logic & Memory Experiments Using TTL Integrated Circuits

by E & L Instruments, Inc.

Howard W. Sams & Co., Inc.
4300 WEST 62ND ST. INDIANAPOLIS, INDIANA 46268 USA

Preface

We welcome you again to the "wonderful world of digital electronics." This is the second book in the Blacksburg Continuing Education Series™ that treats the 7400-series of TTL integrated-circuit chips. Most of the chips that you will be scrutinizing in this book use *medium scale integration* (MSI), which means the chips function as simple, self-contained logic systems that are comprised of up to 100 logic gates. Included in the MSI category are the decoders, counters, multiplexers, shift registers, memories, and arithmetic elements in the 7400-series chips. You will discover that it is quite easy to work with these more complicated chips, since much of the tedious and difficult wiring has been performed within the chip itself. You are left with the simple task of making a few external connections to logic switches, pulsers, lamp monitors, clocks, seven-segment LED displays, and other integrated-circuit chips.

This book is a laboratory-oriented text in a series of books that approach the field of electronics in a somewhat different manner. Rather than start you out with experiments in electronic *components,* such as resistors, capacitors, diodes, and transistors, as is so often done in introductory electronics courses, we introduce you instead to *integrated-circuit chips* immediately. You also are introduced immediately to the concepts of logic switches, lamp monitors, pulsers, and displays, and shown how you can use auxiliary functions. You are provided with many experiments that are based on connecting combinations of integrated-circuit chips and such devices. All this is done in *Logic & Memory Experiments Using TTL Integrated Circuits, Books 1 and 2.*

We again emphasize our conviction that digital electronics is not a difficult subject. You are not required to master difficult mathematical equations or specialized digital design techniques, such as Boolean algebra, state minimization, or Karnaugh mapping. Gates are inexpensive—four cents each—and you need not optimize your circuits. The 7400-series integrated-circuit chips can be considered to be the ABCs of digital electronics. With them, you can build almost any digital circuit given sufficient time, wire, pc boards, breadboarding sockets, and patience. At the completion of this book, you should test yourself by designing, constructing, and testing a digital circuit of modest complexity.

We have found wide acceptance of our books in formal classes as well as by individual users in the United States and abroad who find the experiment-based approach a much simplified way to learn digital electronics.

PETER R. RONY AND DAVID G. LARSEN

Contents

tive and Negative Edges—Inversion Circles—The 7474 D-Type
Positive-Edge–Triggered Flip-Flop—A Simple 7474 Circuit—Preset
and Clear Inputs—Edge- and Level-Triggered Flip-Flops—The 7474
Latch—Comparison of 7474 and 7475 Latches—The 74100 Latch—
The 74174 and 74175 D-Type Positive-Edge–Triggered Flip-Flops—
Hewlett-Packard Latch/Displays—Some Additional Flip-Flops—Mas-
ter-Slave Flip-Flops—J and K Inputs—The J-K Flip-Flop with Preset
and Clear—Manufacturer's Literature—Comparison of J-K Flip-Flops
—Comparison of Latches—The 74279 R-S Flip-Flop—Monostable
Multivibrators—The 74121 Monostable Multivibrator—The 74122
Retriggerable Monostable Multivibrator—The 74123 Dual Retrigger-
able Monostable Multivibrator—The 555 Monostable Multivibrator—
The 555 Astable Multivibrator—Introduction to the Experiments—
What Have You Accomplished in This Chapter?

CHAPTER 9

CHAPTER 10

APPENDIX

6

Light-Emitting Diodes and Light-Emitting Diode Displays

INTRODUCTION

In Book 1,Chapter 5, we were tempted to demonstrate the operation of a Hewlett-Packard 5082-7415 five-element LED display in
conjunction with a pair of 7490 decade counters, a 7442 bcd-to-
decimal decoder, and a 7448 bcd-to-seven-segment decoder/driver.
Such a circuit, which will be given in the experimental section in
this chapter, would have demonstrated the use of sequencers and
decoder/drivers at the same time.

We concluded, however, that the experiment was a bit too complicated to wire from scratch without understanding some of the
basic principles of light-emitting diodes (LED), cathodes, anodes,
and the like. In this chapter, we have decided to give a brief description of three kinds of light-emitting diode devices,

- A simple light-emitting diode (LED)
- Two different seven-segment light-emitting diode (LED) displays, one with a common *anode* and the other with a common
  cathode
- A five-element seven-segment LED display manufactured by
  Hewlett-Packard and used in all of their elegant pocket calculators

Our discussion of LEDs will not be comprehensive. For further
information, we refer you to a very readable book on the subject,
LED Circuits & Projects, by Forest M. Mims, III, Howard W. Sams
& Co., Inc., Indianapolis, Indiana, 1973. While recommending books,

let us not forget one which we have found to be extremely useful in aiding the novice to develop an understanding of transistor-transistor logic (TTL) circuits, *TTL Cookbook*, by Donald E. Lancaster, Howard W. Sams & Co., Inc., Indianapolis, Indiana, 1974.

OBJECTIVES

At the completion of this chapter, you will be able to do the following:

- Construct a lamp monitor using a simple light-emitting diode, an npn transistor, and two resistors.
- Construct a seven-segment LED display using both a common cathode and a common anode red numeric display.
- Construct a five-digit seven-segment LED display.
- Demonstrate the operation of a MAN-2A 7 × 5 dot matrix display.
- Use a five-state sequencer to sequence the five digits in a five-digit seven-segment display and the five columns in a 7 × 5 dot matrix display.

DEFINITIONS

anode—The positive electrode; the element to which the principal stream of electrons flows.[1]

cathode—The negative electrode; the element from which the principal stream of electrons flows. When a semiconductor diode is biased in the forward diode, the cathode is that terminal of the diode which is negative with respect to the other terminal.[1]

current-limiting resistor—A resistor inserted into an electric circuit to limit the flow of current to some predetermined value.[1]

diode—An electronic device that allows current to pass in one direction but not in the opposite direction.

dot matrix—A matrix of dots that can be individually lighted to produce symbols, letters, and numerals.

forward bias—An external voltage applied in the conducting direction of a pn junction. The positive terminal is connected to the p-type region and the negative terminal to the n-type region.[1]

light-emitting diode—A pn junction that emits light when biased in the forward direction.[1]

numeric display—A display that can only display the digits 0 through 9.

reverse bias—An external voltage applied to a semiconductor pn junction to reduce the flow of current across the junction and thereby widen the depletion region. It is the opposite of forward bias.[1]

seven-segment display—An electronic display that contains seven lines or segments spatially arranged in such a manner that the digits 0 through 9 can be represented through the selective lighting of certain segments.

transistor—An active semiconductor device, usually made of silicon or germanium, having three or more electrodes. The three main electrodes are the emitter, base, and collector.[1]

WHAT IS A DIODE?

A *diode* is a semiconductor, an electronic device that allows current to pass in one direction but not in the opposite direction. The schematic symbol for a diode is shown in Fig. 6-1.

Fig. 6-1. Schematic symbol for a diode.

The arrow indicates the typically used convention in electronics that current can flow from a positive potential ($+$) in the direction of a negative potential ($-$). Thus, if we had the situation shown in Fig. 6-2, current would flow. When a significant current flows

Fig. 6-2. Forward biased diode.

$+5V$ ─────▶│───── GND

across a diode, we state that the diode is *forward biased*. On the other hand, if we had the situation presented in Fig. 6-3, no current would flow. We state that this particular diode is *reverse biased*.

Fig. 6-3. Reverse biased diode.

GND ─────▶│───── $+5V$

Two important terms that are used when discussing the properties of diodes are the terms *anode* and *cathode*. For a typical diode, the anode and cathode are as shown in Fig. 6-4. Based on these definitions for anode and cathode, we can make the following important conclusions:

Fig. 6-4. Semiconductor diode anode and cathode relationship.

Anode ─────▶│───── Cathode

- A *diode will block current flow when its anode is negative with respect to its cathode* (*reverse biased*).
- A *diode will conduct current when its anode is positive with respect to its cathode* (*forward biased*).

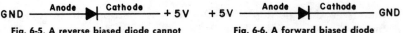

| Fig. 6-5. A reverse biased diode cannot conduct current. | Fig. 6-6. A forward biased diode conducts current. |

Thus, in the Fig. 6-5, the diode is reverse biased and will not conduct current. In Fig. 6-6, the diode is forward biased and will conduct a current.

WHAT IS A LIGHT-EMITTING DIODE?

A *light-emitting diode,* or *LED,* is simply a diode that emits light when it is forward biased and can conduct a current. The symbol for a light-emitting diode is given in Fig. 6-7. The anode and cathode ends of the LED (Fig. 6-8) are the same as they are for an ordinary diode.

Fig. 6-7. Schematic symbol for a light-emitting diode (LED).

Fig. 6-8. LED anode and cathode relationship.

Finally, there are two similar conclusions that can be made regarding the operation of a light-emitting diode.

- A *light-emitting diode (LED) will emit light when its anode is positive with respect to its cathode (forward biased).*
- A *light-emitting diode (LED) will not emit light when its anode is negative with respect to its cathode (reverse biased).*

Fig. 6-9. A forward biased LED emits light.

Thus, in Fig. 6-9, the LED is forward biased and will emit light. In Fig. 6-10, the LED is reverse biased and will not emit light.

Fig. 6-10. A reverse biased LED does not emit light.

WHAT IS A CURRENT-LIMITING RESISTOR?

All diodes, including light-emitting diodes, are rather delicate semiconductor devices that can burn out if too high a potential difference is applied across the anode and cathode. When working with LEDs, it is mandatory that a *current-limiting resistor* be provided to restrict the current through the LED to a level that will not burn it out yet at a level that would permit sufficient light to be emitted from the LED.

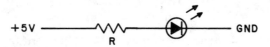

+5V ——————/\/\/——————(▶|)— GND
R

Fig. 6-11. LED and current-limiting resistor in series.

Let us consider Fig. 6-11 which shows a diagram for a light-emitting diode. The LED is connected to a +5-volt power source and has a current-limiting resistor, R, in series with it. A current-limiting resistor is required to reduce the current through the LED. In analyzing this situation, remember that the LED also has an equivalent resistance at constant current. This resistance must be taken into account when computing the current through the circuit. Thus, we can schematically represent the above circuit by its equivalent, as shown in Fig. 6-12.

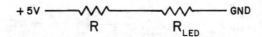

+5V ——————/\/\/——————/\/\/—— GND
R   R$_{LED}$

Fig. 6-12. Equivalent circuit for a current-limiting resistor and an LED.

Now, recalling Ohm's law, we can write

$$5 \text{ volts} = I(R + R_{LED})$$

where I is the current through resistor R and through light-emitting diode resistance R_{LED}. For a typical red-emitting LED composed of the semiconductor material gallium-arsenide-phosphide, GaAsP, experience has shown that the quantity IR_{LED} is equal to approximately 1.8 volts.

$$IR_{LED} = 1.8 \text{ volts}$$

Therefore, substituting this result into the above equation, we obtain

$$3.2 \text{ volts} = IR$$

We are now in a position to decide what I must be and then compute the required current-emitting resistor, R. Again from experience, we know that the current in a continuously operating LED should be approximately 5 mA to 40 mA, where the term *mA* represents milliamperes, or one-thousandth of an ampere. Let us choose a current of 20 mA, or

$$I = 20 \text{ mA} = 0.020 \text{ A}$$

Our final result for the current-limiting resistor is

$$R = 3.2 \text{ volts}/0.020 \text{ ampere}$$
$$= 160 \text{ ohms}$$

In general, resistors of 100 ohms to 500 ohms are quite effective as current-limiting resistors. In case there is any question concerning what the specific value R should be, start with a high value and decrease the value until the light intensity emitted from the LED is satisfactory. Try to operate at the highest possible value of R to minimize current drain on your power supply or lantern battery. In general, we use either a 220-ohm resistor or a 330-ohm resistor.

A LIGHT-EMITTING DIODE AS A LAMP MONITOR

One of the reasons that we have decided to discuss LEDs and LED displays is to provide you with the ability to make your own lamp monitors and seven-segment LED displays. As a first application for an LED, let us construct a lamp monitor.

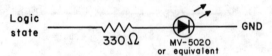

Fig. 6-13. Simple lamp monitor.

The simplest possible lamp monitor circuit consists of an LED, such as an MV-5020 or equivalent, a 330-ohm resistor, and several wires. When wired as shown in Fig. 6-13, the LED is capable of detecting both a logic 0 state and a logic 1 state. For example, a logic 1 input to the circuit will light the LED (Fig. 6-14), whereas a logic 0 input to the circuit will cause the LED to remain unlit (Fig. 6-15).

For completeness, it should be noted that the LED will be unlit for two other possible conditions that may occur if you incorrectly wire the circuit (Fig. 6-16).Therefore, if you can make the LED light, you know that you are on the right track.

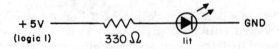

Fig. 6-14. A logic 1 input lights the LED.

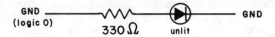

Fig. 6-15. A logic 0 input causes the LED to be unlighted.

The problem with the above lamp monitor circuit, however, is that it requires too much current to operate and thus acts as a current drain on the output of an integrated-circuit chip. *In many*

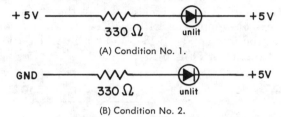

(A) Condition No. 1.

(B) Condition No. 2.

Fig. 6-16. A reverse biased LED is unlighted.

situations, the above circuit is entirely acceptable as a lamp monitor, but in some situations, it is desirable to reduce the input current to the circuit. This can be done by the simple expedient of adding an npn transistor and a current-limiting resistor to the base of the

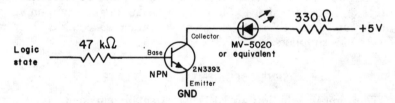

Fig. 6-17. A useful lamp monitor circuit requiring very low input current.

transistor. We are not prepared to discuss here the operation of a transistor, why we use the symbol given below, or why the transistor is called "npn." We simply wish to present a circuit that is highly effective as a lamp monitor. The circuit is shown in Fig. 6-17.

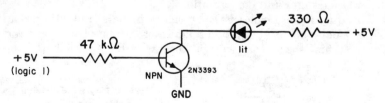

Fig. 6-18. A logic 1 input to the lamp monitor lights the LED.

Let us compare the behavior of the two circuits that we have for a lamp monitor. The first circuit requires only an LED and a 330-ohm resistor, but draws, according to our measurements, a total of 9 mA for a logic 1 state. The second circuit requires an LED, an npn transistor, a 330-ohm resistor, and a 47K resistor and draws only 0.09 mA, or 90 microamperes. Despite this low current drain from the integrated circuit, the current through the LED is still approximately 9 mA for a logic 1 state input to the circuit. Thus, the light intensity for both circuits is the same for a logic 1 state, yet the second circuit draws one-hundredth the amount of current. With this second circuit, the LED will be lit when a logic 1 state is applied at the input (Fig. 6-18), and not lit when a logic 0 state is applied at the input (Fig. 6-19).

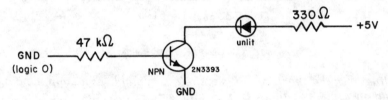

Fig. 6-19. With a logic 0 input to the lamp monitor, the LED is unlighted.

Occasionally, you may need one or more extra lamp monitors. The preceding circuits show you how to make them. Light-emitting diodes are currently quite inexpensive, under 25 cents each from electronics suppliers.

SEVEN-SEGMENT LED DISPLAYS

The typical red-emitting LED has a small semiconductor wafer electrically mounted on a metal base and to which a small thin wire is attached at the top (Fig. 6-20). The assembly is potted with clear epoxy plastic lens in a configuration such that the small emitting area appears to the eye as a much larger area. The reason for the epoxy lens is related to a property of light known as the index of refraction. Consult *LED Circuits & Projects* for a discussion of LED packages and configurations.

The question is, can LEDs be made in bars and other shapes which could be used for other kinds of displays? The answer is yes. The first shape that we will discuss is the "bar" shape, seven

Fig. 6-20. Diagram of a typical light-emitting diode.

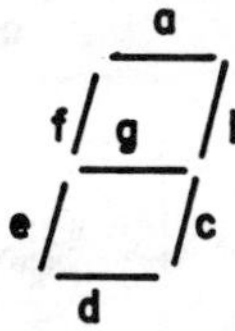

Fig. 6-21. Segments in a typical
seven-segment display.

of which can be assembled to produce what is known as the *seven-segment LED display*, shown in Fig. 6-21. This display was shown previously, but we shall discuss it in greater detail here. Note that there is usually a decimal point in addition to the seven segments a, b, c, d, e, f, and g. In Chapter 5, it was shown how to create any decimal numeral between 0 and 9 simply by lighting only certain segments. For example, the number "4" can be obtained by lighting segments b, c, f, and g (Fig. 6-22). A wide variety of inexpensive seven-segment LED displays can now be obtained from hobby sources.

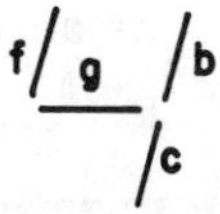

Fig. 6-22. Numeral 4 can be obtained by
selectively lighting segments b, c, f, and g.

THE OPCOA SLA-1 COMMON ANODE RED
NUMERIC LED DISPLAY

The pin configuration of the Opcoa SLA-1 seven-segment red numeric LED display is shown in Fig. 6-23. The SLA-1 display is schematically represented in Fig. 6-24, and electronically represented in Fig. 6-25.

The symbol for a light-emitting diode is used to represent each of the seven segments as well as the decimal point (DP). The following conclusions can be drawn from the preceding diagrams:

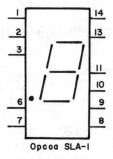

Fig. 6-23. Opcoa SLA-1 common anode red
numeric LED display pin configuration.

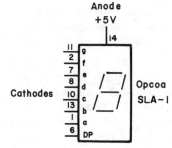

Fig. 6-24. Schematic representation for
Opcoa SLA-1 display.

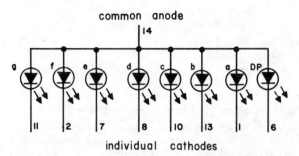

Fig. 6-25. Electronic representation of Opcoa SLA-1 display.

- Pins 4, 5, and 12 are missing from the 14-pin DIP chip.
- There is a common anode at pin 14. You set this anode at +5 volts.
- There are a total of eight individual cathodes, seven for the segments a, b, c, d, e, f, and g, and one for the decimal point.
- There are no electrical outputs from the 14-pin DIP chip. Everything is an input. The only "output" from the display is light from the LEDs.

We now come to an important question: How do we wire the display so that we can light the various segments correctly? This question will be answered in the following section.

THE 7447 BCD-TO-SEVEN-SEGMENT DECODER/DRIVER

In this section, we shall demonstrate how to do the following:

- Light a single segment on a seven-segment LED display by grounding one of the cathodes with the aid of a suitably chosen current-limiting resistor.
- Light a group of segments on the LED display by grounding several of the cathodes using identical and suitably chosen current-limiting resistors.
- Light any decimal number between 0 and 9 using a 7447 bcd-to-seven-segment decoder/driver.

Let us first light a single segment on the LED display. This can be done by applying +5 volts at the common anode and by connecting a current-limiting resistor between ground and any of the individual cathodes on the SLA-1 display. According to our measurements on such a circuit, a resistance of 100 ohms will allow 22 mA of current through the segment, whereas a resistance of 150 ohms will allow only 15 mA. The segment becomes dimmer only when a 330-ohm resistor is employed; such a resistor drops the cur-

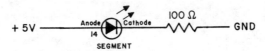

Fig. 6-26. Typical lighted segment in the Opcoa SLA-1 display.

rent through the LED segment to 8 mA. The segment is brightly lit and readable in all three cases, however.

If you connect 100-ohm resistors between ground and pins 13, 10, 2, and 11, respectively, a decimal numeral "4" will appear on the display. A typical segment has the circuit diagram shown in Fig. 6-26, and the complete circuit required to produce decimal 4 is shown in Fig. 6-27.

The important point in the preceding discussion is the need to ground the cathodes on the SLA-1 display. You need a decoder and, perhaps, a decoder/driver that will provide a logic 0 state for those segments that must be lit. This is accomplished using the 7447 bcd-to-seven-segment decoder/driver. The 7447 truth table is given in Table 6-1. For decimal 3, segments a to d and g are at a logic 0 state.

Table 6-1. Truth Table for the 7447 BCD-to-Seven-Segment Decoder/Driver Integrated Circuit

Decimal Numeral	Inputs				Outputs						
	D	C	B	A	a	b	c	d	e	f	g
0	0	0	0	0	0	0	0	0	0	0	1
1	0	0	0	1	1	0	0	1	1	1	1
2	0	0	1	0	0	0	1	0	0	1	0
3	0	0	1	1	0	0	0	0	1	1	0
4	0	1	0	0	1	0	0	1	1	0	0
5	0	1	0	1	0	1	0	0	1	0	0
6	0	1	1	0	0	1	0	0	0	0	0
7	0	1	1	1	0	0	0	1	1	1	1
8	1	0	0	0	0	0	0	0	0	0	0
9	1	0	0	1	0	0	0	0	1	0	0

With the aid of current-limiting resistors, the 7447 decoder/driver gives a decimal "3" on the LED display; provided, of course, that the DCBA input into the 7447 chip is 0011_2. The circuit diagram is shown in Fig. 6-28. By the application of the proper binary coded

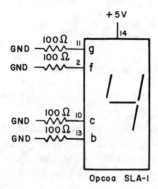

Fig. 6-27. Complete circuit for lighting the numeral 4 in the Opcoa SLA-1 display.

decimal word at the DCBA inputs, it is possible to produce 0, 1, 2, 3, 4, 5, 6, 7, 8, and 9 on the Opcoa SLA-1 display. The operation of the decoder/driver and display should be clear from a knowledge of the truth table given previously.

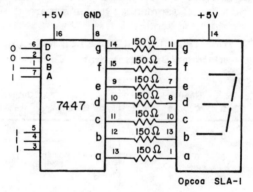

Fig. 6-28. Schematic for a 7447 decoder/driver and Opcoa SLA-1 common anode display; the bcd input corresponds to the numeral 3.

THE LITRONIX DATA-LIT 704 COMMON CATHODE RED NUMERIC LED DISPLAY

The pin configuration for the Litronix Data-Lit 704 seven-segment red numeric display is given in Fig. 6-29. The 704 is schematically represented in Fig. 6-30, and electronically represented in Fig. 6-31, where again we use the symbol for an LED to represent each of the seven segments and the decimal point (DP). As was done with the Opcoa SLA-1, the following conclusions can be drawn:

- The pin configuration of the Data-Lit 704 is different from the SLA-1.

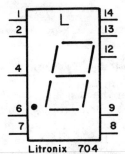

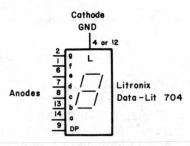

Fig. 6-29. Pin configuration for Litronix Data-Lit 704 common cathode red numeric LED display.

Fig. 6-30. Schematic for Litronix Data-Lit 704 display.

- Pins 3, 5, 10, and 11 are missing from the 14-pin DIP chip.
- There is a common cathode both at pin 4 and pin 12. A connection to either pin will do. You set this cathode to ground potential.
- There are a total of eight individual anodes, seven for the segments a, b, c, d, e, f, and g, and one for the decimal point.
- There are no electrical outputs from the 14-pin DIP chip. Everything is an input. The only "output" from the display is light from the LEDs.

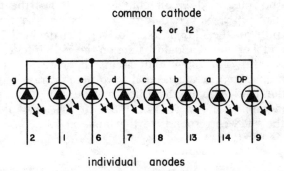

Fig. 6-31. Electronic representation of Litronix Data-Lit 704 display.

In the following section, we describe how you can wire the Litronix Data-Lit 704 display.

THE 7448 BCD-TO-DECIMAL DECODER/DRIVER

If you wish to light a single segment on the Litronix Data-Lit 704 display, you can use the circuit in Fig. 6-32.

First, apply a connection to ground at the common cathode and connect a 100-ohm current-limiting resistor between +5 volts and

Fig. 6-32. Typical lighted segment in the Litronix 704 display.

any of the individual common anodes on the display. A resistance of 100 ohms allows 26 mA through the segment; this is a bit high. A 150-ohm current-limiting resistor will reduce this current to 18 mA, a 330-ohm resistor will reduce it still further to 8 mA. A segment is brightly lit only for the 100-ohm and 150-ohm resistors, but it is still somewhat difficult to distinguish it from a neighboring unlit segment. The Litronix Data-Lit 704 is inferior in readability to the Opcoa SLA-1.

If you connect 330-ohm resistors between +5 Volts and pins 13, 8, 1, and 2, respectively, a number 4 will appear on the display. The complete circuit required to produce number 4 is given in Fig. 6-33.

You must connect each anode to +5 Volts with a current-limiting resistor in order to light a segment. This is just the reverse of the Opcoa SLA-1 display, where you had to ground the cathode input to a segment. To light any numeral between 0 and 9, a decoder or decoder/driver is needed that will provide a logic 1 state for each segment that must be lit. The 7448 bcd-to-seven-segment decoder/driver is the integrated-circuit chip to use. It has the truth table given in Table 6-2. Notice that the outputs are the complements of the outputs for the 7447 decoder/driver. For decimal 5, segments a, c, d, f, and g are all at a logic 1 state on the 7448 integrated circuit, whereas on the 7447 integrated circuit they are all at a logic 0 state. The final step in this section is to demonstrate how you can connect the 7448 chip to the Litronix Data-Lit 704 display. The wiring diagram is shown in Fig. 6-34. In this example, the bcd input to the 7448 corresponds to the numeral 5.

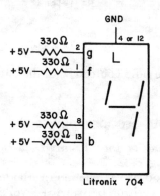

Fig. 6-33. Complete circuit for lighting numeral 4 in the Litronix 704 display.

Table 6-2. Truth Table for the 7448 BCD-to-Seven-Segment Decoder/Driver Integrated Circuit

Decimal Numeral	D	C	B	A	a	b	c	d	e	f	g
0	0	0	0	0	1	1	1	1	1	1	0
1	0	0	0	1	0	1	1	0	0	0	0
2	0	0	1	0	1	1	0	1	1	0	1
3	0	0	1	1	1	1	1	1	0	0	1
4	0	1	0	0	0	1	1	0	0	1	1
5	0	1	0	1	1	0	1	1	0	1	1
6	0	1	1	0	1	0	1	1	1	1	1
7	0	1	1	1	1	1	1	0	0	0	0
8	1	0	0	0	1	1	1	1	1	1	1
9	1	0	0	1	1	1	1	1	0	1	1

Note that you do not connect the current-limiting resistors between the two 14-pin DIP chips; rather, you use the resistors as "pull-up" resistors and tie them all to +5 volts. The outputs of the 7448 integrated circuit are *open-collector* outputs (see Chapter 7) and require this type of connection.

With this circuit, it is possible to produce the decimal numerals 0, 1, 2, 3, 4, 5, 6, 7, 8, and 9 provided that you choose the proper values for the DCBA inputs to the 7448. You can use the 7448 truth

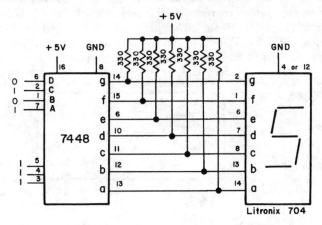

Fig. 6-34. Schematic for 7448 decoder/driver and Litronix 704 common cathode display.

table in Table 6-2 to confirm the operation of the seven-segment LED display.

THE HEWLETT-PACKARD FIVE-DIGIT SEVEN-SEGMENT SOLID-STATE NUMERIC INDICATOR

So far, we have discussed the characteristics of single-digit red numeric LED displays. You can construct a five-digit LED display simply by arranging five single-digit LED displays side by side and by making the appropriate wire connections. Or, you can employ a multi-digit LED display, such as the Hewlett-Packard five-digit seven-segment red numeric display, which is a 14-pin DIP containing a cluster of five digits (Fig. 6-35).

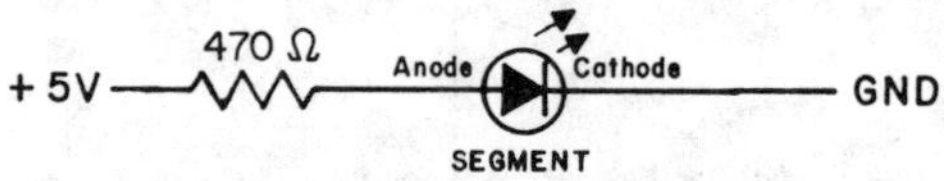

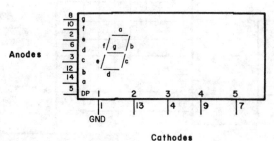

$$+ 5V \underset{470\,\Omega}{-\!\!\!\bigwedge\!\!\!\bigwedge\!\!\!-} \quad \text{Anode} \quad \text{Cathode} \quad -\!\!\!\text{GND}$$

SEGMENT

Fig. 6-35. Pin configuration of Hewlett-Packard five-digit seven-segment common cathode red numeric display.

The schematic representation for the five-digit display is shown in Fig. 6-36. Note that there are eight anodes, including the decimal point, and five cathodes, and a total of 35 different segments plus five different decimal points. You can select any one of the 40 light-emitting diodes by choosing one of the eight anodes and one of the five cathodes. In effect, you have an 8-by-5 input matrix to the five-digit seven-segment display.

As with the preceding Litronix 704 display, you can light a single segment by connecting the common cathode to ground and the anode through a current-limiting resistor, R, to +5 volts. The specifications for this five-digit display, which is listed by Hewlett-Packard as 5082-7415, indicate that the maximum average current per segment should be 5 mA. Using the following current-limiting resistors, we have measured the following LED currents (Table

Fig. 6-36. Schematic of Hewlett-Packard five-digit seven-segment display.

**Table 6-3. Measured Values for the LED Segment Current
as a Function of the Current-Limiting Resistor**

Current-Limiting Resistor (ohms)	Observed Current (mA)
100	28
330	10
470	7
1000	2.3

6-3). With a current of 28 mA, the segment is extremely bright and gives the impression that it might burn out at any moment. On the other hand, currents of 7 mA or 8 mA are acceptable for the continuous operation of any segment. We recommend the use of a current-limiting resistor that is no less than 330 ohms (Fig. 6-37).

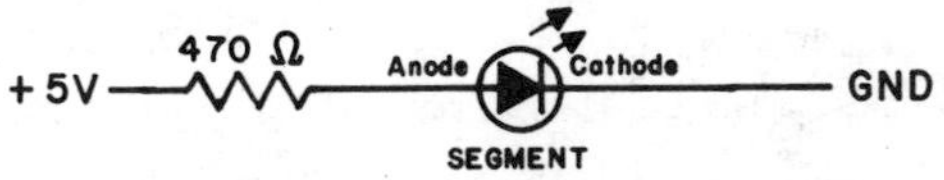

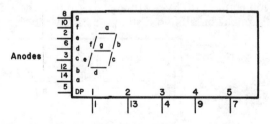

Fig. 6-37. Typical lighted segment in the Hewlett-Packard five-digit seven segment display.

Fig. 6-38 is a schematic representation of the pins required to light the first digit in the five-digit display. This representation closely resembles the Litronix Data-Lit 704 single-digit common-cathode numeric display discussed previously. If you wish to light the numeral 4 on the Hewlett-Packard display, connect 470-ohm resistors between pins b, c, f, and g and +5 Volts, as shown in Fig. 6-39.

Next step, connect the abcdefg inputs to the Hewlett-Packard five-digit display to the abcdefg outputs from the 7448 bcd-to-seven-segment decoder/driver (Fig. 6-40), as you did with the Litronix Data-Lit 704 (Fig. 6-34). You again use the 470-ohm

Cathodes

Fig. 6-38. To light first digit on the left, ground cathode at pin 1 and apply appropriate logic states to eight anodes.

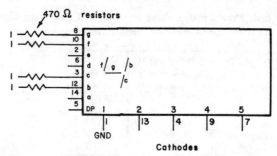

Fig. 6-39. Example of lighting the numeral 4 as first digit on the left.

resistors as pull-up resistors that are connected to +5 volts. Note the similarity between this circuit and the one shown in Fig. 6-34. The bcd input to the 7448 corresponds to numeral 8.

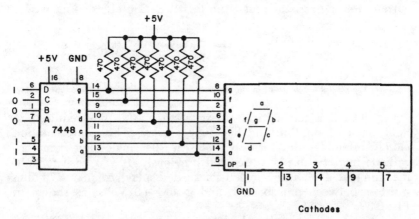

Fig. 6-40. Schematic for 7448 decoder/driver and Hewlett-Packard five-digit seven-segment display.

Your remaining task is to learn how to scan all five digits on the display. If you connect all five cathodes to ground, the same numeric reading will appear on all five displays, as shown in Fig. 6-41. Thus,

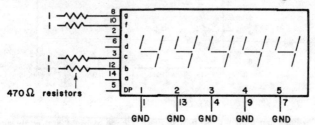

Fig. 6-41. Example of lighting the numeral 4 at all five digit positions.

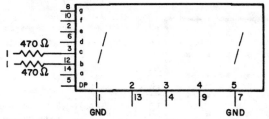

Fig. 6-42. Example of lighting the numeral 1 at digit position 1 and 5.

you must scan the digits one at a time and *leave sufficient time intervals between digits for the abcdefg inputs to be changed.* In Figs. 6-42 and 6-43, we show situations in which more than one digit is lit for the same set of inputs to the display.

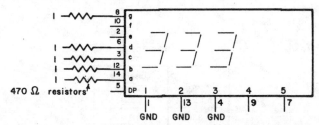

Fig. 6-43. Example of lighting the numeral 3 at digit positions 1, 2, and 3.

The trick is to construct a sequencer that sequences the five digits in any manner desired. It is customary to sequence the display starting with either the least-significant digit at the right or the most-significant digit at the left. Each time the circuit sequences to a new digit, it simultaneously receives new digital information at the eight anodes so that it can determine which number and whether a decimal point should be displayed. You will perform such an experiment later using a 7490 decade counter, a 7442 bcd-to-decimal decoder, and a 7404 inverter in addition to the Hewlett-Packard 5082-7415 display and a 7448 decoder/driver.

THE MONSANTO MAN-2A 0.32-INCH RED ALPHANUMERIC DISPLAY

As our final display, we will describe the Monsanto MAN-2A 0.32-inch red alphanumeric display, which is a seven-row by five-column matrix plus a decimal point. It is mounted on a dual in-line 14-pin substrate with a clear epoxy lens, as shown in Fig. 6-44. According to the manufacturer's specifications, the maximum current through a single LED is 20 mA. Using the experimental setup shown in Fig. 6-45, we have determined the current for several different

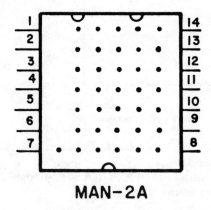

Fig. 6-44. Pin configuration of MAN-2A dot matix display.

MAN-2A

Table 6-4. Measured Values for the LED Dot Current

R (ohms)	Observed Current (mA)
330	10
470	7
1000	2.3

Fig. 6-45. A lighted dot in the MAN-2A dot matrix display requires a current-limiting resistor.

values of the current-limiting resistor, R (Table 6-4). A 330-ohm current-limiting resistor gives ample brightness for each dot in the matrix.

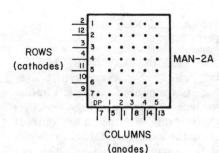

Fig. 6-46. Schematic representation of the MAN-2A dot matrix display inputs.

Fig. 6-47. Typical lighted dot in the MAN-2A dot matrix display. See Fig. 6-48 for dot location.

The MAN-2A display is known as a 7 × 5 *dot matrix,* a term which accounts for the fact that there are seven rows and five columns. A schematic representation of the 14-pin display is shown in Fig. 6-46; row 1, column 1 is in the upper left-hand corner and row 7, column 5 is in the lower right-hand corner. If you wish to

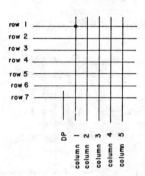

Fig. 6-48. Location of the lighted dot for the circuit in Fig. 6-47.

light the upper left-hand dot in the matrix of 35 dots, you simply use the circuit in Fig. 6-47 to obtain the result shown in Fig. 6-48. On the other hand, if you desire to light the four corners of the matrix, use the circuit in Fig. 6-49 to obtain the result shown in Fig. 6-50. The amazing characteristic of the 7 × 5 dot matrix is that

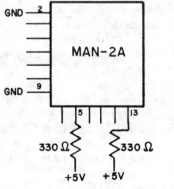

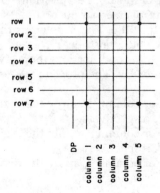

Fig. 6-49. Circuit for lighting four dots on the MAN-2A dot matrix display.

Fig. 6-50. Location of the four lighted dots for the circuit in Fig. 6-49.

it can be used to represent the entire 64-character half-ASCII code described previously in Book 1, Chapter 5. In addition to the letters of the alphabet, symbols such as [,], !, ", #, $, %, &, ', (,), *, +, ,, -, ., /, :, ;, =, ?, etc., can be represented. Examples are shown in Table 6-5.

The lighting of the MAN-2A alphanumeric display requires sophisticated integrated-circuit chips. A discussion of such chips is beyond the scope of this book. However, it is appropriate to summarize the principles whereby an actual alphanumeric readout is produced on the display. Let us consider the letter "T" which we wish to light on the 7 × 5 dot matrix. If we assume that the letter dots are defined by a logic 0 state and the background by a logic 1 state, then we wish to obtain the matrix of logic states shown in Fig. 6-51, which lead to the letter "T", shown in Fig. 6-52, as a

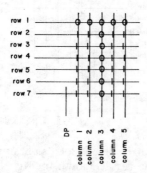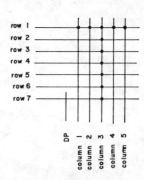

Fig. 6-51. Logic states corresponding to capital letter T in a common cathode MAN-2A dot matrix display.

Fig. 6-52. Location of the lighted dots for capital letter T in a 5 × 7 dot matrix display.

series of dots. The question now is how do we maintain such a display over a period of time sufficient for the naked eye to read the letter "T"? The problem is that the diodes do not stay lit permanently, but must be *refreshed* or "relighted" about one hundred times a second so that they give the impression that they are lit permanently. The procedure is as follows:

- For column 1, apply the digital word 0111111 to rows 1 through 7, respectively.
- For column 2, apply the digital word 0111111 to rows 1 through 7, respectively.
- For column 3, apply the digital word 0000000 to rows 1 through 7, respectively.
- For column 4, apply the digital word 0111111 to rows 1 through 7, respectively.

Table 6-5. Letters, Numerals, and Symbols Produced on 7-Row by 5-Column Dot Matrix Display

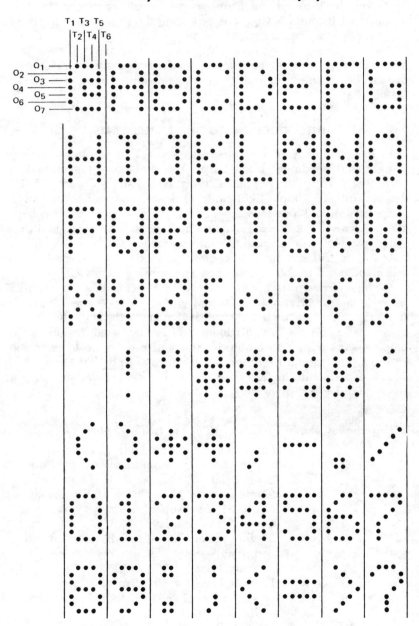

- For column 5, apply the digital word 0111111 to rows 1 through 7, respectively.
- Cycle back to column 1 and repeat the above process for columns 1 through 5. Continue repeating the process one hundred times per second for each column.

We use a 0, 1, 2, 3, 4, sequencer to cycle among the five columns. We shall give an example of the above procedure in an experiment in this chapter.

INTRODUCTION TO THE EXPERIMENTS

In this chapter, you will construct circuits that employ a variety of light-emitting diode (LED) displays, including the Opcoa SLA-1, Litronix Data-Lit 704, Hewlett-Packard 5082-7415, Monsanto MAN-2A, as well as a simple light-emitting diode. You will learn how a lamp monitor and a seven-segment LED display operate. This chapter requires some knowledge about choosing resistors; a section that will assist you is attached to this introduction.

It is easy to burn out a light-emitting diode, so be very careful when you perform the experiments. The only cause of LED burnout is *too high a current in the diode.* Never connect a diode or segment in a display directly to +5 volts and ground. Always use a current-limiting resistor to minimize excessive currents through the diodes or segments. If you are in doubt concerning what resistance to employ, start with a 1000-ohm resistor and proceed to lower value resistors. You should never go below a resistance of 100 ohms.

The experiments in this chapter can be summarized by stating the type of LED display studied. Thus,

Experiment No.	Type of LED Display
1	Simple light-emitting diode (LED)
2	Construction of a lamp monitor from a simple LED
3	Single segment in an Opcoa SLA-1 display
4	Opcoa SLA-1 display
5	Opcoa SLA-1 display
6	Single segment in a Litronix Data-Lit 704 display
7	Litronix Data-Lit 704 display
8	Litronix Data-Lit 704 display
9	Single segment in a Hewlett-Packard 5-digit display
10	Hewlett-Packard 5-digit display

11	Hewlett-Packard 5-digit display
12	Single dot in a Monsanto MAN-2A display
13	Monsanto MAN-2A display
14	Monsanto MAN-2A display

You should enjoy many of these experiments. If you are familiar with analog electronics, obtain an ammeter in the 0- to 30-mA range and measure the currents that pass through the diode segments and dots.

Choosing Resistors

The subject of fixed composition resistors properly belongs in a discussion of analog electronics. Nevertheless, you will need to know something about how to read values of resistors from the different colored bands that are painted on them.

A typical resistor, whether it be rated for ⅛ watt, ¼ watt, or 2 watts, has a series of four bands painted on one end of the resistor, as shown in Fig. 6-53. The bands indicate both the resistance value as well as the "tolerance" of the resistance value. Thus, we have the following:

Fig. 6-53.

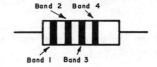

Band 1—is the first digit of a two significant digit number. The colors correspond to the following decimal numbers:

Black	0
Brown	1
Red	2
Orange	3
Yellow	4
Green	5
Blue	6
Violet	7
Gray	8
White	9

Band 2—is the second digit of a two significant digit number. The colors correspond to the same decimal numbers given for Band 1 above.

Band 3—is the power of ten by which the two-digit number must be multiplied in order to obtain the correct total resistance value. The colors correspond to the following powers of ten:

Black	1
Brown	10
Red	100
Orange	1000
Yellow	10,000
Green	100,000
Blue	1,000,000
Violet	10,000,000
Gold	0.1
Silver	0.01

Band 4—is the tolerance of the resistor, i.e., how close the resistance value of the resistor is to that stated on the series of bands. The colors correspond to the following tolerances:

Gold	±5%
Silver	±10%
No Band	±20%

It is useful to give several examples of resistors that you will use in this and subsequent chapters. The following resistors have a tolerance of ±10% (silver band).

100 ohms:	red-red-brown-silver $= 22 \times 10$
220 ohms:	red-red-brown-silver $= 22 \times 10$
330 ohms:	orange-orange-brown-silver $= 33 \times 10$
470 ohms:	yellow-violet-brown-silver $= 47 \times 10$
1000 ohms:	brown-black-red-silver $= 10 \times 100$
4700 ohms:	yellow-violet-red-silver $= 47 \times 100$
10,000 ohms:	brown-black-orange-silver $= 10 \times 1000$
47,000 ohms:	yellow-violet-orange-silver $= 47 \times 1000$
100 kilohms:	brown-black-yellow-silver $= 10 \times 10,000$
1 megohm:	brown-black-green-silver $= 10 \times 100,000$
10 megohms:	brown-black-blue-silver $= 10 \times 1,000,000$

EXPERIMENT NO. 1

Purpose

The purpose of this experiment is to demonstrate the operation of a simple red light-emitting diode (LED) such as the MV-5020 or the equivalent.

Schematic Diagrams of Circuits (Fig. 6-54)

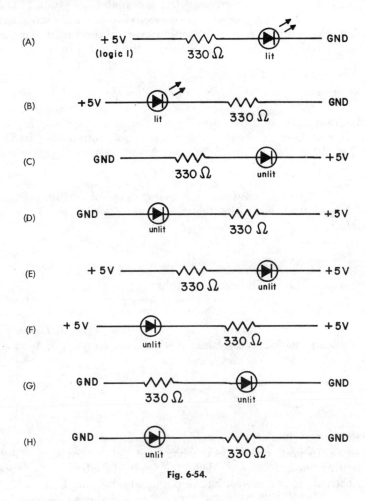

Fig. 6-54.

Step 1

The object of this experiment is to light the LED without burning it out. You can protect the LED from burnout by making sure that a 330-ohm resistor is present in the circuit somewhere between ground potential and +5 volts. Either a 220-ohm or 470-ohm resistor can be used in place of the 330-ohm resistor.

Connect the 330-ohm resistor to +5 volts with the other end of the resistor connected to one of the 128 sets of five interconnected terminals on the solderless breadboard. Connect a wire between an adjacent set of five interconnected terminals and ground. Then, insert the LED so that one end is connected to the 330-ohm resistor and the other end is grounded. Apply power to the breadboard and answer in the space below whether or not the LED is lit.

If the answer is yes, then your circuit is represented by diagram (A) in Fig. 6-54. If the answer is no, then your circuit is represented by diagram (D). If the answer is no, simply reverse the LED. It should now become lighted. If it does not, either the LED is faulty or there is something wrong with your source of power.

Step 2

Wire the LED as shown in schematic diagram in Fig. 6-54B. It should light with approximately the same intensity as Fig. 6-54A produced.

Step 3

Wire the LED as in diagrams in Figs. 6-54C, D, E, F, G, and H. In each case, the LED should not light.

Step 4

Draw a picture in the following space of the LED that you used and indicate which connection is the anode and which is the cathode.

Question

1. Define, in your own words, what is meant by the term, "light-emitting diode." In your definition, indicate whether the anode or cathode is at a more positive potential when the LED is lit.

EXPERIMENT NO. 2

Purpose

The purpose of this experiment is to demonstrate the use of an npn transistor as an LED driver that reduces the current drain from an integrated circuit.

Schematic Diagrams of Circuits (Fig. 6-55)

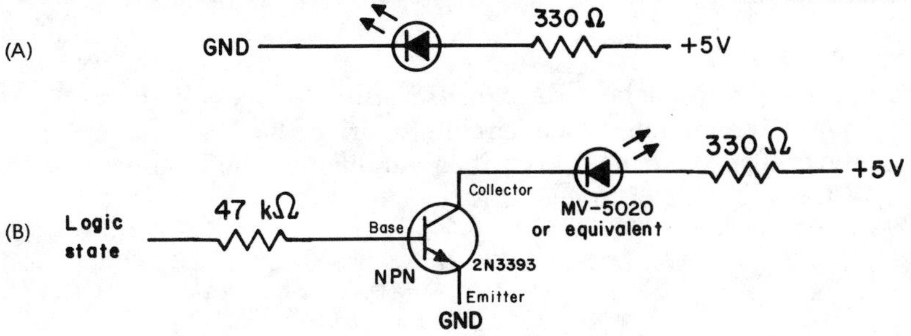

(A)
GND
330 Ω
+5V
(B)
Logic state
47 kΩ
Base
Collector
Emitter
NPN
2N3393
330 Ω
+5V
MV-5020 or equivalent
GND

Fig. 6-55.

Step 1

Identify the *base* (B), *collector* (C), and *emitter* (E) wires on the npn transistor that you are using. Wire the circuit as shown in Fig. 6-55A and apply power to the breadboard. The LED should light.

Step 2

Disconnect the power to the breadboard and now add the npn transistor and 47K resistor to the circuit of Step 1. Transistors are generally very sensitive electronic devices that can be easily burned out, so please be careful.

Step 3

At the input to the base of the transistor, apply a logic 1 state. The LED should light.

Next, apply a logic 0 to the base of the transistor that is connected to the 47K resistor. The LED should be unlit.

Step 4

If you have a volt-ohm milliammeter (vom), you may wish to measure the current to the base of the transistor for the logic 1 state. The circuit is shown in Fig. 6-56. The measured current should

Logic state
47 kΩ
A
VOM set to 1–10 mA position
NPN
2N3393
GND
330 Ω
+5V

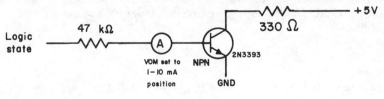

Fig. 6-56.

be approximately 50 to 200 microamperes, much smaller than 9 milliamperes.

Question

1. Can you suggest how the npn transistor reduces the current required for an integrated circuit to drive the LED? Hint: The npn transistor acts as a current amplifier. Explain the function of the 47K resistor in your answer.

EXPERIMENT NO. 3

Purpose

The purpose of this experiment is to light a single segment in a common-anode red numeric seven-segment LED display. In this experiment, you will use the SLA-1 LED display.

Schematic Diagram of Circuit (Fig. 6-57)

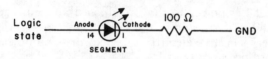

Fig. 6-57.

Step 1

This is a simple experiment. Gently press the seven-segment LED display chip into the SK-10 socket. Find the common anode and, with the power to the breadboard disconnected, wire it to +5 volts. Connect a 100-ohm to 330-ohm resistor between ground and segment a on the display. Apply power to the breadboard and observe that the segment lights.

Step 2

Now connect the resistor to +5 volts. The segment should no longer be lit. In the following space, explain why the segment is not lit.

The reason is that either there is no potential difference across the segment or the segment is reverse biased.

Step 3

Each cathode segment requires its own 100-ohm resistor between the input pin to the segment and ground. In the space below, explain why it is inadvisable to connect each cathode to ground without the aid of a resistor. For example, if you should do such a thing, the circuit would be as follows:

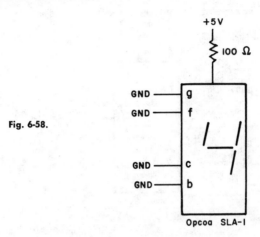

Fig. 6-58.

The circuit in Fig. 6-58 is incorrect! Explain why in the following space.

To answer this question, you should refer to the electronic representation provided in Fig. 6-25. The current through the 100-ohm resistor is split four ways into segments b, c, f, and g in Fig. 6-58. Thus, the current through an individual segment is one-fourth the total current. As a consequence, the segment intensity is much less. Such intensity would also vary with the number of segments that are lit.

Question

1. How many 100-ohm resistors would you need to light the numeral 4? The numeral 1? The numeral 9? The numeral 8?

EXPERIMENT NO. 4

Purpose

The purpose of this experiment is to light the numeral 4 using four 100-ohm resistors and an Opcoa SLA-1 common-anode seven-segment LED display.

Schematic Diagram of Circuit (Fig. 6-59)

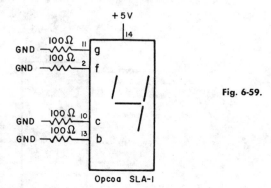

Fig. 6-59.

Step 1

This experiment is an extension of Experiment No. 3. Wire the circuit shown in Fig. 6-59. Apply power to the breadboard and observe that the numeral 4 becomes lit.

Questions

1. You have seven 100-ohm resistors in your possession and wish to wire the numeral 6. What input pins on the Opcoa SLA-1 display do you connect to ground using the resistors? How many resistors are required?

2. Repeat Question 1 for the numeral 7.

3. Repeat Question 1 for the numeral 3.

4. Repeat Question 1 for the numeral 2.

5. Repeat Question 1 for the decimal point.

6. Repeat Question 1 for the numeral 8.

EXPERIMENT NO. 5

Purpose

The purpose of this experiment is to demonstrate the use of the 7447 bcd-to-seven-segment decoder/driver in conjunction with the Opcoa SLA-1 seven-segment LED display.

Pin Configuration of Integrated Circuit (Fig. 6-60)

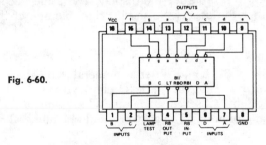

Fig. 6-60.

7447

Schematic Diagram of Circuit (Fig. 6-61)

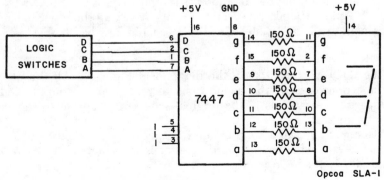

Fig. 6-61.

Step 1

With the power to the breadboard disconnected, wire the above circuit. Seven identical resistors in the 100-ohm to 470-ohm range are satisfactory replacements for the 150-ohm resistors shown. Be careful that none of the seven resistors contact each other. You might light or blank two segments, if a pair of resistors do touch. Once you wire this circuit and correctly demonstrate its operation, you will understand why the seven-segment LED display works the way it does.

Step 2

With the four logic switches set at DCBA = 0000, apply power to the breadboard. You should observe decimal 0 on the display.

With the four logic switches set at DCBA = 1111, explain whether or not you see a number on the display.

The display should be blank.

Step 3

Fill in the truth table for the display. Write the decimal numeral or symbol that you observe in the far right column of the following table.

Step 4

Set DCBA = 0111 and observe numeral 7 on the display. Now ground input pin 3 on the 7447 IC chip. This is the LAMP TEST input pin. It lights all seven segments. What numeral do you observe with this pin grounded? The answer should be numeral 8.

Step 5

Set DCBA = 0111 and again connect pin 3 to a logic 1 state. Now ground input pin 4 on the 7447 IC chip. This is the BLANKING INPUT pin. It blanks all seven segments by setting the input to each segment to a logic 1 state. The display should now be blank.

Step 6

Set DCBA = 0000 as in the diagram in Fig. 6-62. All the other connections, except the connections to pins 4 and 5 on the 7447 chip, are the same as in the original schematic diagram to this experiment.

Connect pin 4 to a lamp monitor. Apply power to the breadboard and observe whether the lamp monitor is lit or not when pin 5 on the 7447 is at a logic 1 state.

The lamp monitor should be lit.

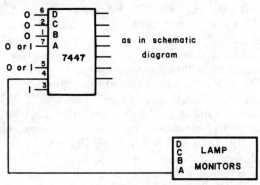

Fig. 6-62.

D	C	B	A	Numeral or Symbol
0	0	0	0	0
0	0	0	1	1
0	0	1	0	
0	0	1	1	
0	1	0	0	
0	1	0	1	
0	1	1	0	
0	1	1	1	
1	0	0	0	
1	0	0	1	
1	0	1	0	
1	0	1	1	
1	1	0	0	
1	1	0	1	
1	1	1	0	
1	1	1	1	blank

Step 7

With DCBA = 0000, ground pin 5 on the 7447 IC chip. Now the lamp monitor should not be lit. With pin 5 still grounded, set DCBA to any value except 0000. In all cases, you should observe that the lamp monitor becomes lit.

You now may ask, What is the purpose for pin 4 on the 7447 chip? It is at a logic 0 state only when DCBA = 0000 and pin 5 is grounded. The answer is that the output from pin 4 is used as a RIPPLE BLANKING INPUT to other 7447 chips to eliminate unnecessary zeros. Keep in mind that a lit segment or group of segments draw power and thus cause a drain on a battery. If we have a number such as 00067.90000 on a calculator, it would be quite useful to eliminate all the forward and trailing zeros to obtain 67.9. We save considerable power by doing so. Most good calculators and other battery-powered digital electronic devices with seven-segment LED readouts have this feature. They achieve the desired result in different ways, however.

To repeat the results from this experiment, pin 4 will be at logic 0 only when both DCBA = 0000 and pin 5 is at logic 0 state. Also, pin 3 must be at a logic 1 state.

Question

1. What is the logic state of input pins 3, 4, and 5 when they are unconnected? Does the answer to this question explain why you do not always observe either a totally lit or totally blank LED display?

EXPERIMENT NO. 6

Purpose

The purpose of this experiment is to light up a single segment in the Litronix Data-Lit 704 common-cathode seven-segment LED display.

Schematic Diagram of Circuit (Fig. 6-63)

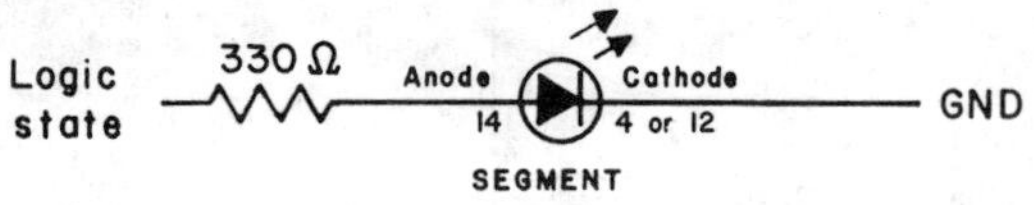

Fig. 6-63.

Step 1

Gently press the seven-segment Litronix LED display into the SK-10 socket. Wire the common cathode, either pin 4 or pin 12, to ground. Connect a 100- to 330-ohm resistor between pin 14, the *a* segment, and +5 Volts. Apply power to the breadboard and observe that the segment becomes lit.

Step 2

Now connect the 330-ohm resistor to ground. The segment should no longer be lit. In the following space, draw a circuit that explains why the segment is not lit.

Step 3

Each anode requires its own 330-ohm resistor between the input pin and +5 Volts. In the following space, explain why it is inadvisable simply to use a single 330-ohm resistor connected between pin 4 and ground, with the input anode segments tied directly to +5 Volts. To illustrate this point, we show the circuit in Fig. 6-64. It is incorrect!

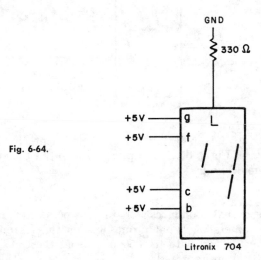

Fig. 6-64.

To answer this question, you may wish to refer to the electronic representation in Fig. 6-31. The current through a single segment will depend on how many other segments are also lit. The diode segments, in effect, function as a group of parallel resistors that are in series with the 330-ohm resistor. According to Ohm's law, the more diodes in parallel, the lower will be the current through each of them. The numeral 1 will be brighter than the numeral 8.

Question

1. Compare the properties of the common anode Opcoa SLA-1 display with the common cathode Litronix Data-Lit 704 display. In what way are these two types of seven-segment red numeric displays different?

EXPERIMENT NO. 7

Purpose

The purpose of this experiment is to light the numeral 4 using four 330-ohm resistors and a Litronix Data-Lit common cathode seven-segment LED display.

Schematic Diagram of Circuit (Fig. 6-65)

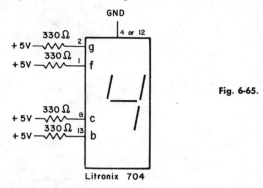

Fig. 6-65.

Step 1

This experiment is an extension of Experiment No. 6. Wire the circuit shown in Fig. 6-65 and apply power to the breadboard. The numeral 4 should be lit.

Questions

1. You have seven 330-ohm resistors in your possession and desire to wire the numeral 6. What input pins on the Litronix Data-Lit 704 display do you wire to +5 volts using these resistors? How many resistors are required?

2. Repeat Question 1 for the numeral 7.

3. Repeat Question 1 for the numeral 3.

4. Repeat Question 1 for the numeral 2.

5. Repeat Question 1 for the decimal point.

6. Repeat Question 1 for the numeral 8.

EXPERIMENT NO. 8

Purpose

The purpose of this experiment is to demonstrate the use of the 7448 bcd-to-seven-segment decoder/driver in conjunction with the Litronix Data-Lit 704 LED display.

Pin Configuration of Integrated Circuit (Fig. 6-66)

Fig. 6-66.

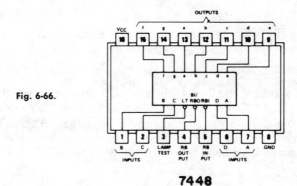

7448

Schematic Diagram of Circuit (Fig. 6-67)

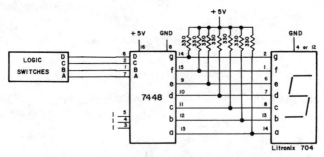

Fig. 6-67.

Step 1

Wire the above circuit with the power to the breadboard disconnected. As in Experiment No. 5, be careful that none of the seven resistors contact each other. Hollow plastic tubing known as *spaghetti* or *noodles* can be used to cover the resistor leads.

Step 2

Set the four logic switches DCBA to 0000 and apply power to the breadboard. You should observe a decimal 0 on the display. When DCBA = 1111, the display should be blank.

Step 3

Fill in the following truth table for the display. Write the numeral or symbol that you observe in the far right column.

Step 4

Set DCBA = 0111 and observe the numeral 7 on the display. As you did in Experiment No. 5 with the 7447 chip, ground input pin 3 on the 7448 decoder/driver. This is the LAMP TEST input pin, and it should light all seven segments when grounded. You should observe a numeral 8 when pin 3 is grounded.

Step 5

With DCBA = 0111, connect pin 3 to a logic 1 state but ground pin 4 on the 7448 chip. Pin 4 is the BLANKING INPUT pin which, when at a logic 0 state, blanks all seven segments by setting the input to each segment to a logic 0 state. The display should be blank.

D	C	B	A	Numeral or Symbol
0	0	0	0	0
0	0	0	1	
0	0	1	0	
0	0	1	1	
0	1	0	0	
0	1	0	1	
0	1	1	0	
0	1	1	1	
1	0	0	0	
1	0	0	1	
1	0	1	0	
1	0	1	1	
1	1	0	0	
1	1	0	1	
1	1	1	0	
1	1	1	1	blank

Step 6

As shown in Fig. 6-68, connect pin 3 to a logic 1 state, pin 4 to a lamp monitor, and pin 5 to a logic 1 state. Also set DCBA = 0000. The lamp monitor should be lit.

Set DCBA to any other value and observe that the lamp monitor remains lit.

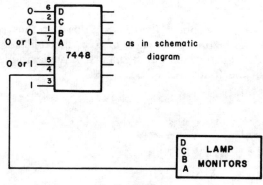

Fig. 6-68.

Step 7

With DCBA = 0000, ground pin 5 on the 7448 chip. The lamp monitor should not now be lit. With pin 5 still grounded, set DCBA to any value except 0000 and observe that the lamp monitor becomes lit again.

Pin 4 will be at a logic 0 state only when DCBA = 0000, pin 3 is at logic 1, and pin 5 is at logic 0. As we explained in Experiment No. 5, this feature, where the output from pin 4 is used as a RIPPLE BLANKING INPUT to other 7448 chips, serves to blank out segments that have zeros, thus conserving power.

Questions

1. Can you draw a schematic diagram for three or four 7448 or 7447 chips that demonstrates how the RIPPLE BLANKING IN-PUT capability is used to blank out leading or trailing zeros? Do so in the following space. You can omit the connections to the seven segments, the ABCD connections, and the power connections. Just explain or demonstrate how pins 3, 4, and 5 are connected together from one chip to another.

2. What is the logic state of input pins 3, 4, and 5 on the 7448 chip when they are left unconnected?

3. How would you connect five 7448 chips together so that you could test the segments in each of five different seven-segment LED displays for burned out segments? Give a simple schematic diagram in the following space.

EXPERIMENT NO: 9

Purpose

The purpose of this experiment is to light up a single segment in the Hewlett-Packard 5082-7415 five-digit seven-segment LED display.

Schematic Diagram of Circuit (Fig. 6-69)

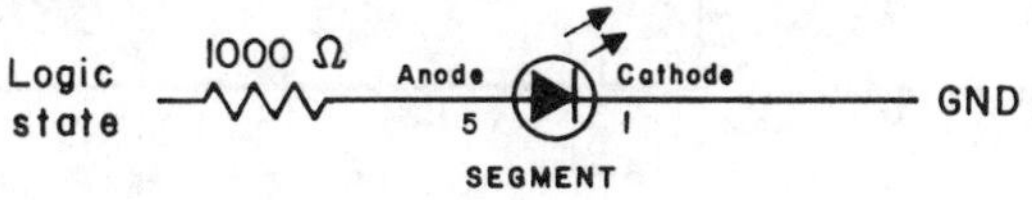

Fig. 6-69.

Step 1

Gently press the five-digit seven-segment display into the breadboard. Connect pin 1 to ground and pin 5 through a 1000-ohm resistor to +5 Volts. Apply power to the breadboard and demonstrate that the decimal point becomes lit.

Step 2

Now connect the 1000-ohm resistor to ground. The decimal point should become unlit.

Step 3

With the 1000-ohm resistor connected to +5 Volts at one end, touch in turn the following pins: 5, 14, 12, 3, 6, 2, 10, and, finally, 8. By doing so, you should successively light up the decimal point and the seven segments in the first digit of the five-digit display.

Questions

1. What pin must you connect to ground in order to light the third digit from the left side of the display?

2. What pin must you connect to ground in order to light the fourth digit from the left side of the display?

EXPERIMENT NO. 10

Purpose

The purpose of this experiment is to light the numeral 4 in each of the five digits on the Hewlett-Packard 5082-7415 five-digit seven-segment LED display.

Schematic Diagram of Circuit (Fig. 6-70)

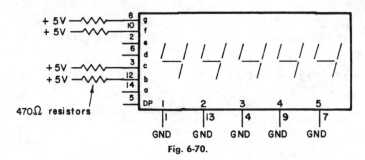

Fig. 6-70.

Step 1

Wire the circuit as shown and apply power to the breadboard. You should see a series of five dimly lit decimal 4s on the display.

Step 2

Eliminate the connection from pin 1 and ground. The numeral 4 in the first digit on the far left should disappear and the remaining numeral 4s should appear a little brighter.

Step 3

Eliminate the connection from pin 13 and ground as well. Now only three numeral 4s should be lit, all a little brighter than observed in Step 2.

Step 4

Eliminate the connections between ground and pins 1, 13, 4, and 9. Now only a single numeral 4 should remain. At what digit does it appear? Is it brighter than the 4s which you observed in Steps 2 and 3?

Step 5

What pin must be grounded in order to make the numeral 4 appear in the middle digit? Test your prediction.

What pin must you ground to make the 4 appear in the second digit from the left? Try it.

Questions

1. Why do you believe that the digits become dimmer as more decimal 4s are present?

2. Can you think of any good use for five digits each exhibiting the same decimal numeral? If your answer is yes, please explain. If your answer is no, please go to the next question.

3. How would you make the five-digit display read the number 59037? What type of connections would be required to obtain such a result? This is a difficult question. Answer it if you have time.

4. What problems do you have in making the number 59037 appear on the Hewlett-Packard five-digit seven-segment display that you do not have with a group of five separate 7447/seven-segment LED pairs? In other words, why is it more difficult to operate the Hewlett-Packard display than it is to operate five 7447/Opcoa SLA-1 displays?

5. What advantage does the Hewlett-Packard five-digit display have over the Opcoa SLA-1 display or the Litronix Data-Lit 704 display?

EXPERIMENT NO. 11

Purpose

The purpose of this experiment is to demonstrate how the Hewlett-Packard five-digit seven-segment LED display can be sequenced using a 7442 bcd-to-decimal decoder and a 7490 decade counter.

The numbers on the display will change between 0 and 9 with the aid of a 7448 decoder/driver and 7490 decade counter. Four integrated circuits and one five-digit display are required in this experiment.

Pin Configurations of Integrated Circuits (Figs. 6-71 through 6-74)

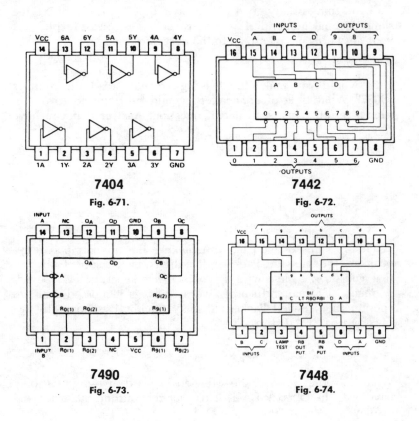

7404
Fig. 6-71.

7442
Fig. 6-72.

7490
Fig. 6-73.

7448
Fig. 6-74.

Schematic Diagram of Circuit (Fig. 6-75)

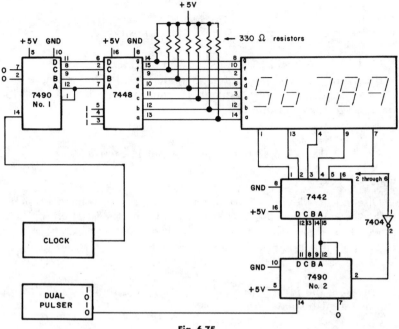

Fig. 6-75.

Step 1

With the power to the breadboard disconnected, wire the above circuit. It can fit nicely on a single breadboarding socket. We have found it advantageous to situate the five-digit display in the center of the board, a 7448 chip on its right, followed by a 7490 counter, and a 7442 chip to the left of the display, followed by a 7490 counter and, finally, a 7404 hex inverter chip. With such a setup, only short wire interconnections are required between the chips.

Step 2

One of the most important connections in the circuit is the one between pin 1 on the 7404 inverter and either pin 2, 3, 4, 5, or 6 on the 7442 chip. During the course of the experiment, you will vary the pin location on the 7442 chip. This is the only wire connection that you will vary in the circuit.

Step 3

Connect pin 2 on the 7442 chip to pin 1 on the 7404 chip. Apply power to the breadboard. In the following space, describe what

53

you observe. (NOTE: *Do not forget to connect pins 14 and 7 on the 7404 to +5 volts and ground, respectively.*)

We observed counting from 0 to 9 at digit position 1.

Step 4

Press and release the pulser repeatedly. Do you observe any change in the five-digit display? If your answer is yes, describe the change that you observe.

We observed no change from the behavior in Step 3.

Step 5

Disconnect the power to the breadboard. Now connect pin 3 rather than pin 2 on the 7442 chip to pin 1 on the 7404 chip. Apply power to the breadboard, repeatedly press and release the pulser; explain what happens in the following space.

By pressing the pulser, we could choose either digit 1 or digit 2 on the five-digit display.

Step 6

Disconnect the power to the breadboard. Now connect pin 4 rather than pins 2 or 3 on the 7442 chip to pin 1 on the 7404 chip. Apply power to the breadboard, repeatedly press and release the pulser, and note the difference in behavior on the five-digit display. Explain what you observe in the following space.

By pressing the pulser, we could choose either digit 1, digit 2, or digit 3 on the five-digit display.

Step 7

Disconnect the power to the breadboard. Now connect pin 5 rather than pins 2, 3, or 4 on the 7442 chip to pin 1 on the 7404 chip. Apply power to the breadboard, repeatedly press and release the pulser, and note what happens. Describe your observations in the following space.

We could choose digit 1, digit 2, digit 3, or digit 4.

Step 8

Finally, connect pin 6 rather than pins 2, 3, 4, or 5 on the 7442 chip to pin 1 on the 7404 chip. Apply power to the breadboard, repeatedly press and release the pulser, and observe the final change in the experiment. Describe what you see in the following space.

We could choose any of the five digits for the counting sequence from 0 to 9.

Questions

1. The circuit in this experiment contains a decimal counter, a sequencer, and a decoder-driven five-digit display. Which chips do the sequencing? Which chip does the counting? Which chip is the decoder/driver for the display?

2. In your own words, and on a separate piece of paper, explain the behavior of the circuit in this experiment.

EXPERIMENT NO. 12

Purpose

The purpose of this experiment is to light a single dot on the MAN-2A 7 × 5 dot matrix alphanumeric LED display.

Schematic Diagrams of Circuit (Figs. 6-76 and 6-77)

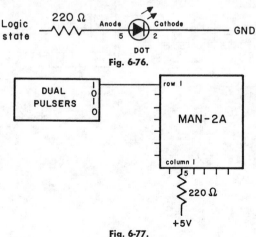

Fig. 6-76.

Fig. 6-77.

Step 1

With the power to the breadboard disconnected, wire the above circuit. Only a single 220-ohm resistor and a single wire connection are required. A 150- or 330-ohm resistor could be used instead of the 220-ohm resistor.

Step 2

Apply power to the breadboard and repeatedly press and release the pulser. The dot should light when you press the pulser, and should extinguish when you release the pulser. You may wish to substitute a 1000-ohm resistor for the 220-ohm resistor and demonstrate that it is still possible to see the illuminated dot.

EXPERIMENT NO. 13

Purpose

The purpose of this experiment is to use the MAN-2A alphanumeric display as an aid in the determination of truth tables for the 7447/7448 decoder/driver integrated-circuit chips. *Save this circuit for the following experiment!*

Pin Configurations of Integrated Circuits (Figs. 6-78 and 6-79)

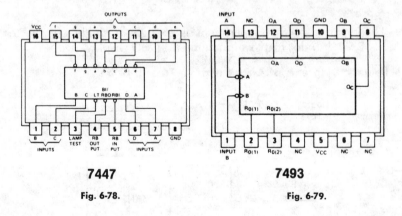

7447   **7493**

Fig. 6-78.   Fig. 6-79.

Schematic Diagram of Circuit (Fig. 6-80)

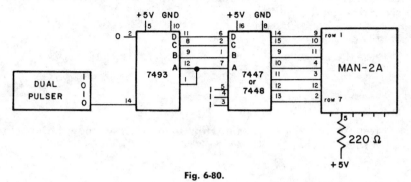

Fig. 6-80.

Step 1

The schematic diagram shown in Fig. 6-80 applies either for the 7447 or for the 7448 decoder/driver integrated-circuit chips. No change in wiring is required; simply exchange one chip for the other.

Step 2

We must decide what the relationship is between one of the seven outputs on the 7447 or 7448 chip and whether or not a dot is lit on the seven-row alphanumeric display. Each row is a separate cathode, which means that current will flow through the light-emitting diode on the display only when the cathode is at a logic 0 state. The 220-ohm resistor connected to column 1 is the required current-limiting resistor for the LEDs. Thus, we conclude the following:

- A logic 0 output from the 7447 or 7448 chip will light a dot on the display.
- A logic 1 output from the 7447 or 7448 chip will keep a dot unlit on the display.

Step 3

Place a 7447 decoder/driver in the appropriate position on the breadboard and wire the circuit shown.

Step 4

Apply power to the breadboard. How many lighted dots do you observe on the MAN-2A alphanumeric display in the first column?

The number of lit dots that you observe will depend on the warm-up characteristics of your 7493 binary counter. We have observed both six and seven dots initially.

Step 5

Press the pulser once. How many dots are now lit?

Step 6

Press the pulser once again. How many dots are now lit, and in what rows are they?

Step 7

Continue to press and release the pulser. Note that the number and location of lit dots constantly change. It is not immediately clear that there is a distinct pattern for these lit dots. We shall show that there is in the following steps.

Step 8

To better demonstrate what is happening in the circuit, we recommend that you add a seven-segment LED display at the ABCD outputs from the 7493 binary counter chip. Shown in Fig. 6-81 is a partial schematic diagram that illustrates how you must make this additional group of connections. All you are going to do is add the LED display to the circuit. You are not going to change any of the previous wire connections.

Apply power to the breadboard and note the first reading on the seven-segment display. Several illuminated dots should appear on the MAN-2A alphanumeric display. Cycle through the various states of the 7493 binary counter using the pulser until you reach

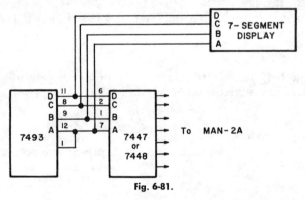

Fig. 6-81.

numeral 0 on the display. How many dots are lit on the alphanumeric display now?

You should observe six illuminated dots.

Step 9

You will now complete a truth table that summarizes your observations. In the following truth table, *a lit dot on the alphanumeric display will correspond to a logic 0 state from the output of the 7447 or 7448 chip, and an unlit dot on the alphanumeric display will correspond to a logic 1 state from the output of the 7447 or 7448 chip.* This is a very important point which you must take into consideration when you construct the truth table for the 7447 and 7448 chips. It is very tempting to consider a lit dot to be a logic 1 state. To do so would be incorrect. As a first step, let us construct a truth table for the 7447 chip.

Decimal Numeral or Symbol	Row Number						
	1	2	3	4	5	6	7
0	0	0	0	0	0	0	1
1							
2							
3							
4							
5							
6							
7							
8	0	0	0	0	0	0	0
9							
⊏							
⊐							
⊔							
⊑							
⊨							
blank	1	1	1	1	1	1	1

We have given some assistance in setting up the preceding truth table. Confirm the results given for numerals 0 and 8, then complete the remaining parts of the truth table.

Step 10

Replace, with the power off, the 7447 chip by the 7448 chip and complete the following truth table.

Decimal Numeral or Symbol	Row Number						
	1	2	3	4	5	6	7
0	1	1	1	1	1	1	0
1							
2							
3							
4							
5							
6							
7							
8							
9							
⊏							
⊐							
⊔							
⊏							
⊨							
blank	0	0	0	0	0	0	0

When you fill in the two truth tables, keep in mind the following points:

- The decimal numeral or symbol is that which you observe on the seven-segment LED display.
- A lit dot on the alphanumeric display corresponds to a logic 0 entry in the truth table.
- An unlit dot on the alphanumeric display corresponds to a logic 1 entry in the truth table.
- Row 1 corresponds to segment a, row 2 to segment b, row 3 to segment c, row 4 to segment d, row 5 to segment e, row 6 to

segment f, and row 7 to segment g on the 7447 and 7448 decoder/driver chips.

Step 11

Now compare the truth tables that you obtained experimentally with the truth tables for the 7447 and 7448 chips given in this chapter. They should be identical! If you have done this experiment correctly, you have demonstrated that the MAN-2A alphanumeric display can be used to monitor the outputs from a bcd-to-seven-segment decoder/driver integrated circuit.

Question

1. Does the intensity of the dots in column 1 change with the number of dots that are actually lit? In other words, if only one dot is lit, is it very intense when compared to the situation when seven dots are lit? If your answer is yes to both of these questions, can you explain why this happens? Do so in the following space.

EXPERIMENT NO. 14

Purpose

The purpose of this experiment is to demonstrate how to *refresh* a 7 × 5 dot matrix LED display so that a permanent nonflickering image is produced. You will use a five-state sequencer to cycle among the five columns of the display.

Pin Configurations of Integrated Circuits (Figs. 6-82 through 6-85)

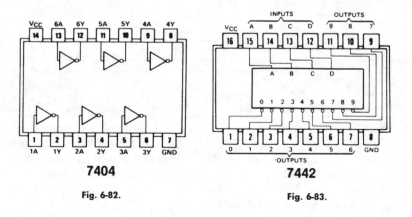

Fig. 6-82.   7404

Fig. 6-83.   7442

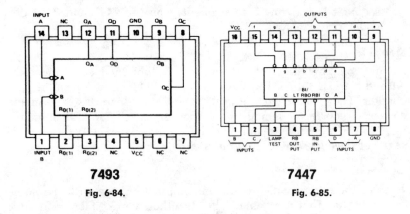

7493

Fig. 6-84.

7447

Fig. 6-85.

Schematic Diagram of Circuit (Fig. 6-86)

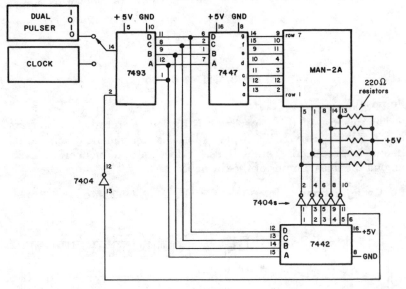

Fig. 6-86.

Step 1

Carefully study the circuit in Fig. 6-86 and note that it is quite similar to the circuit given in the preceding experiment. We have added a 7442 decoder, some 7404 inverters, several additional current-limiting resistors, and a clock. The 7493/7442 group of chips functions as a five-state sequencer.

Step 2

Wire the circuit as shown. When you have finished, apply power to the breadboard and repeatedly press and release the pulser, which acts as a clock input to the 7493 binary counter. You should observe that the MAN-2A alphanumeric display repeatedly cycles through the five columns. Each column of dots is different from the other. The columns form the equivalent seven-segment logic states for the numerals 0, 1, 2, 3, and 4. Numeral 0 corresponds to column 1, numeral 1 to column 2, numeral 2 to column 3, numeral 3 to column 4, and numeral 4 to column 5.

Step 3

Now connect a clock operating at a frequency greater than 1000 Hz to input pin 14 on the 7493 chip. What do you observe? Is there any flicker? Explain in the following space.

The flicker disappears and a seemingly permanent dot pattern appears on the MAN-2A display. The eye cannot detect changes that occur at frequencies greater than 40 Hz, so it averages the light intensity that appears at each light-emitting diode.

Step 4

If you have performed this experiment correctly, you should have observed a steady display of dots on the alphanumeric display. These dots do not correspond to any particular letter, numeral, or symbol, but their pattern suggests how a letter or numeral can be formed on the 7 × 4 dot matrix display. In our experiment, the intensity of the lit dots appeared to be uniform over the entire display. You may wish to substitute a 7448 decoder/driver for the 7447 chip. If you do so (disconnect the power when you make the substitution), you should observe the complementary lit dot pattern to the 7447 chip, i.e., if a dot was lit in the 7447 circuit, it would not be lit in the 7448 circuit, and vice versa. In this particular circuit configuration, both the 7447 and 7448 function as *read-only memories*. We shall discuss the subject of memories in Chapter 9.

Questions

1. Can you guess from the behavior of the 7447 and 7448 chips in this experiment what a *read-only memory* (*ROM*) must be? Explain if you can.

2. Why are the dot patterns for the 7447 and 7448 chips the complement of each other?

3. Why is a high frequency clock input required to maintain the "permanent" display?

4. What do we mean by a "refresh" circuit? In the preceding experiment, you rapidly refreshed the logic states at the inputs to the MAN-2A display. This statement should be a sufficient hint to enable you to answer this question.

WHAT HAVE YOU ACCOMPLISHED IN THIS CHAPTER?

Review of Objectives

We stated in the Introduction to this chapter that at the end you would be able to do the following:

- Construct a lamp monitor using a simple light-emitting diode, an npn transistor, and two resistors.

  You did this in Experiment No. 2.

- Construct a seven-segment LED display using both a common cathode and a common anode red numeric display.

  You constructed a common anode seven-segment LED display in Experiment No. 5 and a common cathode seven-segment LED display in Experiment No. 8. The 7447 and 7448 decoder/driver integrated-circuit chips were respectively employed in the two experiments. You probably observed that the Opcoa SLA-1 common-anode display was easier to read.

- Construct a five-digit seven-segment LED display.

  You did this in Experiment Nos. 10 and 11.

- Demonstrate the operation of a MAN-2A 7 × 5 dot matrix display.

Busing: Tri-State and Open Collector Outputs

INTRODUCTION

In Chapter 5, we discussed the languages of digital electronics, digital codes, and indicated that digital electronic devices communicate among themselves using a variety of such languages, among which binary, binary coded decimal, and ASCII are currently the most important. As an increasing number of electronic devices are converted from analog to digital operation, the problem of digital communications between such devices becomes an ever more significant concern of the electronic design engineer. In this chapter, we shall discuss one of the more elegant solutions to interdevice communications, the *bus*. The use of bus lines is quite common in computers, minicomputers and microprocessors and is becoming steadily more important in the design of certain kinds of digital electronic instruments.

OBJECTIVES

At the completion of this chapter, you will be able to do the following:

Construct a multiplexer using a pair of 74126 integrated circuits containing eight three-state bus buffer gates.
Determine an acceptable value for a "pull-up" resistor connected to the output of a 7405 inverter with an open collector output.
Construct a "wired-OR" circuit.

You did this in Experiment Nos. 13 and 14.

- Use a five-state sequencer to sequence the five digit digit seven-segment display and the five columns in a matrix display.

These were probably the most interesting but the cult experiments in this chapter. You constructed the five-digit seven-segment LED display in Experiment the sequenced 7×5 dot matrix display in Experime

d
m
a
re
d
ol
m
ch
de
m
co
di

lo

- Pass a test in which you are asked to define the following terms:
  - positive logic
  - negative logic
  - positive bus
  - negative bus
  - wired-OR circuit
  - three-state output
  - open collector output
  - bus

DEFINITIONS

bus—A path over which digital information is transferred, from any of several sources to any of several destinations. Only one transfer of information can take place at any one time. While such transfer is taking place, all other sources that are tied to the bus must be disabled.

to bus—To interconnect several digital devices, which either receive or transmit digital signals by a common set of conducting paths, called a bus, over which all information between such devices is transferred.

negative bus—A bus in which, when no information is being transmitted, the bus lines are at +5 volts. When information is being transmitted over the bus, the bus lines vary between ground potential and +5 volts, where a pulse at ground potential corresponds to "data" or to a logic 1 state.

negative logic—A form of logic in which the more positive voltage level represents logic 0 and the more negative level represents logic 1.[1]

open collector output—An output from an integrated-circuit device in which the final "pull-up" resistor in the output transistor for the device is missing and must be provided by the user before the circuit is completed.

positive bus—A bus in which, when no information is being transmitted, the bus lines are at ground potential. When information is being transmitted over the bus, the bus lines vary between ground potential and +5 volts, where a pulse at +5 volts corresponds to "data" or to a logic 1 state.

positive logic—A form of logic in which the more positive voltage level represents logic 1 and the more negative level represents logic 0.[1]

receiver—A device that accepts information from a transmitter or source of information.

transmitter—A device that provides information that is ultimately accepted by a receiver.

Tri-state® device, three-state device—A semiconductor logic device in which there are three possible output states: (1) a logic 0 state, (2) a logic 1 state, or (3) a state in which the output is, in effect, disconnected from the rest of the circuit and has no influence on it.

wired-OR circuit—A circuit consisting of two or more semiconductor devices with open collector outputs in which the outputs are wired together. The output from the circuit is at a logic 0 if device A *or* device B *or* device C *or* . . . is at a logic 0 state.

WHAT IS A BUS?

We can define the noun, *bus,* and the verb, *to bus,* as follows:

bus—A path over which digital information is transferred, from any of several sources to any of several destinations. Only one transfer of information can take place at any one time. While such transfer is taking place, all other sources that are tied to the bus must be disabled.

to bus—To interconnect several digital devices, which either receive or transmit digital signals, by a common set of conducting paths, called a bus, over which all information between such devices is transferred.

Basically, the purpose of a bus is to minimize the number of interconnections and integrated-circuit chips required to transfer information between digital devices and also to save wire. Buses are commonly used in computers, where there is a necessity to transfer digital information between a *central processing unit* (CPU) or *arithmetic element* and random access memories (RAMs), read-only memories (ROMs), programmable read-only memories (PROMs), and a variety of input/output (I/O) devices such as teletypewriters, line printers, CRTs, high-speed card readers, tape cassettes, magnetic tape units, etc.

EXAMPLE OF A SIMPLE BUS SYSTEM

Shown in Fig. 7-1 is a simple example of a bus system in which there are two transmitters (A and C)—devices that provide digital information to the bus—and two receivers (B and D)—devices that accept information from the bus. The important points to remember about the operation of this bus system are:

- If gates A and C are disabled, no information is provided to the bus.
- If gates B and D are disabled, no information is accepted from the bus.

- Gates A and C cannot both be enabled at the same time. One or the other of these two sets of gates must be disabled.
- Gates B and D can both be enabled at the same time. There is no limit as to how many output devices can receive information from the bus at the same time, provided that the bus drivers can drive all of the devices on the bus.

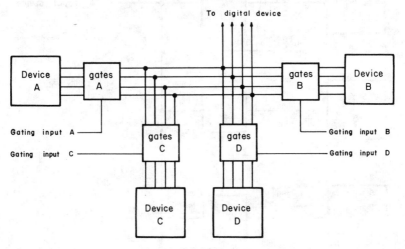

Fig. 7-1. Simple bus system.

- Six different modes of information transfer are possible.

A to D

A to D

C to B

C to D

A to B and D

C to B and D

Bus systems in which there are two or three transmitters and up to ten or fifteen receivers are quite common in digital electronics. Even digital instruments are increasingly using buses, particularly input/output buses. In typical laboratories, it will become quite common to have several digital instruments bused together and transmitting information to the same receiver located somewhere else in the laboratory.

It is easy to see that it is possible to tie a number of receivers to a single bus line. Not so obvious, however, is the fact that all the transmitters must also be tied to the single bus line. So far during this laboratory workbook, we have not shown how to tie outputs together from different gates or integrated-circuit chips.

The problem is shown in Fig. 7-2, where four transmitters (A, B, C, and D) are connected to a single bus line through the outputs of gates A, B, C, and D, respectively. With TTL chips that possess normal outputs, it is impossible to do this! However, several TTL

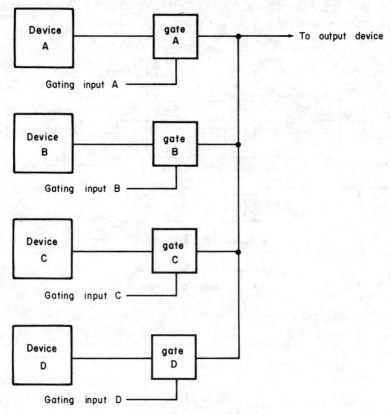

Fig. 7-2. A four-transmitter single-bit bus system.

integrated-circuit chips have unusual outputs that permit the wiring of the outputs of gates together. The outputs from such chips have special names, and are known either as *three-state outputs* or as *open collector outputs*. Both kinds of outputs permit you to tie the outputs of a number of gates together, thus facilitating the task of busing several input devices. We would now like to discuss these outputs in greater detail. We shall start with three-state outputs, since they essentially have replaced devices with open collector outputs.

THREE-STATE LOGIC

In a gate with TRI-STATE® logic, (the term, TRI-STATE® is a trademark registered by National Semiconductor; the generic names are TSL, three-state logic, three-state TTL, and three-state outputs) there are three possible output states:

- A logic 0 state
- A logic 1 state
- A state in which the output is, in effect, disconnected from the rest of the circuit and has no influence on it.

The third state, of course, is the one that makes TRI-STATE® logic devices unique.

All logic-state devices have an extra input called an *enable/disable* gating input, which permits the logic device either to behave normally, or else disconnects the output of the gate from the rest of the circuit. When the logic device is enabled, the output of the device can either be at a logic 0 or at a logic 1 state, but not both. When the logic device is disabled, then the output (or outputs) is disconnected from the rest of the circuit and the logic device is, in effect, disconnected from the rest of the circuit.

The enable/disable gating input will accept either a logic 0 or logic 1 input and will either enable or disable the logic device. Some three-state devices are enabled by a logic 0 state, while others are enabled by a logic 1 state.

Perhaps the most important three-state logic device is the three-state buffer, two versions of which are shown in Figs. 7-3 and 7-4. Two integrated-circuit chips which contain such buffers are the

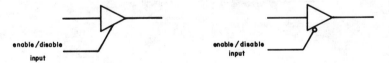

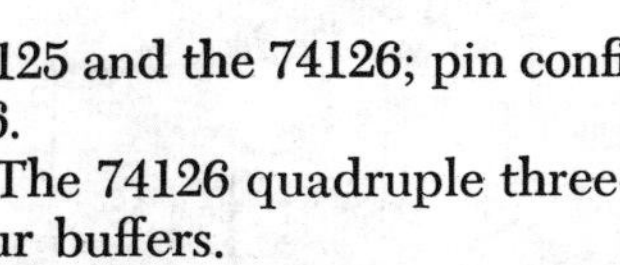

Fig. 7-3. A logic 1 enables this three-state buffer.

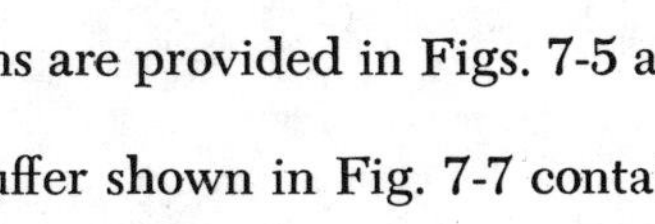

Fig. 7-4. A logic 0 enables this three-state buffer.

74125 and the 74126; pin configurations are provided in Figs. 7-5 and 7-6.

The 74126 quadruple three-state buffer shown in Fig. 7-7 contains four buffers.

The 74125 quadruple three-state buffer contains four buffers as well (Fig. 7-8). The little circle in the 74125 gates indicates that the output is enabled when the enable/disable gating input is at a logic 0 state. With the 74126 gates, the output is enabled when the gating input is at a logic 1 state.

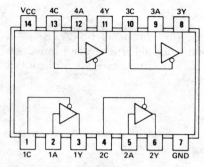

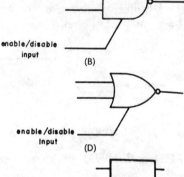

74125

Fig. 7-5. Pin configuration for 74125 IC, which contains four independent three-state buffers.

74126

Fig. 7-6. Pin configuration for 74126 IC, which contains four independent three-state buffers.

Fig. 7-7. Diagrams of four independent three-state buffers in 74126 IC.

Fig. 7-8. Diagrams of four independent three-state buffers in 74125 IC.

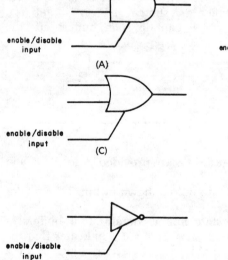

Fig. 7-9. Examples of three-state devices.

It is possible to manufacture three-state AND, NAND, OR, NOR, and other devices. Examples of such logic devices are shown in Fig. 7-9.

Three-state logic devices are becoming increasingly popular because they exhibit less noise and considerably higher speeds than open collector output devices, which are also used to bus devices together. Up to 128 outputs can be bus-connected at room temperature using three-state logic devices.

EXAMPLES OF THREE-STATE LOGIC CIRCUITS

When we connect the outputs of several three-state logic devices together, we basically create a data selector/multiplexer circuit in which the enable/disable gating inputs perform the function of the data select inputs on a regular TTL data selector/multiplexer (Fig. 7-10).

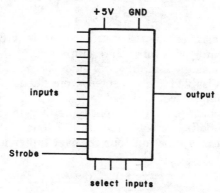

Fig. 7-10. Typical TTL data-selector/multiplexer.

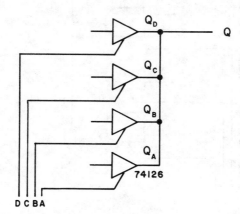

Fig. 7-11. Four-bit multiplexer circuit consisting of four bused three-state buffers.

For example, we can use four three-state bus buffer gates to produce a 4-line-to-1-line data selector/multiplexer (Fig. 7-11). The difference between such a multiplexer and the 74153 chip is that the select inputs DCBA can have only a single logic 1 state among them, i.e., they can either be 1000, 0100, 0010, or 0001. It is not possible to select two or more of the bus buffer gates at the same time. The truth table that applies for such a circuit is given in Table 7-1. Note that it is forbidden to enable two buffers simultaneously. Thus, only four truth table entries are needed.

Table 7-1. Truth Table for the Circuit in Fig. 7-11

D	C	B	A	Q
0	0	0	1	Q_A
0	0	1	0	Q_B
0	1	0	0	Q_C
1	0	0	0	Q_D

In a similar manner, we can select one of four different 2-input positive NAND gates with three-state outputs (Fig. 7-12). Again, we can only select a single 2-input NAND gate at a time. The other three NAND gates are disabled (disconnected) from the output Q.

As a final example, we show in Fig. 7-13 a single-line eight-device bus system in which several different types of gates drive up to four three-state bus buffer gates. Whereas only one of the transmitters can be enabled at a time, all four receiver buffer gates can be en-

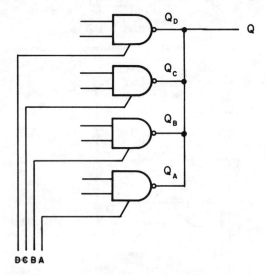

DCBA

Fig. 7-12. Four 2-input three-state NAND gates bused together.

abled and receive information in parallel. It should be observed that it is easy to bus receivers together; special types of gate outputs are not required and up to ten or more TTL receivers can be bused without any special precautions.

Such is not the case for transmitters to a bus line. We cannot connect the outputs of normal TTL devices together unless the outputs are of a special type that permit such connections, i.e., the outputs

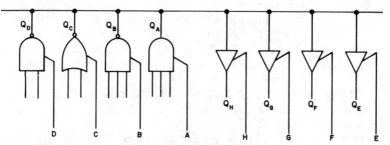

Fig. 7-13. Single-bit bus system consisting of four transmitters and four receivers.

are either three-state or open collector. So, all the fuss in this chapter is over the problem of connecting the outputs of logic devices together. In Fig. 7-13, three-state outputs are required for gates A, B, C, and D but not for the buffer gates E, F, G, and H.

SOME THREE-STATE INTEGRATED CIRCUITS

Although several chips in the 7400-series have three-state outputs, including the 74125 and 74126 bus buffer, gates many more three-state devices are available from National Semiconductor, who first introduced the TRI-STATE® gate in 1970. As described in their *Digital Integrated Circuits* catalog, the following is a list of some of the TRI-STATE devices that are available:

DM74200	TRI-STATE 256 random access memory
DM8093	TRI-STATE quad buffer
DM8094	TRI-STATE quad buffer
DM8095	TRI-STATE hex buffer
DM8097	TRI-STATE hex buffer
DM8098	TRI-STATE hex inverter
DM8123	TRI-STATE quad 2-input multiplexer
DM8214	TRI-STATE dual 4:1 multiplexer
DM8219	TRI-STATE 16-line to 1-line multiplexer
DM8230	TRI-STATE demultiplexer
DM8542	TRI-STATE quad I/O register
DM8544	TRI-STATE quad switch debouncer

DM8551	TRI-STATE quad-D flip-flop
DM8552	TRI-STATE decade counter/latch
DM8553	TRI-STATE 8-bit latch
DM8554	TRI-STATE binary-counter/latch
DM8555	TRI-STATE programmable decade counter
DM8556	TRI-STATE programmable binary counter
DM8574	TRI-STATE 1024-bit field-programmable read only memory
DM8696	TRI-STATE 4096-bit bipolar read only memory
DM8597	TRI-STATE 1024-bit read only memory
DM8598	TRI-STATE 256-bit read only memory
DM8599	TRI-STATE 64-bit random access read/write memory
DM8696	TRI-STATE 4096-bit bipolar read only memory
DM8831	TRI-STATE line driver
DM8832	TRI-STATE line driver
DM8833	quad TRI-STATE transceiver
DM8834	quad TRI-STATE transceiver
DM8835	quad TRI-STATE transceiver
DM8875A	TRI-STATE 4-bit multiplier
DM8875B	TRI-STATE 4-bit multiplier

More three-state devices are coming on the market and more manufacturers are "second sourcing" the above devices. By "second sourcing," we mean that the electrical specifications of an integrated circuit of one manufacturer are copied by another, usually with the former's consent, creating two sources for the chip. Purchasers of the chip are thus assured that it will be available, independent of strikes, floods, and bankruptcy.

Three-state busing is important also because it is the dominant busing technique currently used in microcomputers, semiconductor memories, and programmable interface chips. Open collector busing has essentially disappeared from the microcomputer-oriented integrated circuits.

OPEN COLLECTOR OUTPUTS

An older, slower, less expensive, and "noisier" way to bus the outputs of logic devices together is through the use of *open collector outputs*. In an open collector device, the final "pull-up" resistor in the output transistor for the device is missing and must be provided by the user before he completes his circuit. However, because the pull-up resistor is missing from all logic devices with open collector outputs, it is possible to connect all such outputs together and use a single pull-up resistor.

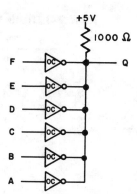

+5V

1000 Ω

F — Q

E

D

C

B

A

Fig. 7-14. Six open collector inverters bused
together to form a 6-input NOR gate.

For example, we can use the six inverters with open collector outputs which exist in the 7405 hex inverter integrated circuit to construct the circuit in Fig. 7-14. The six inverter outputs on the 7405
integrated circuit are tied together to +5 volts using a single 1000-
ohm pull-up resistor. The output, Q, is at a logic 1 state only if
ABCDEF = 000000. If any of the six inputs is at a logic 1 state,
the output from such an inverter is at a logic 0 state and grounds,
or pulls down, the outputs of the remaining five inverters. Under
such conditions, the output, Q, is at a logic 0 state. The truth table
for such a circuit is reminiscent of a multi-input NOR gate (Table

Table 7-2. Truth Table for Circuit in Fig. 7-14

F	E	D	C	B	A	Q
0	0	0	0	0	0	1
all other states						0

7-2). It is clear that the circuit in Fig. 7-14 functions as a 6-input
positive NOR gate. Such a gate is infrequently called a "wired-NOR"
gate, as is done by D. Lancaster on page 138 of the *TTL Cookbook*
(Howard W. Sams & Co., Inc., Indianapolis, Indiana). We show a
6-input NOR gate in Fig. 7-15.

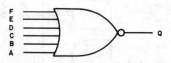

Fig. 7-15. Symbol for circuit in Fig. 7-14.

For a pair of 2-input positive NAND gates with open collector
outputs that are wired together (Fig. 7-16), the truth table is as
shown in Table 7-3. This table states that if the output of either
gate 1 *or* gate 2 is at a logic 0, then Q = 0. Does this table remind
you of an AND-OR-INVERT gate? See Chapter 3, Book I. Open collector

Table 7-3. Truth Table for Circuit in Fig. 7-16

D	C	B	A	Q
0	0	0	0	1
0	0	0	1	1
0	0	1	0	1
0	0	1	1	0
0	1	0	0	1
0	1	0	1	1
0	1	1	0	1
0	1	1	1	0
1	0	0	0	1
1	0	0	1	1
1	0	1	0	1
1	0	1	1	0
1	1	0	0	0
1	1	0	1	0
1	1	1	0	0
1	1	1	1	0

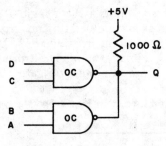

Fig. 7-16. Two 2-input NAND gates bused together.

gates that are wired together behave in rather unusual ways; they cannot be used to create simple gates! We recommend that you proceed with caution when you use several 2-input gates that are wired together. One exception to this rule is the use of open collector AND

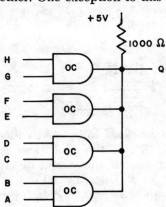

Fig. 7-17. Four 2-input AND gates bused together.

gates such as in Fig. 7-17, which has the truth table given in Table 7-4.

Table 7-4. Truth Table for Circuit in Fig. 7-17

H	G	F	E	D	C	B	A	Q
			all other states					0
1	1	1	1	1	1	1	1	1

SYMBOLS FOR OPEN COLLECTOR LOGIC DEVICES

We have not detected much standardization for the symbols that apply to gates containing open collector outputs. In most cases, traditional gate symbols are employed and you must deduce from

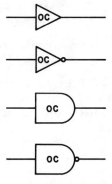

Fig. 7-18. Open collector devices often identified by "OC" within symbol. Exception is MSI IC 7489—a memory chip with open collector outputs (see Chapter 9).

the text or from the presence of a pull-up resistor that open collector gates are being used. In this book, we shall place the letters "OC" within the appropriate logic gate symbols, as shown in Fig. 7-18.

WIRED-OR CIRCUITS

According to what we have learned about open collector circuits, we would conclude, for the circuit shown in Fig. 7-19, that the output, Q, will be at logic 0 if either gate G1 *or* gate G2 *or* inverter G3 *or* gate G4 has an output of logic 0. People in the digital electronics area have called such a circuit a "wired-OR" circuit, but we believe that the use of the term "wired-OR" can be a bit misleading, owing to the fact that the circuit in no way behaves as a simple multiple-input OR gate. We urge you to be very careful whenever you encounter the term "wired-OR".

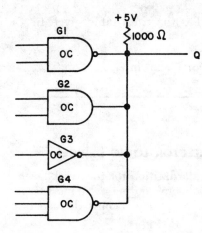

Fig. 7-19. Output Q is at logic 0 if gate G1 or G2 or inverter G3 or gate G4 is at logic 0 state in this example of "wired-OR" concept.

SOME TYPICAL OPEN COLLECTOR INTEGRATED-CIRCUIT CHIPS

In this unit, you will perform experiments using six common and simple open collector gate integrated circuits:

- The 7401 quad 2-input positive NAND gate with open collector output
- The 7403 quad 2-input positive NAND gate with open collector output
- The 7405 hex inverter with open collector output
- The 7409 quad 2-input positive AND gate with open collector output
- The 7415 triple 3-input positive AND gate with open collector output
- The 7422 dual 4-input positive NAND gate with open collector output

We shall comment on them briefly in the pages that follow.

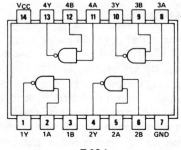

Fig. 7-20. Pin configuration for 7401 quad positive NAND gate with open collector output.

7401

THE 7401 QUAD 2-INPUT POSITIVE NAND GATE
WITH OPEN COLLECTOR OUTPUT

The pin configuration for the 7401 quad 2-input positive NAND gate with open collector output is shown in Fig. 7-20.

There are four independent 2-input positive NAND gates with open collector outputs, which are schematically represented in Fig. 7-21.

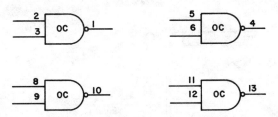

Fig. 7-21. Diagrams of independent 2-input NAND gates with open collector outputs in 7401 IC.

THE 7403 QUAD 2-INPUT POSITIVE NAND GATE
WITH OPEN COLLECTOR OUTPUT

The 7403 quad 2-input positive NAND gate with open collector output is identical in function to the 7401 chip, but has a different pin configuration (Fig. 7-22).

Fig. 7-22. Pin configuration for 7403 quad 2-input positive NAND gate with open collector output.

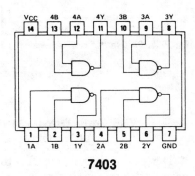

7403

Four independent 2-input positive NAND gates with open collector outputs are also present (Fig. 7-23).

THE 7405 HEX INVERTER WITH OPEN COLLECTOR OUTPUT

The 7405 hex inverter with open collector output chip has the pin configuration shown in Fig. 7-24.

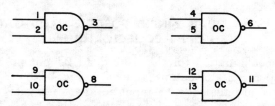

Fig. 7-23. Diagrams of four independent 2-input NAND gates with open collector outputs in 7403 IC.

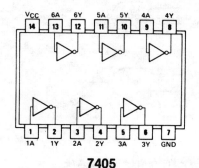

7405

Fig. 7-24. Pin configuration for 74035 hex inverter with open collector output.

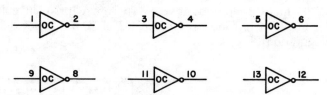

Fig. 7-25. Diagrams of six independent inverters with open collector outputs in 7405 IC.

The 7405 contains six independent inverters with open collector outputs (Fig. 7-25).

THE 7409 QUAD 2-INPUT POSITIVE AND GATE WITH OPEN COLLECTOR OUTPUT

The pin configuration for the 7409 quad 2-input positive AND gate with open collector output (Fig. 7-26) is similar to the 7403 integrated circuit (Fig. 7-22).

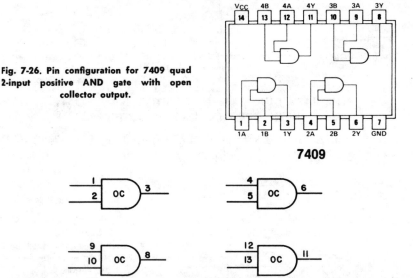

Fig. 7-26. Pin configuration for 7409 quad 2-input positive AND gate with open collector output.

7409

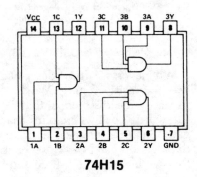

Fig. 7-27. Diagrams of four independent 2-input AND gates with open collector outputs in 7409 IC.

The 7409 contains four independent 2-input positive AND gates with open collector outputs (Fig. 7-27).

THE 7415 TRIPLE 3-INPUT POSITIVE AND GATE WITH OPEN COLLECTOR OUTPUT

The infrequently used 7415 triple 3-input positive AND gate with open collector chip has the pin configuration shown in Fig. 7-28.

Fig. 7-28. Pin configuration for 7415 triple 3-input positive AND gate with open collector output.

74H15

The 74H15 contains three independent 3-input positive AND gates with open collector outputs (Fig. 7-29).

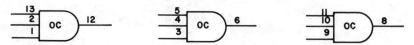

Fig. 7-29. Diagrams of three independent 3-input positive AND gates with open collector outputs in 7415 IC.

THE 7422 DUAL 4-INPUT POSITIVE NAND GATE
WITH OPEN COLLECTOR OUTPUT

The final integrated circuit is the infrequently used 7422 dual 4-input positive NAND gate with open collector output (Fig. 7-30).

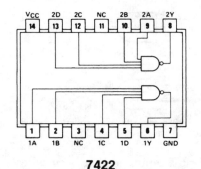

7422

Fig. 7-30. Pin configuration for 7422 dual 4-input positive NAND gate with open collector output.

The 7422 has only two independent 4-input positive NAND gates with open collector outputs (Fig. 7-31).

Fig. 7-31. Diagrams of two independent 4-input positive NAND gates with open collector outputs in 7422 IC.

POSITIVE VS. NEGATIVE LOGIC

Whenever we have described a gate, we have indicated that it was a "positive" gate. We have never indicated why it is useful to make the distinction that it was "positive." In fact, the use of the word "positive" implies that there exists some different type of gate. Such reasoning is entirely correct, for there exists four "negative" gates that bear close relationship to the four "positive" gates that we have already discussed: AND, NAND, OR, and NOR.

The important point to remember is that *the devices—the integrated circuits—remain the same; what changes is our designations for the ground and +5-volt input and output states.*

A truth table for a 2-input 7408 gate can be written as follows in terms of ground and +5 volts, the actual electronic conditions that we observe with this integrated circuit (Table 7-5). When we have

Table 7-5. Truth Table for 7408 Integrated-Circuit Gate, in Terms of Voltages, Measured Experimentally

A	B	Q
GND	GND	GND
GND	+5 V	GND
+5 V	GND	GND
+5 V	+5 V	+5 V

positive logic, we imply that the more positive voltage is at a logic 1 state. Thus, for positive logic, GND = 0 and +5 V = 1. The truth table for positive logic is given in Table 7-6.

Table 7-6. Truth Table Corresponding to Table 7-5 When GND = Logic 0 and +5 V = Logic 1. This Is Positive Logic, and the Table Shown Corresponds to a 2-input AND Gate

A	B	Q
0	0	0
0	1	0
1	0	0
1	1	1

Now let us try negative logic, where the more positive voltage is at a logic 0 state. For negative logic, GND = 1 and +5 V = 0, and the truth table for the 2-input AND integrated circuit becomes something different (Table 7-7).

Table 7-7. Truth Table Corresponding to Table 7-6 When GND = Logic 1 and +5 V = Logic 0. This Is Negative Logic, and the Table Shown Corresponds to a Positive 2-Input OR Gate

A	B	Q*
1	1	1
1	0	1
0	1	1
0	0	0

*Denotes negative logic.

This is the truth table for a 2-input positive OR gate! Thus, we conclude that *the truth table for a 2-input negative AND gate is identical to the truth table for a 2-input positive OR gate.*

The truth table for a 2-input 7400 gate, in terms of GND and +5 V, which are the electronic inputs and outputs actually observed, is shown in Table 7-8. For a negative logic 2-input NAND gate, the truth table becomes Table 7-9, which is identical to the truth table

Table 7-8. Truth Table, Written in Terms of Voltages, for the 7400 Integrated-Circuit Gate

A	B	Q
GND	GND	+5 V
GND	+5 V	+5 V
+5 V	GND	+5 V
+5 V	+5 V	GND

Table 7-9. Truth Table Corresponding to Table 7-8, in Which GND = Logic 1 and +5 V = Logic 0. This Is Negative Logic, and the Table Corresponds to a Positive 2-Input NOR Gate

A	B	Q*
1	1	0
1	0	0
0	1	0
0	0	1

*Denotes negative logic.

for a 2-input positive NOR gate. Therefore, *the truth table for a 2-input negative NAND gate is identical to the truth table for a 2-input positive NOR gate.*

Next, we have the truth table, in terms of GND and +5 V, for the 7432 gate (Table 7-10), which becomes, with negative logic, Table 7-11, which is the truth table for a 2-input positive AND gate. Thus,

Table 7-10. Truth Table, Written in Terms of Voltages, for the 7432 Integrated-Circuit Gate

A	B	Q
GND	GND	GND
GND	+5 V	+5 V
+5 V	GND	+5 V
+5 V	+5 V	+5 V

Table 7-11. Truth Table Corresponding to Table 7-10, in Which GND = Logic 1 and +5 V = Logic 0. This Is Negative Logic, and the Table Corresponds to a Positive 2-Input AND Gate

A	B	Q*
1	1	1
1	0	0
0	1	0
0	0	0

*Denotes negative logic.

the truth table for a 2-input negative OR *gate is identical to the truth table for a 2-input positive* AND *gate.*

Finally, the truth table for a 2-input 7402 gate (Table 7-12), becomes for negative logic, Table 7-13. Therefore, *the truth table*

Table 7-12. Truth Table, Written in Terms of Voltages, For the 7402 Integrated-Circuit Gate

A	B	Q
GND	GND	+5 V
GND	+5 V	GND
+5 V	GND	GND
+5 V	+5 V	GND

Table 7-13. Truth Table Corresponding to Table 7-12, in Which GND = Logic 1 and +5 V = Logic 0. This Is Negative Logic, and the Table Corresponds to a Positive 2-Input NAND Gate

A	B	Q*
1	1	0
1	0	1
0	1	1
0	0	1

*Denotes negative logic.

for a 2-input negative NOR *gate is identical to the truth table for a 2-input positive* NAND *gate.*

The conclusions that we have reached can be summarized as follows:

Integrated Circuit Gate	Positive Logic	Negative Logic
7408	AND	OR
7400	NAND	NOR
7432	OR	AND
7402	NOR	NAND

The question now arises, When do we use negative logic? In general, we use negative logic whenever it significantly simplifies the overall circuitry that we are using to accomplish a certain function. Keep in mind that the hardware is not changed; a positive-logic NAND gate is the same piece of hardware as a negative-logic NOR gate!

One of the more interesting ways that we can view positive and negative logic is as follows:

- In positive logic, "data" = 1 and "no data" = 0.
- In negative logic, "data" = 0 and "no data" = 1.

By the term, "no data," we mean that the line over which we are transferring digital information is at the logic state in question when no information is being transferred. Another way of saying the above is

- In positive logic, "data" =+5 V and "no data" = GND.
- In negative logic, "data" = GND and "no data" = +5 V.

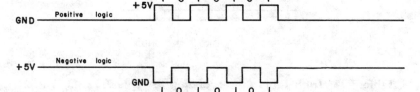

Fig. 7-32. Serial transmission of data over both positive-logic bus and negative-logic bus; the latter, once popular with minicomputers such as the PDP-8, are no longer in vogue due to the advance of positive-logic three-state bus technology.

This is best seen in the timing diagram given in Fig. 7-32, where we are transmitting the digital word, 1010101 in both positive and negative logic. In positive logic, the line is at GND potential when no data is being transmitted, whereas in negative logic, the line is at +5 volts when no data is being transmitted.

POSITIVE VS. NEGATIVE BUSES

What we are driving at in our discussion of positive and negative logic is a distinction between a *positive bus* and a *negative bus*. In a positive bus, "no data" = GND. Three-state logic leads to positive-bus systems, whereas open collector logic leads to negative-bus systems. Let us discuss the negative-logic bus of open collector systems in a little bit more detail, as it may not be obvious why such systems function as negative-bus systems.

In Fig. 7-33, we have a negative bus in which four logic devices with open-collector outputs are tied to the bus. When nothing is happening, the bus line is at +5 volts. If the output from gate G1 *or* gate G2 *or* Gate 3 *or* inverter G4 goes to a logic 0 state, the bus line drops to ground potential and a change in logic state occurs in the output logic devices G5 through G7, provided that such devices are enabled.

The characteristics of a negative bus system, as typified by Fig. 7-33, can be summarized as follows:

- The quiescent state of the bus line, the state in which the least power is consumed, corresponds to +5 volts.

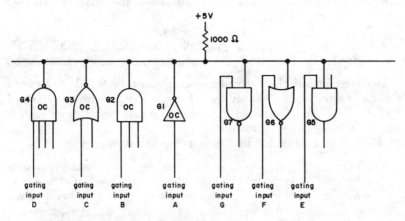

Fig. 7-33. Single-bit bus system with four open collector transmitters and four receivers.

- When no information is being transmitted over the bus, the bus line remains at +5 volts.
- When information is being transmitted over the bus, the bus line varies between ground and +5-V potential, where ground potential corresponds to a logic 1 state and +5 V corresponds to a logic 0 state.

INTRODUCTION TO THE EXPERIMENTS

In this chapter, you will construct several simple circuits that use gates or buffers that have either three-state or open collector outputs. In some of the experiments, you will be asked to use a volt-ohm-milliammeter (vom) to determine either the resistance or voltage of an open collector output. In the following paragraphs, we have given you a few hints concerning the use of a vom.

Using a Volt-Ohm-Milliammeter (VOM)

A typical volt-ohm-milliammeter consists of a group of resistors connected in such a manner that you can measure electrical quantities such as dc volts, ac volts, dc milliamperes, and ohms. An internal battery in the vom is required for all resistance measurements; the ohms scales are calibrated with an "ohms adjust" knob to compensate for the slowly declining voltage of the internal battery.

To operate the vom, you must do the following:

- Adjust the scale-selector knob to the scale that you desire.
- Locate the correct scale on the face of the meter.

- Connect the $(+)$ and $(-)$ leads from the vom to the electrical circuit of interest.
- Read the measured value on the meter.
- If measuring resistance, multiply the measured value on the meter by the indicated power of ten on the scale-selector knob.

We recommend that you attempt to measure the dc voltage of the battery or power supply that you are using with your breadboard. The voltage should be approximately +5.0 volts, but it may be a little larger or smaller.

We can offer several hints for choosing and using a vom:

- When storing the vom, set the scale-selector knob to 500 dc volts or 500 ac volts. There is little likelihood that someone would accidentally touch the two leads to a +500-volt power supply, but even if such an accident occurs, no damage would result to the vom.
- Do not store the vom with the scale-selector knob set at a resistance scale. If you do, there is an excellent chance that you will drain the dry battery within the vom.
- The best vom models are those that have the highest "sensitivity," a quantity which is measured in units of "ohms per volt." A cheap vom has a sensitivity of 10,000 ohms per volt. An expensive vom has a sensitivity of 100,000 ohms per volt. In the experiments in this chapter, we used a vom with a sensitivity of 20,000 ohms per volt.

EXPERIMENT NO. 1

Purpose

The purpose of this experiment is to demonstrate the operation of a 74126 bus buffer gate with three-state output.

Pin Configuration of Integrated-Circuit (Fig. 7-34)

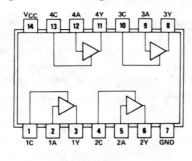

Fig. 7-34.

74126

Schematic Diagram of Circuit (Fig. 7-35)

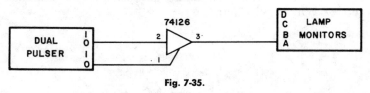

Fig. 7-35.

Step 1

Wire the circuit as shown in Fig. 7-35. The 74126 chip contains four independent bus buffer gates; use only one of them. You may find it more convenient to use logic switches instead of the pulsers.

Step 2

With pulser No. 1 released, repeatedly press and release pulser No. 2. What do you observe? Write it down in the following space.

We observed that nothing happened. The lamp monitor did not light.

Step 3

Press pulser No. 1, thus enabling the bus buffer gate and repeatedly press and release pulser No. 2. What happens?

In our case, we observed that the lamp monitor went on and off, thus indicating that it was making transistions between logic 0 and logic 1 states. We concluded that a logic 1 state applied at pin 1 of the 74126 chip enables the first bus buffer gate, and that a logic 0 applied at this pin disables the bus buffer gate.

That is all there is to the experiment.

Questions

1. Would it be useful to connect the outputs of all four bus buffer gates on the 74126 chip together? Why or why not?

2. Would it be useful to connect the enable/disable inputs to all four bus buffer gates on the 74126 chip together? Why or why not?

3. Would it be useful to connect the four bus buffer gate outputs together and, at the same time, the enable/disable inputs together? Why or why not?

EXPERIMENT NO. 2

Purpose

The purpose of this experiment is to create a 4-line to 1-line multiplexer by wiring the outputs of the 74125 bus buffer gates together.

Pin Configuration of Integrated Circuit (Fig. 7-36)

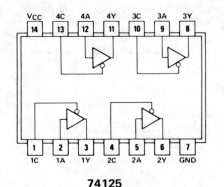

Fig. 7-36.

74125

Schematic Diagram of Circuit (Fig. 7-37)

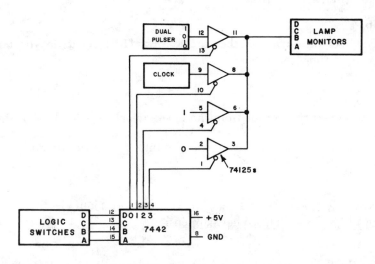

Fig. 7-37.

Step 1

Since the bus buffer gates each have three-state outputs, it is possible to wire pins 3, 6, 8, and 11 on the 74125 chip together. With the exception of integrated circuits with open collector outputs, this is the only time that you can wire outputs from TTL chips together. In the circuit diagram, note that you are able to select the pulser, the clock, or either a logic 0 or logic 1 as an output to the lamp monitor. Since these inputs are quite different from each other, it should be easy for you to demonstrate the fact that the circuit is operating correctly.

Step 2

With the power disconnected, wire the circuit as shown in Fig. 7-37.

Step 3

Set logic switches DCBA to DCBA = 1110. What do you observe at the lamp monitor?

We observed that the lamp monitor output followed the output state of the pulser. When we did not press the pulser, the lamp monitor remained unlit.

Step 4

Now set the logic switches to DCBA = 1101. What do you observe this time?

We observed the output from the clock, which provided clock signals at a frequency of 0.7 Hz. When we removed the capacitor from the clock, the frequency was too high for us to observe clock pulses.

Step 5

Now set the logic switches in turn first to DCBA = 1011 and then to DCBA = 0111. What happens?

With the first setting of the switches, we observed a logic 1 state at the lamp monitor; with the second setting, we observed a logic 0 state.

Questions

1. Do you have any idea how many 74125 bus buffer gates you can bus together? Ten? Thirty? How many?

2. You wish to multiplex the four outputs from three decade counters into a single seven-segment LED display. How many 74125 bus buffer gates are required? How many 74125 chips are required?

3. Can you draw a circuit in which both a 7490 decade counter and a 7493 binary counter are multiplexed together into a single seven-segment LED display? Do so.

EXPERIMENT NO. 3

Purpose

The purpose of this experiment is to multiplex a 7490 decade counter and a 7493 binary counter to a single seven-segment LED display using two 74126 integrated circuits.

Pin Configurations of Integrated Circuits (Figs. 7-38 through 7-40)

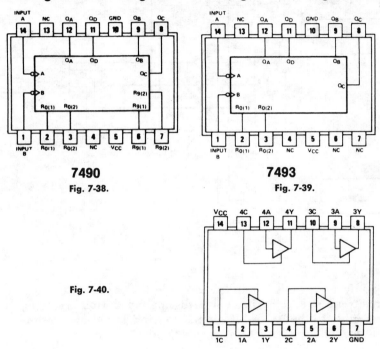

7490

Fig. 7-38.

7493

Fig. 7-39.

Fig. 7-40.

74126

Schematic Diagram of Circuit (Fig. 7-41)

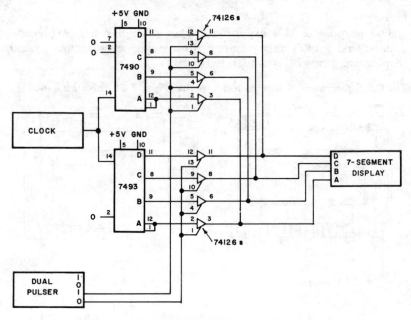

Fig. 7-41.

Step 1

Study the circuit carefully, and note that two 74126 integrated circuits are required. The enable/disable inputs from each chip are tied either to the "0" or "1" output on a single pulser. This ensures that one set of buffer gates is enabled while the other set is disabled.

Step 2

Wire the circuit. Apply power to the breadboard and observe the counting on the seven-segment LED display. Which counter, the 7490 or the 7493, is operating?

In our case, the 7490 counter appeared on the seven-segment LED display. The reason for this is that the pulser, in its released state, disabled the 7493 counter with the "0" output and enabled the 7490 counter with the "1" output.

Step 3

Press the pulser and keep it pressed. Do you now observe a 0 to 15 count on the LED display? You should! In the following space, explain why you observe the output from the 7493 binary counter when the pulser is pressed.

We observed the binary count because, upon pressing the pulser, the 7493 was enabled and the 7490 disabled.

Question

1. In the following space, draw a circuit using three 74126 chips in which you multiplex three 7490 decade counters to a single seven-segment LED display.

EXPERIMENT NO. 4

Purpose

The purpose of this experiment is to observe the behavior of a 7405 inverter using a vom set at a high resistance scale.

Pin Configuration of Integrated Circuit (Fig. 7-42)

Fig. 7-42.

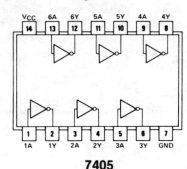

7405

Schematic Diagram of Circuit (Fig. 7-43)

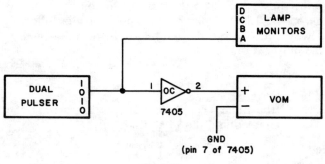

Fig. 7-43.

Step 1

Wire the circuit shown in Fig. 7-43. Set the vom to the highest resistance scale. In our case, we had only two resistance scales, ×10 and ×1000. We picked the ×1000 scale, which means that we multiply the resistance observed on the vom by 1000 to obtain the actual measured resistance.

Step 2

It is important to note that the resistance of a semiconductor device changes with the current that is passing through it. The ouputs of open collector devices are no exception to this rule. Therefore, the only important aspect of the vom measurement of resistance is *whether the resistance has a "high" value, such as 10,000 to 30,000 ohms, or a "low" value, such as 10 ohms.* We are not nearly as concerned about the actual value of the resistance measured.

Step 3

Apply power to the breadboard and repeatedly press and release the pulser. You should observe that the needle on the vom varies between a "high" reading and a "low" reading. With the needle of the vom at a "low" reading, use the Ohms-Adjust knob on the vom to set the needle exactly to 0 ohms.

Step 4

Now repeatedly press and release the pulser. What is the logic state of the pulser when the vom reading is "high"?

It should be logic 0. What is the logic state of the pulser output when the vom reading is "low"? It should be logic 1.

Step 5

Now attach the lamp monitor in the diagram as shown in Fig. 7-44 to the output of the 7405 inverter (pin 2). Repeatedly press and release the pulser. Does the lamp monitor light up either for a "logic 0" or a "logic 1" input to the inverter? Answer yes or no.

If you have done this experiment correctly, you will conclude that this inverter is quite different from the 7404 inverter studied previously. The output from the 7405 inverter is unable to light a lamp monitor.

Questions

1. Why do you think the 7405 inverter cannot light a lamp monitor when the input to the inverter is either at a logic 0 or a logic 1 state?

2. What is meant by the term, open collector output?

EXPERIMENT NO. 5

Purpose

The purpose of this experiment is to demonstrate the behavior of four 7405 inverters with open collector outputs wired together and tied to an output device such as a vom or a lamp monitor.

Pin Configuration of Integrated Circuit (Fig. 7-44)

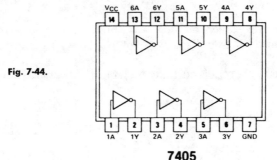

Fig. 7-44.

7405

Schematic Diagram of Circuit (Fig. 7-45)

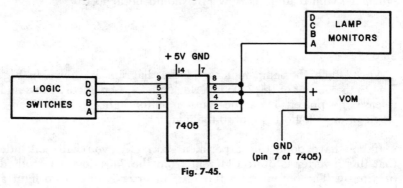

Fig. 7-45.

Step 1

Study the schematic in Fig. 7-45 and in the following space re-write it using the traditional symbol for an inverter with open collector output. You will need to use four inverter symbols.

Step 2

Wire the preceding circuit. Note that pins 2, 4, 6, and 8 are connected. Set the logic switches DCBA initially to 0000. Apply power to the breadboard and determine whether the resistance value on the vom is "high" or "low." Write your answer in the space below.

The vom resistance reading was "high" in our experiment. Is the lamp monitor lit or unlit?

In our case, we observed that the lamp monitor was unlit.

Step 3

Now set the logic switches DCBA to 1111. Is the vom reading "high" or "low" and is the lamp monitor lit or unlit?

The vom reading was "low" and the lamp monitor was still unlit.

Step 4

Vary the logic settings of the four logic switches. How many different settings of the four logic switches produce a "high" resistance reading on the vom?

How many different logic switch settings produce a "low" resistance reading on the vom?

In our case, we observed that quite a few logic states produced a "low" reading; the exact number was fifteen different logic combinations.

Step 5

Fill in the table on the following page.

Step 6

If you set a "high" resistance reading = 1 and a "low" resistance reading = 0, what type of 4-input logic gate have you constructed using the four 7405 inverters? Write the name and the symbol of the gate in the following space.

The answer is, a four-input NOR gate.

Question

1. Explain why you obtained the truth table in Step 5. Why do four 7405 inverters whose open collector outputs are connected together behave in such a way?

D	C	B	A	Resistance Reading ("Low" or "High")
0	0	0	0	
0	0	0	1	
0	0	1	0	
0	0	1	1	
0	1	0	0	
0	1	0	1	
0	1	1	0	
0	1	1	1	
1	0	0	0	
1	0	0	1	
1	0	1	0	
1	0	1	1	
1	1	0	0	
1	1	0	1	
1	1	1	0	
1	1	1	1	

EXPERIMENT NO. 6

Purpose

The purpose of this experiment is to monitor the output of a single 7405 inverter using a vom, a lamp monitor, and a seven-segment LED display while at the same time varying the magnitude of the pull-up resistor to +5 volts.

Pin Configuration of Integrated Circuit (Fig. 7-46)

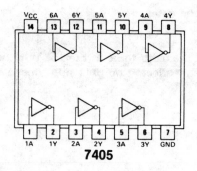

Fig. 7-46.

7405

Schematic Diagram of Circuit (Fig. 7-47)

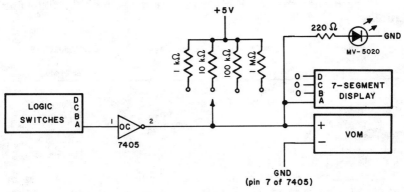

Fig. 7-47.

Step 1

Study the circuit diagram in Fig. 7-47. You will vary the magnitude of the pull-up resistor in this experiment.

Step 2

Set the vom to the 5 V dc scale. Measure the positive voltage that is being applied to the breadboard. You may need to go to the next higher dc voltage scale to do so, however. We measured a voltage of about +5.25 volts ±0.05 volt.

Step 3

Wire the circuit as shown. Apply power to the breadboard. Vary the resistance of the pull-up resistor and note the condition of the MV-5020 LED, whether there is a 0 or a 1 on the seven-segment LED display, and the value of the voltage. Write what you observe in the appropriate places in the following table. Set logic switch A to a logic 0 state.

Pull-up Resistor (ohms)	VOM Voltage (volts)	Seven-Segment LED Display, 0 or 1	MV-5020 LED, Unlit, Lit, or Dimly Lit
1000			
10,000			
100,000			
1,000,000			
10,000,000			
none			

Step 4

We performed the above experiment and obtained the following results:

Pull-up Resistor (ohms)	VOM Voltage (volts)	Seven-Segment LED Display, 0 or 1	MV-5020 LED, Unlit, Lit, or Dimly Lit
1000	+2.2	1	dimly lit
10,000	+1.5	1	dimly lit
100,000	+1.3	1	unlit
1,000,000	+1.3	1	unlit
10,000,000	+1.3	1	unlit
none	+1.3	1	unlit

It can be observed that none of the voltage levels determined by the vom is greater than 2.2 volts, which is considerably less than the +5 volts that we have expected to observe for a logic 1 state. The answer to this dilemma is that:

- We observe a logic 1 output state whenever the voltage output from a gate or inverter is greater than +2.0 volts.
- We observe a logic 0 output state whenever the voltage output from a gate or inverter is between 0 and +0.8 volt.
- The output voltage region between +0.8 volt and +2.0 volts is an indeterminate region that in general should be avoided. Usually, a voltage of +1.3 volts will correspond to a logic 1 state, but not always.
- *The problem with the unexpectedly low values for the output voltages, as measured by the vom, is with our lamp monitor, which simply consisted of a light-emitting diode (LED) and a 220-ohm resistor. The lamp monitor circuit in Fig. 7-48 is totally unsuitable for the circuit, since it "loads down" the output of the 7405 IC chip and reduces the voltage to no more than +2.2 volts with a 1000-ohm pull-up resistor.*

Here is strong experimental evidence for the need of a "driver" transistor to drive the LED. In the following step, we shall repeat the above experiment, only this time we shall use the following circuit (Fig. 7-49) for the lamp monitor.

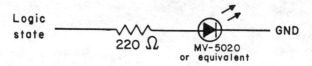

Logic state — 220 Ω — MV-5020 or equivalent — GND

Fig. 7-48.

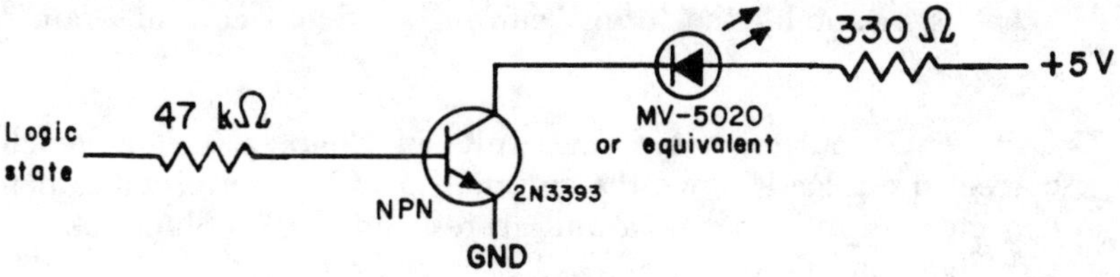

Fig. 7-49.

Step 5

In this step, we repeat the table in which we compare the 7405 output as a function of the resistance of the pull-up resistor. The object here is to demonstrate how the results differ when the lamp monitor no longer acts as a "current sink" (or a current drain) and reduces the output voltage to unacceptably low levels. We obtained the following results:

Pull-up Resistor (ohms)	VOM Voltage (volts)	Seven-Segment LED Display, 0 or 1	MV-5020 LED with Transistor-Driver, Lit, Unlit, or Dimly Lit
1000	+5.1	1	lit
10,000	+4.2	1	lit
100,000	+1.5	1	lit
1,000,000	+1.3	1	lit
10,000,000	+1.3	1	lit
none	+1.3	1	lit
2200	+5.0	1	lit
4700	+4.7	1	lit
6800	+4.5	1	lit

This table of voltages is much more acceptable. It should be clear that 2200 ohms is an acceptable choice as a pull-up resistor for a single 7405 inverter with open collector output. Resistors in excess of about 20,000 ohms are completely unsuitable as pull-up resistors.

We conclude that a lamp monitor consisting of a LED and a current-limiting resistor is unacceptable; it "loads down" the output of a gate or inverter and reduces the output voltage to the indeterminate region between voltages that clearly correspond to either a logic 0 or logic 1 state.

Questions

1. What is meant by "loading down" the output of an integrated circuit?

2. What is meant by the terms "current sink" or "current drain"?

3. Can you calculate, based on results in Chapter 6, how much current drain loads down the output of a 7405 inverter with open collector output? Assume a pull-up resistor of 1000 ohms. This is a difficult question.

4. What is the current "fan in" of one TTL input load? You may not automatically know the answer to this question. Look up the term, "fan in," in a digital electronics dictionary.

EXPERIMENT NO. 7

Purpose

The purpose of this experiment is to demonstrate the behavior of four 7405 inverters whose open collectors are connected to a 1000-ohm pull-up resistor tied to +5 volts.

Pin Configuration of Integrated Circuit (Fig. 7-50)

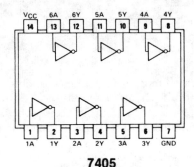

Fig. 7-50.

7405

Schematic Diagram of Circuit (Fig. 7-51)

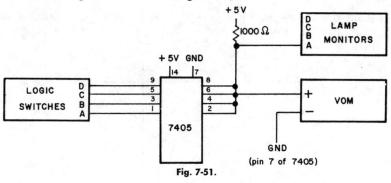

Fig. 7-51.

Step 1

In this experiment, you will use both a transistor-driven LED as a lamp monitor as well as a vom to follow the output from the 7405 chip.

Step 2

Wire the circuit as shown in Fig. 7-51. Set the vom to the +5-volts scale. Apply power to the breadboard and set the four logic switches to DCBA = 0000. Is the lamp monitor lit or unlit?

Step 3

What is the voltage reading on the vom?

We observed a reading of 4.8 volts and a lit lamp monitor. We concluded that the output from our four inverters was at a "logic 1" state.

Step 4

With DCB = 000, set A = 1. What happens both to the lamp monitor and to the vom?

In our case, the lamp monitor became unlit and the vom gave a reading of +0.1 volt. We concluded that the output was at a logic 0 state.

Step 5

Fill in the following truth table. A logic 0 state corresponds to an unlit lamp monitor and a logic 1 state corresponds to a lit lamp monitor.

D	C	B	A	Q
0	0	0	0	1
0	0	0	1	0
0	0	1	0	
0	0	1	1	
0	1	0	0	
0	1	0	1	
0	1	1	0	
0	1	1	1	
1	0	0	0	
1	0	0	1	
1	0	1	0	
1	0	1	1	
1	1	0	0	
1	1	0	1	
1	1	1	0	
1	1	1	1	

To what type of 4-input gate does the truth table correspond? Draw a schematic diagram of the gate in the following space.

A 4-input NOR gate.

EXPERIMENT NO. 8

Purpose

The purpose of this experiment is to demonstrate a "wired-OR" circuit using four 7401 2-input positive NAND gates with open collector outputs.

Pin Configuration of Integrated Circuit (Fig. 7-52)

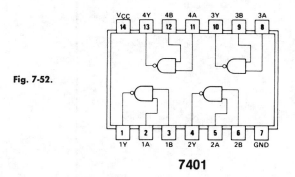

Fig. 7-52.

7401

Schematic Diagram of Circuit (Fig. 7-53)

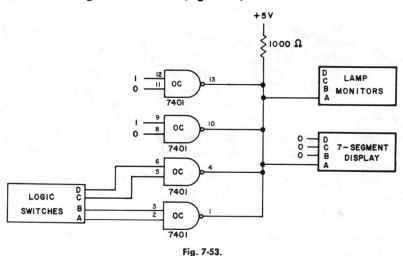

Fig. 7-53.

Step 1

Wire the circuit as shown in Fig. 7-53. Note that you only have four logic switches, but eight inputs to the four 7401 2-input NAND gates. We have arranged the circuit so that the outputs from the two top NAND gates are both at logic 1.

Step 2

Apply power to the breadboard and fill in the following truth table.

D	C	B	A	Q
0	0	0	0	
0	0	0	1	
0	0	1	0	
0	0	1	1	
0	1	0	0	
0	1	0	1	
0	1	1	0	
0	1	1	1	
1	0	0	0	
1	0	0	1	
1	0	1	0	
1	0	1	1	
1	1	0	0	
1	1	0	1	
1	1	1	0	
1	1	1	1	

Step 3

Explain in the following space how the preceding circuit acts as a "wired-OR" circuit. What is "wired" and why do you use the word "OR"?

Questions

1. The truth table in Step 2 was written for positive logic. Convert the table to negative logic. Use the following truth table.

D	C	B	A	Q

2. Change the schematic diagram in this experiment so that the 7403 quad 2-input positive NAND gate with open collector output IC chip can be used instead of the 7401 chip. What pin numbers must now apply to the four 2-input NAND gates?

EXPERIMENT NO. 9

Purpose

The purpose of this experiment is to further demonstrate a "wired-OR" circuit with the aid of three different gates: the 7409 2-input positive AND gate, the 7415 3-input positive AND gate, and the 7422 4-input positive NAND gate. All three of these gates have open collector outputs that are tied to +5 volts using a 1000-ohm pull-up resistor.

Pin Configurations of Integrated Circuits (Figs. 7-54 through 7-56)

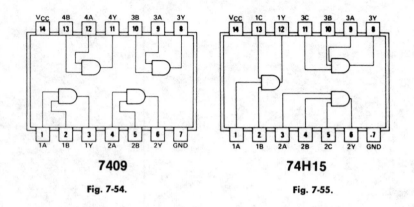

7409

Fig. 7-54.

74H15

Fig. 7-55.

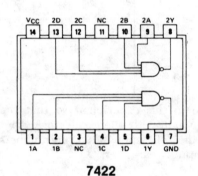

7422

Fig. 7-56.

Schematic Diagram of Circuit (Fig. 7-57)

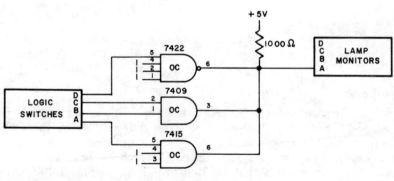

Fig. 7-57.

Step 1

Study the circuit in Fig. 7-57 carefully, then wire it as shown.

Step 2

Fill in the following truth table.

D	C	B	A	Q
0	0	0	0	
0	0	0	1	
0	0	1	0	
0	0	1	1	
0	1	0	0	
0	1	0	1	
0	1	1	0	
0	1	1	1	
1	0	0	0	
1	0	0	1	
1	0	1	0	
1	0	1	1	
1	1	0	0	
1	1	0	1	
1	1	1	0	
1	1	1	1	

Step 3

In the space below, explain how the above circuit acts as a "wired-OR" circuit.

Question

1. Draw a schematic diagram of a "wired-OR" circuit that contains two 7405 inverters, one 7422 4-input NAND gate, one 7401 2-input NAND gate, one 7409 2-input AND gate, and one 7415 3-input AND gate. Use a 1000-ohm pull-up resistor. Use a separate sheet of paper for your answer.

TEST

This test probes your understanding of the digital electronic concepts that we have described in this chapter. Please write your answers on a separate piece of paper.

1. In your own words, define the following terms:

> positive logic
> negative logic
> positive bus
> negative bus
> wired-OR circuit
> three-state output
> open collector output
> bus

2. Write the correct truth tables for the following gates:

> 2-input negative AND gate
> 2-input negative NAND gate
> 2-input negative OR gate
> 2-input negative NOR gate

3. Draw the correct timing diagram (i.e., digital waveform) for the transmission of the following digital information:

- the digital word 0111 in negative logic
- the digital word 1001 in positive logic
- the digital word 1000 in negative logic
- the digital word 0000 in negative and in positive logic
- the digital word 0101 in negative logic
- the digital word 11001101010 in positive logic

Assume that the least-significant bit in each of the above digital words is transmitted first. The LSB is on the far right.

Your performance on this test will be acceptable if you can answer all of the above questions correctly in a one-hour closed book examination. You have encountered all of the above concepts in this chapter.

WHAT HAVE YOU ACCOMPLISHED IN THIS CHAPTER?

Review of Objectives

We stated in the Introduction to this chapter that at the end you would be able to do the following:

- Construct a multiplexer using a pair of 74126 integrated circuits containing eight three-state bus buffer gates.

  You multiplexed a 7490 decade counter and a 7493 binary counter using a pair of 74126 chips in Experiment No. 3.

- Determine an acceptable value for a "pull-up" resistor connected to the output of a 7405 inverter with an open collector output.

  In Experiment No. 6 you determined that a pull-up resistor of 1000 ohms, and perhaps 2200 ohms, was acceptable when connected to the output of a 7405 inverter and tied to +5 volts.

- Construct a "wired-OR" circuit.

  You constructed wired-OR circuits both in Experiment No. 8 and in Experiment No. 9.

- Pass a test in which you are asked to define the following terms:

                positive logic
                negative logic
                positive bus
                negative bus
                wired-OR circuit
                three-state output
                open collector output
                bus

  You have been asked to do this in Question No. 1 on the test.

8

Flip-Flops and
Monostable Multivibrators

INTRODUCTION

A basic requirement for every computer, whether large or small, is the requirement to store logic 0 and logic 1 states. Such digital data storage can be temporary or semipermanent. Mass data storage networks consisting of thousands to millions of individual storage elements called *flip-flops* or *bistable elements* are widespread. Some memories are fabricated from semiconductors, while others are fabricated from magnetic material deposited on tapes, disks, floppy disks, drums, and the like. Semiconductor memories are becoming larger, in terms of memory capacity, as well as less expensive; they will play an increasingly important role in mass data storage in the future. In this chapter, you will study the basic semiconductor memory unit, the flip-flop.

You will also be introduced to the use of monostable multivibrators to provide reasonably precise gating pulses in gated counter systems. You will wire two monostables, the 74121—which can generate very short monostable pulse widths but is not very precise—and the 555—which generates longer pulse widths and has greater precision.

OBJECTIVES

At the completion of this Chapter, you will be able to do the following:

- Define bistable element, flip-flop, synchronous input, asynchronous input, D-type flip-flop, latch, preset, clear, and digital waveform.
- Distinguish between a positive edge and a negative edge on a clock pulse.
- Explain how a simple latch circuit, composed of two 2-input NAND gates, can be used to debounce an spdt mechanical switch.
- Explain the differences between rise time, fall time, and propagation delay.
- Describe what inversion circles mean when applied to clocked devices.
- Describe the operation characteristics of the 7474 D-type positive-edge–triggered flip-flop.
- Describe the operation characteristics of the 7475 latch.
- Explain how the preset and clear inputs function in a typical flip-flop.
- Describe three types of flip-flop clocking actions.
- Demonstrate the operation and behavior of the 7470, 7473, 7474, 7475, 7476, 74106, and 74175 flip-flops as either flip-flops or latches, or both.
- Demonstrate the operation of four different monostable multivibrators, the 555, 74121, 74122, and 74123 integrated-circuit chips.
- Construct a one-and-only-one synchronizer.
- Latch four binary coded decimal bits from a 7490 decade counter using a 7475 latch.
- Define astable element, monostable element, and bistable element.
- Describe the operation characteristics of the 74121, 74122, and 74123 monostable chips.
- Explain the differences in the operation of the 555 chip as a monostable and an astable multivibrator.
- Measure the frequency of a clock given a suitable monostable multivibrator chip.
- Measure the pulse width from a monostable multivibrator given a clock of known frequency.

DEFINITIONS

astable element—A two-state element that has no stable elements.

bistable element—Another name for a flip-flop. A circuit in which the output has two stable states and can be caused to go to either of these states by input signals, but remains in that state permanently after the input signals are removed.[4]

asynchronous inputs—Those terminals in a flip-flop that can affect the output state of the flip-flop independent of the clock. Called set, preset, reset or DC set, and reset or clear.[4]

clear—An asynchronous input. Also called reset. It is used to restore the output, Q, of a memory element or flip-flop to logic 0.

clock—A pulse generator that controls the timing of computer switching circuits and memory states and regulates the speed at which the computer central processor operates. It serves to synchronize all operations in a digital system.[4]

clock input—The terminal on a flip-flop whose condition or change of condition controls the admission of data into a flip-flop through its synchronous inputs. The clock signal performs two functions: (1) it permits data signals to enter the flip-flop; (2) after entry, it directs the flip-flop to change state accordingly.[4]

clocked logic—Logic systems that wait until the arrival of a system clock pulse or command, at which time they respond and provide an output or change of output.

fall time—The time required for an output voltage of a digital circuit to change from a logic 1 to a logic 0 state.

flip-flop—A circuit having two stable states and the capability of changing from one state to another with the application of a clock signal, and remaining in that state after the removal of signals.[4] Some of the different types of flip-flops are the D-type flip-flop, J-K flip-flop, the R-S flip-flop, the RST flip-flop, and the T flip-flop.

inversion circle—A shorthand notation for an inverter.

latch—A simple logic storage element. A feedback loop used in a symmetrical digital circuit, such as a flip-flop, to retain a state.

level-triggered—The state of the clock input, being either logic 0 or logic 1, carries out a transfer of information or completes an action.

monostable multivibrator—A circuit having only one stable state, from which it can be triggered to change the state, but only for a predetermined interval, after which it returns to the original state.

negative-edge triggered—Transfer of information occurs on the negative edge of the clock pulse.

positive-edge triggered—Transfer of information occurs on the positive edge of the clock pulse.

preset—An asynchronous input. Also called set. It is used to restore the output, Q, of a memory element or flop-flip to logic 1.

propagation delay—A measure of the time required for a logic signal to travel through a logic device or a series of logic devices. It occurs as the result of four types of circuit delays—storage, rise, fall, and turn-on delay—and is the time between when the input signal crosses the threshold-voltage point and when the responding voltage at the output crosses the same voltage point.[1]

reset—See clear.

ripple-counter—A binary counting system in which flip-flops are connected in series.

rise time—The time required for an output voltage of a digital circuit to change from a logic 0 to a logic 1 state.

set—See preset.

synchronous—Operation of a switching network by a clock pulse generator. All circuits in the network switch simultaneously, and all actions take place synchronously with the clock.[4]

synchronous inputs—Those terminals of a flip-flop through which data can be entered but only upon command of a clock. These inputs do not have direct control of the output, as in the case of a gate, but only when the clock permits and commands. Called conditioning inputs, JK inputs, or AC set and reset inputs.[4]

CLOCKED LOGIC

To quote Lancaster[6]:

> *Clocked, synchronous,* or *step-by-step* logic systems make up the bulk of the sophisticated digital circuits of today, particularly at the package or device level. Instead of providing an output immediately after input conditions change, clocked-logic packages wait till the arrival of a system *clock* pulse or command; only then do they respond and provide an output.

> There are several advantages to clocked logic. The first is that unchecked transitions cannot wildly run through a circuit. Instead, changes can only progress one stage at a time in an orderly manner. This one-step-at-a-time action makes devices like shift registers and elaborate counters possible. The second advantage of clocked logic is that everything in a system happens more or less at the same time. This often eliminates or greatly minimizes *race conditions, glitches,* and timing sequence mixups.

> The cornerstones of clocked logic are the J-K flip-flop and the D-type flip-flop, . . .

MEMORY ELEMENTS: FLIP-FLOPS

A memory element is, generally, any device that can store logic 0 and logic 1 bits in such a manner that a single bit or group of bits can be accessed and retrieved. The most common form of memory in digital electronics is the *bistable element,* more commonly known as a *flip-flop*. Excellent definitions for these two important terms have been given by H. V. Malmstadt and C. G. Enke.[4]

bistable element—Another name for flip-flop. A circuit in which the output has two stable states (output states 0 or 1) and can be caused to go to either of these states by input signals, but remains in that state permanently after the input signals are removed. This differentiates the bistable element from a gate also having two output states but which requires the retention of the input signals to stay in a given state. The characteristic of two stable states also differentiates it from a monostable element, which keeps returning to a specific state, and from an astable element, which keeps changing from one state to the other.

flip-flop—A circuit having two stable states and the capability of changing from one state to another with the application of a control signal, and remaining in that state after the removal of signals.

In other words, flip-flop is an inclusive term for all bistable, or two-state devices, including those that are:

- electronic, such as the semiconductor D-type flip-flops, J-K flip-flops, R-S flip-flops, RST flip-flops, and T flip-flops;
- magnetic, such as magnetic core, magnetic disk, magnetic tape, magnetic wire, and magnetic bubble;
- chemical, such as those devices based upon electrochemical phenomena;
- mechanical, such as the pull-chain light switch; and
- fluidic, such as the fluidic flip-flop.

In this book you will be concerned only with semiconductor flip-flops.

We would like to emphasize the difference between a gate and a flip-flop:

A gate requires the retention of its input signals in order to stay in a given state, whereas a flip-flop does not.

Memory elements permit you to store digital information for later use. Such a capability permits you, among other things, to build complex digital electronic machines called *microcomputers, minicomputers,* or *computers.* Regardless of their sizes, all computers employ thousands to millions of semiconductor memory elements. All computers function by storing and acting on only two logic states: logic 0 and logic 1. While existing computers depend, to a large degree, on magnetic memory elements such as magnetic core and magnetic disc, many individuals in the electronics industry predict that semiconductor memory devices, e.g., read/write memories will play an increasingly important role in the storage of digital information in computers. This is certainly the case today for minicomputers and microcomputers, e.g., dynamic read/write memories.

SOME SIMPLE FLIP-FLOPS

A number of different kinds of flip-flops exist. The simplest flip-flip has a single clock input and a single output, Q (Fig. 8-1). Such

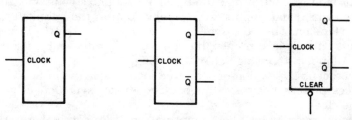

Fig. 8-1. Diagram of simple flip-flop with single input and single output.

Fig. 8-2. Diagram of simple flip-flop with single input and two outputs, one complement of the other.

Fig. 8-3. Adding a clear input permits override of clock input timing and clearing Q to logic 0.

a flip-flop may have a *complementary output*, $\overline{Q}$, that is always at a logic state that is the exact opposite of Q (Fig. 8-2).

A clear input, that permits you to set Q to logic 0 (Fig. 8-3).

A preset input, that permits you to set Q to logic 1 (Fig. 8-4).

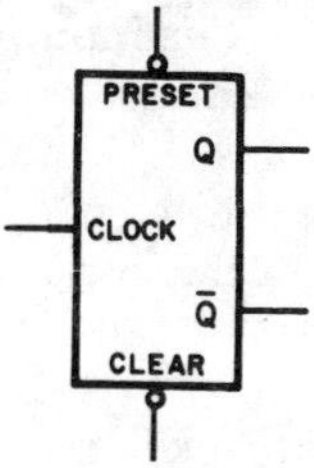

Fig. 8-4. Adding preset input permits you to preset Q to logic 1 also.

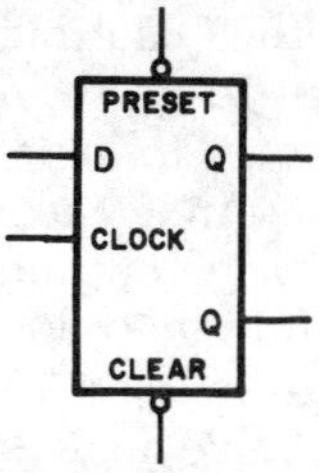

Fig. 8-5. Diagram of D-type flip-flop (D stands for delay or data) which allows you to clock information, present at the D input, to the Q output.

And a data input, D, that is latched at Q when the clock pulse occurs (Fig. 8-5). The clocking action can occur at various times in a clock pulse; this will be discussed later.

Other types of flip-flops include the J-K flip-flop, the RS latch (also known as an R-S flip-flop), the clocked R-S latch, and the T flip-flop. Some of these will be discussed later in this chapter.

Definitions for the above flip-flops are now in order. These definitions are courtesy of Malmstadt and Enke.[4]

D flip-flop—D stands for delay. A flip-flop whose output is a function of the input that appeared one clock pulse earlier; for example, if a logic 1 appeared at the input, the output after the next clock pulse will be a logic 1.

clock—A pulse generator that controls the timing of clocked logic devices and regulates the speed at which such devices operate. It serves to synchronize all operations in a digital system.

clock input—That terminal on a flip-flop whose condition or change of condition controls the admission of data into a flop-flop through the synchronous inputs, and thereby controls the output state of the flip-flop. The clock signals performs two functions: (1) it permits data signals to enter the flip-flop; (2) after entry, it directs the flip-flop to change state accordingly.

synchronous—Operation of a clocked logic system with the aid of a clock pulse generator. All actions take place synchronously with the clock.

asynchronous inputs—Those input pins in a flip-flop that can affect the output state of the flip-flop independent of the clock. Called preset and reset or clear.

synchronous inputs—Those terminals on a flip-flop through which data can be entered but only upon command of the clock. These inputs do not have direct control of the output such as those of a gate, but only when the clock permits and commands. Called JK inputs or D input.

preset, set—An asynchronous input that is used to control the logic state of the Q output. Signals entered through this input cause the Q output to go to logic 1. The preset input cannot cause the Q output to go to logic 0.

clear, reset—An asynchronous input that is used to control the logic state of the Q output. Signals entered through this input cause the Q output to go to logic 0. The clear input cannot cause the Q output to go to logic 1.

latch—A simple logic storage element. A feedback loop used in a symmetrical digital circuit (such as a flip-flop) to retain a logic state.

A latch is used basically as a simple memory element in digital circuits.

A SIMPLE LATCH

We would now like to discuss the properties of a very simple bistable latch that can be constructed from a pair of 7400 2-input positive NAND gates, a pair of 1000-ohm resistors, and either an spdt (single-pole, double-throw) switch or else a single wire connected to ground. A bistable element is a device that is capable of assuming either one of two stable states.

The schematic diagram for the bistable latch is shown in Fig. 8-6; it also includes a truth table for the 2-input NAND gate. Recall that the output of a 2-input NAND gate is logic 0 only if both inputs are at a logic 1 state. With this in mind, we can assign the logic states

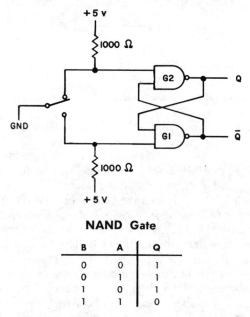

NAND Gate

B	A	Q
0	0	1
0	1	1
1	0	1
1	1	0

Fig. 8-6. Bistable latch circuit schematic composed of two NAND gates; truth table also shown.

given in Fig. 8-7 to the individual inputs and outputs. To obtain these results, we use the following line of reasoning:

The top input to gate G2 must be at logic 0 since this input is grounded. Therefore, *the output from gate G2 must be at logic 1.* Since the output from gate G2 is connected as an input to gate G1, we must have a logic 1 at this input. The remaining input to gate G1 must also be at a logic 1 since this input is "pulled up" to +5 volts with the aid of a 1000-ohm pull-up resistor. Two logic 1 inputs to gate G1 produce a logic 0 output, which is applied at the other input to gate G2.

If we do not move the switch, there will be no change in the bistable latch outputs. They will remain at the indicated logic states indefinitely.

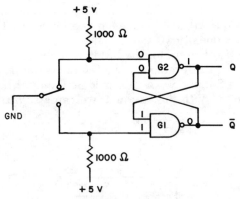

Fig. 8-7. Logic states existing in bistable latch circuit when "key" is up.

Now let us move the switch off of the top connecting wire without touching the switch contact to the lower connecting wire (Fig. 8-8). The question that can be asked is, Does any change in output occur? As shown in Fig. 8-8, the answer is no! The switch contact is between the top and bottom connecting wires. It has not yet touched the bottom wire. The only change that is observable is that the upper input to gate G2 is now a logic 1 state. This change does not cause the unique state (logic 0) to occur at the output of gate G2. We therefore state that the output Q is "latched" at a logic 1 state.

As the final step in our discussion, let us momentarily touch the switch contact to the bottom connecting wire as shown in Fig. 8-9.

A number of logic state changes now occur. The lower input to gate G1 is now grounded and, thus, at a logic 0 state. *This forces the output from gate G1 to be at a logic 1 state.* This same output

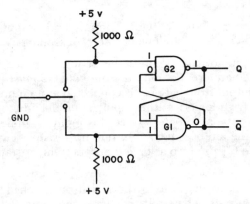

Fig. 8-8. Logic states existing in bistable latch circuit when "key" is in transition between up and down states.

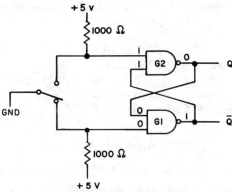

Fig. 8-9. Logic states existing in bistable latch circuit when "key" first touches the down terminal.

serves as one of the inputs to gate G2. Since both inputs to gate G2 are now at logic 1, the unique state for a NAND gate, the output from this gate becomes logic 0. The output from gate G2 is applied to the top input to gate G1. The circuit is now "latched" at a logic 0 state for the output from gate G2. If the switch contact "bounces" off the lower connecting wire *but does not contact the upper connecting wire*, the circuit will remain latched at Q = 0. In fact, the switch contact can bounce on and off the lower connecting wire hundreds of times without changing the latched state of logic 0 at gate G2. This is how a mechanical switch is *debounced*.

A pair of 7402 2-input NOR gates can also be used to debounce a mechanical switch (Fig. 8-10). Such a circuit is not recommended; it draws up to three times more current than the NAND gate debounce circuit. It is also more difficult to pull down a logic level with a resistor than to pull the level up.

Any logic function can be produced with a combination of NAND or NOR gates, from simple flip-flops to the largest computer. A discussion of flip-flop circuits is beyond the scope of this book. We re-

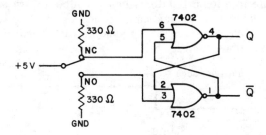

Fig. 8-10. Two 7402 NOR gates used to create a bistable latch.

fer you to more detailed treatment in the following pages from the references listed in the Appendix:

- Reference No. 2, pages 3-1 to 3-13
- Reference No. 4, pages 189 to 197
- Reference No. 5, Module No. 3, pages 254 to 258
- Reference No. 6, pages 188 to 207
- Reference No. 8, Chapter 3.

POSITIVE AND NEGATIVE EDGES

We can define the term, *digital waveform,* as follows:

digital waveform—A graphical representation of a digital signal, showing the variations in logic state as a function of time. This type of representation is also known as a *timing diagram.*

The main reason we use digital waveforms is *to make it possible to show the logic conditions that exist at a particular instant of time in a complex digital circuit.* Actually, the digital circuit need not be complex. However, the use of digital waveforms is essential for complex circuits. For simple logic circuits, it may be necessary to show the digital waveforms for one or only several points in the circuit. For complex circuits, ten or fifteen different digital waveforms may be required to help one understand what is happening.

A commonly observed digital waveform is a *train of clock pulses* (Fig. 8-11). For any digital waveform, time progresses from left to right. The lower state, or baseline, of a digital waveform is usually

time →

Fig. 8-11. Train of clock pulses.

considered to be the logic 0 state. The top of pulses is the logic 1 state, or greater than +2.5 volts. We assume that the change from a logic 0 state to a logic 1 state, which is called a *positive edge,* occurs very quickly (in several nanoseconds or less), essentially instantaneously. We represent such a change by a vertical line in the waveform, as shown in Fig. 8-12.

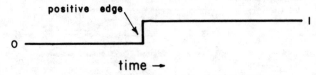

positive edge

0

1

time →

Fig. 8-12. Representation of a positive edge.

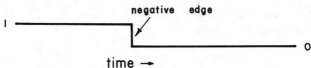

Fig. 8-13. Representation of a negative edge.

We represent a change from logic 1 to logic 0 by a straight line called a *negative edge* (Fig. 8-13).[1]

Again, the transition is assumed to occur instantaneously. In reality, the change in logic state is not instantaneous. There is both a *rise time* and a *fall time,* as defined next.

rise time—The time required for the positive leading edge of a pulse to rise from 10% to 90% of its final value. It is proportional to the time constant and is a measure of the steepness of the pulse wavefront. In digital electronics, the measured length of time required for an output voltage of a digital circuit to change from a low voltage level (logic 0) to a high voltage level (logic 1).[1]

fall time—The time required for the negative trailing edge of a pulse to decrease from 90% to 10% of its initial value. In digital electronics, the measured length of time required for an output voltage of a digital circuit to change from a high voltage level (logic 1) to a low voltage level (logic 0).[1]

While on the subject of rise and fall times, it is useful to define *propagation delay:*

propagation delay—A measure of the time required for a logic signal to travel through a logic device or series of logic devices forming a logic string. It occurs as the result of four types of circuit delays—storage, rise, fall, and turn-on delay—and is the time between when the input signal crosses the threshold-voltage point and when the responding output voltage crosses the same voltage point.[1]

For a regular TTL gate chip, a typical propagation delay is 10 nanoseconds $= 0.000000010$ second $= 10^{-8}$ second. A low-power TTL gate chip has a propagation delay of as much as 33 ns, whereas a Schottky TTL chip has a propagation delay of only 3 ns. When you are working at very high digital frequencies with complex logic circuits, the concept of propagation delay can be quite important.

When designing digital circuits, you should be alert to the possibility of a *race* condition. The term, *race,* can be defined as follows:

race—The condition that occurs when changing the state of a system requires a change in two or more state variables. If the final state is affected by which variable changes first, the condition is a critical race. Also, the condition that exists when a signal is propagated through two or more memory elements during the same clock period.

Race conditions occur when two time-dependent signals are "racing" each other to cause an action or group of actions to take place. Race conditions are often caused by poor design and by propagation delays. In Fig. 8-14, a race condition exists because of the propagation delay of the three inverters, assuming that A and B change state at the same time.

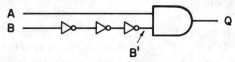

Fig. 8-14. Diagram of circuit in which race conditions exist.

In this case, we would initially expect the output, Q, to remain at logic 0 because A and B change state simultaneously and the required unique state, $A = B = 1$, is not achieved. As shown in the timing diagrams in Fig. 8-15, the propagation delay of the inverters adds a race and produces the "glitch" at Q; the $B = 0$ logic condition takes time to pass through the inverters.

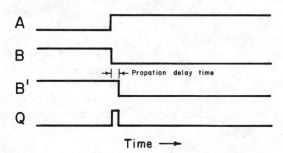

Fig. 8-15. Exaggerated behavior of race circuit in Fig. 8-14; output pulse created is extremely short.

INVERSION CIRCLES

In previous chapters, you have observed that the little circles present at the outputs of AND and OR gates represent *inversion* (Fig. 8-16).

These circles appear frequently in block diagrams of digital devices and circuits, so it is useful to discuss the range of possible meanings for such circles. Before we do, several definitions are in order:

to disable, to inhibit—To prevent the passage of a digital signal into or through a digital device or circuit.

to enable, to strobe, to trigger—To permit the passage of a digital signal into or through a digital device or circuit.

When applied to a clocked logic device, the term *to clock* is frequently used to signify the passage of a digtial signal into or the change of state of a bistable element. We shall use these verbs interchangeably throughout this book.

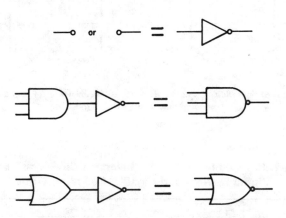

Fig. 8-16. Examples depicting use of inversion circles.

Inversion circles can be applied at both the output (as with NAND and NOR gates) and the input of gates. For example, you can use inversion circles to facilitate the representation of the types of transformations shown in Figs. 8-17 and 8-18, where it is seen that an inversion circle is a shorthand notation for an inverter. The possible

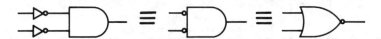

Fig. 8-17. Use of inversion circles to demonstrate equivalence of an AND gate with negated inputs and a NOR gate.

meanings for inversion circles at the inputs or outputs of digital devices are given in Table 8-1.

For inputs to clocked devices or circuits, the following conventions apply:

If there is no circle present at the intersection of the input line and the block diagram (Fig. 8-19), then a positive clock pulse, or positive edge, will enable, strobe, or clock the device or circuit to perform an action.

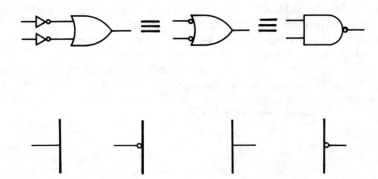

Fig. 8-18. Use of inversion circles to demonstrate equivalence of an OR gate with negated inputs and a NAND gate.

Table 8-1. Possible Meanings for Inversion Circles or Outputs of Digital Devices and Circuits, Excluding Gates

Use	Symbol	Meaning
Inputs		Logic 1 enables device or circuit Logic 0 disables device or circuit Positive edge enables, strobes, triggers, or clocks device or circuit Positive clock pulse strobes or clocks device or circuit Data is presented uninverted
		Logic 0 enables device or circuit Logic 1 disables device or circuit Negative edge enables, strobes, triggers, or clocks device or circuit Negative clock pulse strobes or clocks device or circuit Data is presented inverted
Use	Symbol	Meaning
Outputs		Output from device or circuit is not inverted Output from device or circuit is a positive clock pulse
		Output from device or circuit is inverted Output from device or circuit is a negative clock pulse

If there is a circle present at the intersection of the input line and the block diagram (Fig. 8-20), then a negative clock pulse, or negative edge, will enable, strobe, or clock the device or circuit to perform an action.

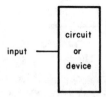

Fig. 8-19. A positive clock pulse or positive edge causes circuit or device to respond.

For outputs from digital devices and circuits, the following conventions apply:

If there is no circle present at the intersection of the output line and the block diagram (Fig. 8-21), then the output from the circuit or device is not inverted and is considered to be unique in the logic 1 state.

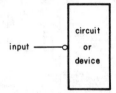

Fig. 8-20. Negative clock pulse or negative edge causes circuit or device to respond.

If there is a circle present at the intersection of the output line and the block diagram (Fig. 8-22), then the output from the circuit or device is inverted and is considered to be unique in the logic 0 state.

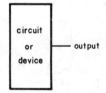

Fig. 8-21. Unique output or normal responses of circuit or device is logic 1 state.

The schematics of chips and circuits provided by manufacturers are generally very reliable with respect to the presence or absence of inversion circles. In the general literature, the inversion circles are frequently omitted. It simply is too time consuming, for example, to draw sixteen inversion circles at the ouputs of the 74154 decoder

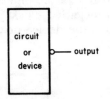

chip. When inversion circles are present, there usually is a very good reason for them to be shown. Be alert when you see them.

THE 7474 D-TYPE POSITIVE-EDGE–TRIGGERED FLIP-FLOP

Our favorite flip-flop, which is actually a latch, is the 7474 D-type positive edge–triggered flip-flop with preset and clear. The pin configuration is shown in Fig. 8-23. A single 7474 integrated circuit contains two independent D-type latches, as can be clearly seen from the pin configuration.

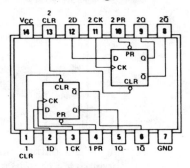

7474

Fig. 8-23. Pin configuration of 7474 D-type positive-edge–triggered flip-flop.

The truth table for this chip, along with the truth tables for other 7400-series flip-flops, is provided in *The TTL Data Book for Design Engineers* by Texas Instruments Incorporated. To understand such truth tables, you will require the following definitions:

- H means logic 1
- L means logic 0
- Q_0 is the level of Q before the indicated input conditions were established.
- $\overline{Q_0}$ is the complement of Q_0.
- * means that this configuration is not stable; that is, it will not persist when the preset and clear inputs return to their inactive (logic 1) state.
- ↑ represents a positive-edge–triggered clock input.
- ↓ represents a negative-edge–triggered clock input

Table 8-2. Truth Table for 7474 D-Type
Positive-Edge–Triggered Flip-Flop

Inputs				Outputs	
Preset	Clear	Clock	D	Q	$\overline{Q}$
L	H	X	X	H	L
H	L	X	X	L	H
L	L	X	X	H*	H*
H	H	↑	H	H	L
H	H	↑	L	L	H
H	H	L	X	Q_0	$\overline{Q_0}$

- ⎍ represents a level-triggered clock input.
- X means that the logic state of this input is irrelevant; it can be either logic 0 or logic 1 and has no influence on the logic state of the output after the active transition of the indicated input.
- TOGGLE means that each output, Q and $\overline{Q}$, changes to the complement of its previous state on each active transition of the clock.

With the above definitions, you should now understand the truth table provided by Texas Instruments Incorporated for the 7474 D-type flip-flop (Table 8-2).

We can rewrite this truth table in terms of logic 0 and logic 1 states (Table 8-3). The asynchronous inputs are PRESET and CLEAR. They override the CLOCK and D inputs when at a logic 0 state. Both PRESET and CLEAR can be simultaneously at logic 0, but this set of states produces ambiguous results. It is a condition that you should avoid in logic designs.

Table 8-3. Truth Table for 7474 Flip-Flop Written in Terms of
Logic 0 and Logic 1 States Rather Than H and L States

Inputs				Outputs	
Preset	Clear	Clock	D	Q	$\overline{Q}$
0	1	X	X	1	0
1	0	X	X	0	1
0	0	X	X	*	*
1	1	↑	1	1	0
1	1	↑	0	0	1
1	1	0	X	Q_0	$\overline{Q_0}$

A SIMPLE 7474 CIRCUIT

One of the first experiments that you will perform with the 7474 D-type latch is to observe the influence of the CLOCK and D inputs on the output, Q, from the latch (Fig. 8-24). The output, Q, will be determined by the logic state of the D input *at the positive edge of each clock pulse applied to the CLOCK input.* For example, consider the timing diagram shown in Fig. 8-25.

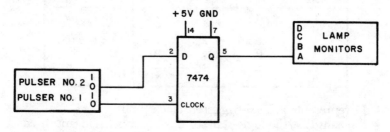

Fig. 8-24. Simple circuit permits demonstrating characteristics of 7474 D-type flip-flop.

Note: When the output, Q, goes to a logic 1 state, it is at the positive edge of the CLOCK signal. Once the output is latched to logic 1, it remains at that logic state until D goes to logic 0 and we have another positive edge. When studying timing diagrams, remember that time proceeds from left to right. The first events are

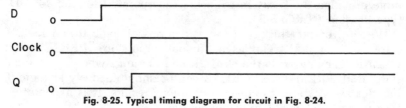

Fig. 8-25. Typical timing diagram for circuit in Fig. 8-24.

at the far left on the diagrams. Propagation delays are usually not shown.

PRESET AND CLEAR INPUTS

The following rules apply to the PRESET and CLEAR inputs to all flip-flops:

The PRESET and CLEAR inputs should not both be enabled. An indeterminate or unstable output from the flip-flop will result.

An enabled PRESET input overrides all synchronous inputs, such as CLOCK, D, J, and K, and sets the output, Q, of the flip-flop to logic 1.

An enabled CLEAR input overrides all synchronous inputs, such as CLOCK, D, J, and K, and sets the output, Q, of the flip-flop to logic 0.

The synchronous inputs on a flip-flop can be enabled only by disabling both the PRESET and CLEAR asynchronous inputs.

Most, if not all, of the 7400-series flip-flops have inversion circles at the PRESET and CLEAR inputs. We can add, therefore, the following rule to the above:

A logic 0 state applied to the PRESET input will set the flip-flop output to logic 1; a logic 0 state applied to the CLEAR output will clear the flip-flop output to logic 0. Logic 0 states should not be simultaneously applied to both the PRESET and CLEAR inputs on a flip-flop.
The negative clock pulse symbol, ⌐⎍⌐ .

is frequently used to indicate that we are either presetting or clearing a flip-flop. The following flip-flops have inversion circles at the PRESET and CLEAR inputs: 7470, 74H71, 7472, 7473, 7474, 7476, 7478, 74101, 74102, 74103, 74106, 74107, 74108, 74109, 74110, 74111, 74112, 74113, and 74114.

EDGE- AND LEVEL-TRIGGERED FLIP-FLOPS

All flip-flops are *clocked logic* devices. Rather than provide an output immediately after the input conditions change—as is the case with all gates—flip-flops wait until the arrival of a clock pulse. Only then do they respond and provide a new or updated output. The term, *triggered,* is synonymous with the term, *clocked,* which means the application of a single clock pulse at the CLOCK input of a flip-flop.

Clock pulses can be either *positive clock pulses* or *negative clock pulses.* A positive clock pulse is a complete logic cycle from logic 0 to logic 1 and back to logic 0 (Fig. 8-26). Whereas a negative clock pulse is a complete logic cycle from logic 1 to logic 0 and back to logic 1 (Fig. 8-27).

The three basic types of clocking actions can be described as follows:

• *Positive-edge–triggered* flip-flops

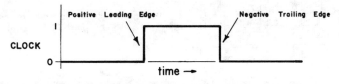

Fig. 8-26. Positive clock pulse.

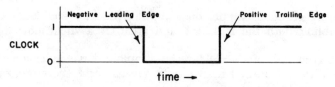

Fig. 8-27. Negative clock pulse.

Transfer of information from the synchronous input(s) to the output of the flip-flop occurs on the positive edge of the clock pulse.

- *Negative-edge–triggered* flip-flops

  Transfer of information from the synchronous input(s) to the output of the flip-flop occurs on the negative edge of the clock pulse.

- *Level-triggered* flip-flops

  The state of the CLOCK input being either logic 0 or logic 1 carries out a transfer of information or completes an action. Normally, flip-flops of the *master-slave* type are level triggered.

The characteristics of master-slave-type flip-flops, such as the 7476 J-K flip-flop, will be discussed later in this chapter.

THE 7475 LATCH

Another useful and popular flip-flop is the 7475 latch. The pin configuration is shown in Fig. 8-28.

Four latches are present on the 7475 chip. Two of these latches are enabled at pin 4, and the remaining two latches are enabled at pin 13. If you connect pin 4 to pin 13, you can enable all four bistable latches simultaneously.

Note that the term, "enable," is used for pins 4 and 13 rather than "clock." The reason is that each 7475 bistable latch behaves some-

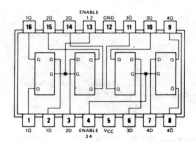

Fig. 8-28. Pin configuration for 7475 latch IC.

7475

what like an AND gate with memory. When pins 4 and 13 are at a logic 1 state, digital input data at the D input to each latch will transfer through each latch and appear almost instantaneously at the output, Q. When a 7475 latch is enabled, we say that it acts as a *follower,* with the output, Q, following the input, D. The propagation delay for a 7475 latch is approximately 30 ns, which is three times the propagation delay for a regular TTL gate such as the 7400.

The 7475 latch differs from an AND gate in the following way: when the enable input makes a logic 1 to logic 0 transition, the instantaneous value of the D input is latched. Thus, a 7475 latch has memory, whereas a 7408 AND gate does not.

Please observe that the 7475 chip has neither PRESET nor CLEAR inputs. The truth table for its operation is given in Table 8-4.

Table 8-4. Truth Table and Description of the 7475 Latch Integrated Circuit

(Each Latch)

Inputs		Outputs	
D	G	Q	$\overline{Q}$
L	H	L	H
H	H	H	L
X	L	Q_0	$\overline{Q_0}$

H = high level, L = low level, X = irrelevant
Q_0 = the level of Q before the high-to-low transition of G

These latches are ideally suited for use as temporary storage for binary information between processing units and input/output or indicator units. Information present at a data (D) input is transferred to the Q output when the enable (G) is high and the Q output will follow the data input as long as the enable remains high. When the enable goes low, the information (that was present at the data input at the time the transition occurred) is retained at the Q output until the enable is permitted to go high.

We can rewrite this truth table in terms of logic 0 and logic 1 states (Table 8-5).

Table 8-5. Truth Table for the 7475 Latch Integrated Circuit Written in Terms of Logic 0 and Logic 1 States

Inputs		Outputs	
D	G	Q	$\overline{Q}$
0	1	0	1
1	1	1	0
X	0	Q_0	$\overline{Q_0}$

The pin configuration of the 7475 chip can be better understood with the aid of the block diagram shown in Fig. 8-29. This diagram clearly shows the existence of four bistable latches, each of which has both a Q and a $\overline{Q}$ output. Latches 1 and 2 are clocked simultaneously, as are latches 3 and 4.

COMPARISON OF 7474 AND 7475 LATCHES

The operation of the 7474 and 7475 latches can be summarized as follows:

7474 latch: If the D input is at a logic 1 state, the Q output goes to or remains at a logic 1 state at the positive edge of the CLOCK pulse. If the D input is at a logic 0 state, the Q output goes to or remains at a logic 0 state at the positive edge of the clock pulse.

7475 latch: If the D input is at a logic 1 state at the negative edge of the clock pulse, the output Q latches a logic 1 state. If the D input is at a logic 0 state at the negative edge of the clock pulse, the output Q latches a logic 0 state. When the enable input is at logic 1, the output Q follows the logic state of the D input with approximately a 30-ns propagation delay.

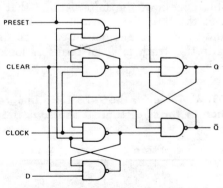

Fig. 8-30. Internal gating circuit for 7474 D-type latch.

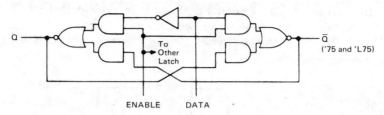

Fig. 8-31. Internal gating circuit for 7475 D-type latch.

The two latches employ two entirely different combinations of gates. For the 7474 latch, six 3-input NAND gates are used (Fig. 8-30), whereas for the 7475 latch, two AND-OR-Invert gates and an inverter are required (Fig. 8-31).

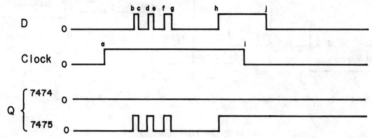

Fig. 8-32. Timing diagrams illustrating some differences between 7474 and 7475 latches.

The difference between the two latches can be seen by considering the timing diagrams when both latches are clocked simultaneously. For example, in the timing diagrams in Fig. 8-32, the output from the 7474 latch remains at logic 0 because its D input was at logic 0 at the positive edge of the clock pulse (point a). On the other hand, the 7475 "follows" the D input for as long as the clock is at logic 1. Latching of the D input on the 7475 occurs on the negative edge of the clock pulse (point i).

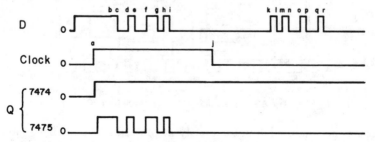

Fig. 8-33. Another set of timing diagrams illustrating differences between 7474 and 7475 latches.

In the timing diagrams in Fig. 8-33, it is evident that the 7475 output follows the input only when the clock input is at logic 1. The circuit that you would use to perform such experiments is provided in Fig. 8-34.

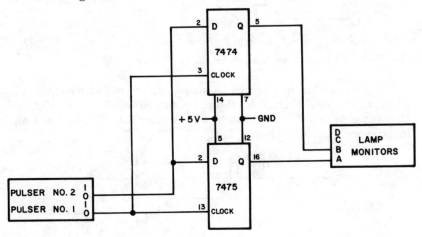

Fig. 8-34. Schematic of circuit that permits comparing behavior of 7474 and 7475 latches.

THE 74100 LATCH

The 74100 latch chip is a 24-pin chip that contains eight bistable latches that are identical in behavior to the 7475 latches. The pin configuration for the chip is shown in Fig. 8-35. You should observe that there are no complementary outputs, $\overline{Q}$, and that four

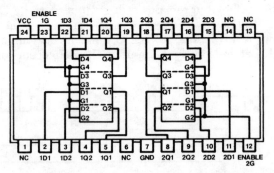

Fig. 8-35. Pin configurations of 74100 latch IC.

latches are enabled simultaneously at pins 12 and 23. These latches are "followers" just as the 7475 latches. The truth table and logic configuration are the same as for the 7475 (Table 8-6 and Fig. 8-36).

Table 8-6. Truth Table for 74100 D-Type Latch

functional block diagram (each latch)

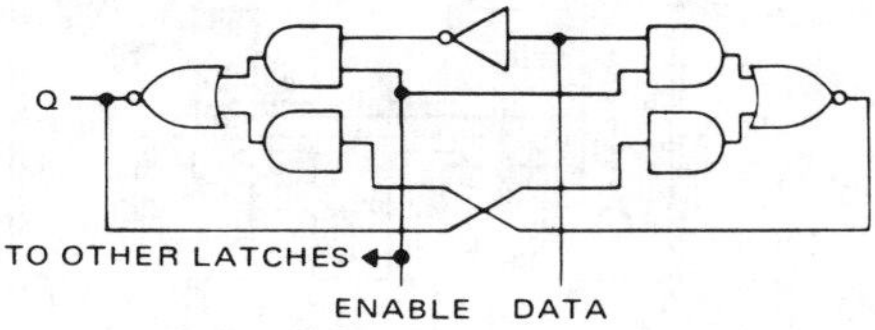

Inputs		Outputs	
(Each Latch)			
D	G	Q	$\overline{Q}$
L	H	L	H
H	H	H	L
X	L	Q_0	$\overline{Q_0}$

H = high level, X = irrelevant
Q_0 = the level of Q before the high-to-low transition of G

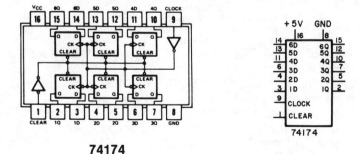

TO OTHER LATCHES

ENABLE   DATA

Fig. 8-36. Internal gating circuit for 74100 latch IC.

These latches are ideally suited for use as temporary storage for binary information between processing units and input/output or indicator units. Information present at a data (D) input is transferred to the Q output when the enable (G) is high and the Q output will follow the data input as long as the enable remains high. When the enable goes low, the information (that was set up at the data input at the time the transition occurred) is retained at the Q output until the enable is permitted to go high.

THE 74174 AND 74175 D-TYPE POSITIVE-EDGE–TRIGGERED FLIP-FLOPS

The D-type flip-flops in the 74174 and 74175 chips are identical in characteristics to the 7474 D-type flip-flop that we have discussed previously. The only difference between the chips is that there are six such D-type flip-flops in the 74174 D-type flip-flop chip and four such flip-flops in the 74175 chip (Figs. 8-37 and 8-38).

All of the flip-flops in the 74174 and 74175 chips are positive-edge triggered. There is a CLEAR input on each chip, but no PRE-

74174

Fig. 8-37. Pin configuration and schematic for 74174 D-type positive-edge–triggered flip-flop IC.

141

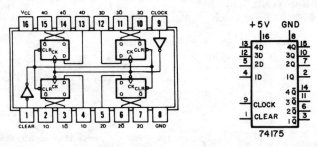

74175

Fig. 8-38. Pin configuration and schematic for 74175 D-type positive-edge–triggered flip-flop IC.

SET input. The CLEAR input clears all four or six flip-flops simultaneously. Similarly, the CLOCK input on each chip clocks the D input into all four or six flip-flops simultaneously. This is shown in Fig. 8-39. The truth table for the two chips is given in Table 8-7.

Table 8-7. Truth Table for 74174 and 74175 D-Type Flip-Flops

(Each Flip-Flop)

Inputs			Outputs	
Clear	Clock	D	Q	$\overline{Q}$†
L	X	X	L	H
H	↑	H	H	L
H	↑	L	L	H
H	L	X	Q_0	$\overline{Q_0}$

H = high level (steady state)
L = low level (steady state)
X = irrelevant
↑ = transition from low to high level
Q_0 = the level of Q before the indicated steady-state input conditons were established
† = '175, 'LS175, and 'S175 only

The details of the CLEAR and CLOCK inputs can be seen in the functional block diagrams from the *TTL Data Book* by Texas Instruments Incorporated (Fig. 8-39). Note that the symbol at the CK input on each flip-flop has the following meaning:

A group of flip-flops that are simultaneously clocked and cleared function as a *register*. They store simultaneously as many bits of information as there are flip-flops in the register. For example, the 74175 chip functions as a 4-bit register, whereas the 74174 chip functions as a 6-bit register. The concept of a register is very important in digital computers.

functional block diagrams

'174, 'LS174, 'S174

'175, 'LS175, 'S175

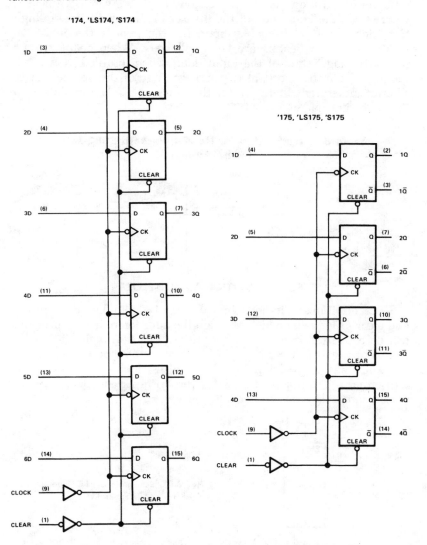

Fig. 8-39. Functional block diagram for 74174 and 74175 D-type latch ICs.

HEWLETT-PACKARD LATCH/DISPLAYS

A very interesting and useful latch is the latch contained within the Hewlett-Packard 5082-7300 series numeric indicators. The characteristics of the 4-bit latch are essentially identical to those of the 7475 and 74100 bistable latch chips. The only difference is that *a logic 0 enables the 5082-7300 series numeric indicators.* The truth table for each bit on the numeric display latch is given in Table 8-8, where Q_0 is the logic state of the display bit before the low-to-high transition of the latch enable input. In other words, the 5082-7300 series numeric indicators are latch/followers. When enabled, they follow the logic state of the input data; when disabled, they latch the logic state that exists at the positive edge of the enable signal. The manufacturer's literature for the numeric displays is shown on the followiing page.

Table 8-8. Truth Table for Hewlett-Packard 5082-7300 Latch/Displays

Inputs		Output
Input Bit	Latch Enable	Display Bit
0	0	0
1	0	1
X	1	Q_0

SOME ADDITIONAL FLIP-FLOPS

Some additional flip-flops include the J-K flip-flop with preset and clear (Fig. 8-40) which, through the addition of a 7404 inverter, can be converted into a D-type flip-flop (Fig. 8-41); the R-S latch, also known as the R-S flip-flop (Fig. 8-42); the clocked R-S latch, also known as the RST flip-flop (Fig. 8-43), which can be converted into either a T flip-flop (Fig. 8-44), or, with the aid of a 7404 inverter, into a D-type flip-flop (Fig. 8-45).

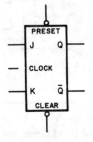

Fig. 8-40. Schematic of J-K flip-flop with preset and clear.

HEWLETT hp PACKARD

COMPONENTS

NUMERIC and HEXADECIMAL INDICATORS

5082-7300 SERIES

FEATURES

- Numeric 5082-7300/-7302
  - 0-9, Test State, Minus Sign, Blank States
  - Decimal Point
    - 7300 Right Hand D.P.
    - 7302 Left Hand D.P.
- Hexadecimal 5082-7340
  - 0-9, A-F, Base 16 Operation
  - Blanking Control, Conserves Power
  - No Decimal Point

- DTL – TTL Compatible
- Includes Decoder/Driver with Memory
  - 8421 Positive Logic Input
- 4 X 7 Dot Matrix Array
  - Shaped Character, Excellent Readibility
- Standard .600 inch X .400 inch Dual-in-Line Package including Contrast Filter
- Categorized for Luminous Intensity
  - Assures Uniformity of Light Output from Unit to Unit within a Single Category

DESCRIPTION

The HP 5082-7300 series solid state numeric and hexadecimal indicators with on-board decoder/driver and memory provide a reliable, low-cost method for displaying digital information.

The 5082-7300 numeric indicator decodes positive 8421 BCD logic inputs into characters 0-9, a "–" sign, a test pattern, and four blanks in the invalid BCD states, The unit employs a right-hand decimal point. Typical applications include point-of-sale terminals, instrumentation, and computer systems.

The 5082-7302 is the same as the 5082-7300, except that the decimal point is located on the left-hand side of the digit.

The 5082-7340 hexadecimal indicator decodes positive 8421 logic inputs into 16 states, 0-9 and A-F. In place of the decimal point an input is provided for blanking the display (all LED's off), without losing the contents of the memory. Applications include terminals and computer systems using the base-16 character set.

The 5082-7304 is a "±1" overrange character, including decimal point, used in instrumentation applications.

PACKAGE DIMENSIONS

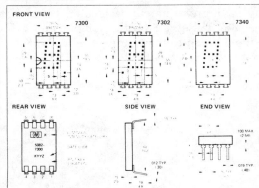

FRONT VIEW — 7300 — 7302 — 7340

REAR VIEW   SIDE VIEW   END VIEW

PIN	FUNCTION	
	5082-7300 and 7302 Numeric	5082-7340 Hexadecimal
1	Input 2	Input 2
2	Input 4	Input 4
3	Input 8	Input 8
4	Decimal point	Blanking control
5	Latch enable	Latch enable
6	Ground	Ground
7	V_{CC}	V_{CC}
8	Input 1	Input 1

NOTES: 1. Dimensions in inches and (millimeters).
2. Unless otherwise specified, the tolerance on all dimensions is ±.015 inches.

145

Some definitions for the above flip-flops, courtesy of Malmstadt and Enke,[4] are provided below. The definition of the D-type flip-flop was given earlier.

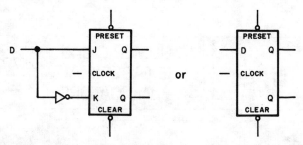

Fig. 8-41. Adding 7404 inverter between J and K inputs, converts J-K flip-flop to D-type latch.

D flip-flop—D stands for delay. A flip-flop whose output is a function of the input that appeared one clock pulse earlier; for example, if a 1 appeared at the input, the output after the next clock pulse will be a 1.[4]

Fig. 8-42. Schematic of R-S flip-flop.

J-K flip-flop—A flip-flop having two inputs designated J and K. At the application of a clock pulse, a 1 on the J input and a 0 on the K input will set the flip-flop to the 1 state; a 1 on the K input and a 0 on the J input will reset it to the 0 state; and 1's simulta-

Fig. 8-43. Schematic of clocked R-S flip-flop.

neously on both inputs will cause it to change state regardless of the previous state. J = 0 and K = 0 will prevent change.[4]

R-S flip-flop—A flip-flop consisting of two cross-coupled NAND gates having two inputs designated R and S. A 1 on the S input and

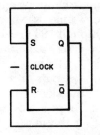

Fig. 8-44. Schematic of T flip-flop.

a 0 on the R input will reset (clear) the flip-flop to the 0 state, and 1 on the R input and 0 on the S input will set it to the 1 state. It is assumed that 0's will never appear simultaneously at both inputs. If both inputs have 1's it will stay as it was; 1 is considered nonactivating. A similar circuit can be formed with NOR gates.[4]

RST flip-flop—A flip-flop having three inputs, R, S, and T. This unit works as the R-S flip-flop except that the T input is used to cause the flip-flop to change states.[4] Also called a clocked R-S flip-flop, where the T input is the clock input.

T flip-flop—A flip-flop having only one input. A pulse appearing on the input will cause the flip-flop to change states. Used in ripple counters.[4]

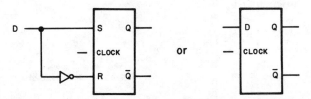

Fig. 8-45. Adding 7404 inverter between R and S inputs converts R-S flip-flop into D-type latch.

MASTER-SLAVE FLIP-FLOPS

A *master-slave flip-flop* is a circuit that contains two flip-flops, a master and a slave. The master flip-flop receives information on the positive leading edge of a clock pulse and transfers information to the slave (the output flip-flop) on the negative trailing edge of the clock pulse. As discussed by Malmstadt and Enke,[4] the following four steps occur at the indicated points on the positive clock pulse shown in Fig. 8-46.

Fig. 8-46. Diagram of positive clock pulse input to master-slave flip-flop. Information transfer occurs at various points on the pulse

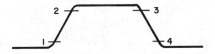

147

The following four steps apply to an R-S master-slave flip-flop constructed from nine NAND gates. For further information, consult pages 197 through 199 in reference 4. The basic object of the master-slave flip-flop is to *isolate the inputs of the flip-flop from the outputs.*

- At point 1, a pair of NAND gates in the slave flip-flop close, thus isolating the slave from the master.
- At point 2, a pair of NAND gates in the master flip-flop open, thus connecting the master to the input information to the master-slave flip-flop.
- At point 3, the pair of NAND gates mentioned at point 2 close, thus isolating the master from the input information.
- At point 4, the pair of NAND gates mentioned at point 1 open, thus connecting the master to the slave and transferring information to the output of the master-slave flip-flop.

J AND K INPUTS

On certain types of flip-flops, what happens to the flip-flop during the clock pulse can be modified by *conditioning inputs,* which change the output characteristics of the flip-flop in a predetermined way. For example, in a J-K flip-flop (a master-slave flip-flop) such as that shown in Fig. 8-47.

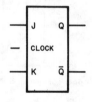

Fig. 8-47. Schematic of J-K flip-flop.

- When J = 0 and K = 1, Q can go to or stay at logic 0 but cannot go to logic 1.
- When J = 1 and K = 0, Q can go to or stay at logic 1 but cannot go to logic 0.
- When J = 0 and K = 0, Q remains at its logic state; the clock has no effect.
- When J = 1 and K = 1, Q changes to the opposite logic state at each clock pulse. In other words, it *toggles*—switches back and forth between the two logic states.

It should be noted, however, that *the CLEAR and PRESET inputs* (Fig. 8-40) *have the highest priority and override the J, K, CLOCK, and similar inputs to a flip-flop.*

THE 7476 J-K FLIP-FLOP WITH PRESET AND CLEAR

A commonly used J-K flip-flop is the 7476 master-slave J-K flip-flop with preset and clear; the pin configuration is shown in Fig. 8-48. A single 7476 integrated circuit contains two independent J-K flip-flops.

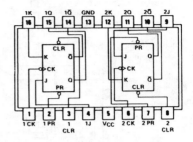

Fig. 8-48. Pin configuration for 7476 J-K flip-flop with preset and clear.

7476

The truth table for this integrated circuit is shown in Table 8-9 and a functional block diagram is given in Fig. 8-49. We shall make no attempt to explain the operation of the master-slave circuit given in Fig. 8-49.

In the 7400-series of integrated–circuit chips, three types of 7476 flip-flop integrated circuits are available: the 7476, shown above in Fig. 8-49; the 74H76, the high-speed version of the 7476; and

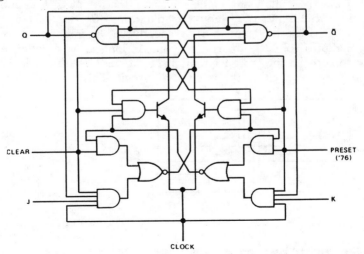

Fig. 8-49. Functional block diagram for 7476 J-K flip-flop with preset and clear; same circuitry found in 7473 and 74107 J-K flip-flop ICs.

Table 8-9. Truth Table for 7476 and 74H76 J-K Flip-Flops

Inputs					Outputs	
Preset	Clear	Clock	J	K	Q	$\bar{Q}$
L	H	X	X	X	H	L
H	L	X	X	X	L	H
L	L	X	X	X	H*	H*
H	H	⎍	L	L	Q_0	$\bar{Q}_0$
H	H	⎍	H	L	H	L
H	H	⎍	L	H	L	H
H	H	⎍	H	H	TOGGLE	

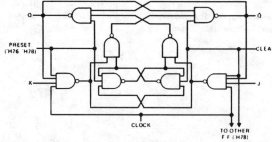

Fig. 8-50. Functional block diagram for 74476 J-K flip-flop with preset and clear; same circuitry found in 74473 and 74478 J-K flip-flop ICs.

the 74LS76, low-power Schottky version of the 7476. The pin configuration for all three chips is the same, as shown in Fig. 8-48. However, the functional block diagram that depicts the gating circuit is different. We show the diagrams for the 74H76 and 74LS76 in Figs. 8-50 and 8-51, respectively. In most cases, such information is of little interest to you. As long as you understand how to use the integrated circuit itself, it matters little what circuitry is present within the integrated circuit. This certainly is true

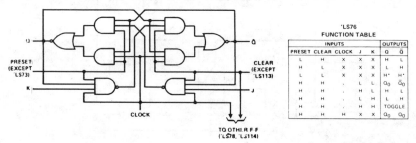

Courtesy Hewlett-Packard

Fig. 8-51. Functional block diagram and truth table for 74LS76 J-K flip-flop with preset and clear; same circuitry found in 74LS73, 74LS78, 74LS112, 74LS113, and 74LS114 ICs. Flip-flops are all negative-edge triggered.

with the much more sophisticated LSI chips marketed today; in most cases, the manufacturers of such chips will not tell you much about what is inside the chips.

MANUFACTURER'S LITERATURE

On several pages following, we give the pin configurations and truth tables for most of the flip-flops and latches in the 7400 series of integrated circuits. The 7475, 74100, 74174, and 74175 flip-flops were omitted from this listing, as they have been described previously in this chapter. You should by now be able to interpret the manufacturer's literature, which is courtesy of Texas Instruments Incorporated. Study the definitions given at the bottom of each table.

COMPARISON OF J-K FLIP-FLOPS

It is useful to compare the behavior of three types of J-K flip-flops: a *positive-edge–triggered* (7470), a *negative-edge–triggered* (74106 and others), and a *level-triggered* (7473, 7476, 74107, and others) J-K flip-flop. Table 8-10 partially summarizes their behavior. The outputs are all the same, but the transfer of information occurs at different points on the clock input pulse.

The only difference between these three types of flip-flops is the time during the clock pulse at which data at the J and K conditioning inputs determine the output of the flip-flops. Thus:

7470: Postive-edge–triggered flip-flop. Data present at the J and K inputs at the positive edge of the clock pulse determine the final output, Q, of the flip-flop. The 7470 is not a master-slave flip-flop.

74106: Negative-edge–triggered flip-flop. Data present at the J and K inputs at the negative edge of the clock pulse determine the final output, Q, of the flip-flop. The 74106 and related flip-flops are of the master-slave type.

Table 8-10. Behavior Summary of 7470, 7473, and 74106 J-K Flip-Flops

Conditioning Inputs		Clock Input			Q Output		
J	K	7470	7473	74106	7470	7473	74106
0	0	↑	⎍	↓	Q	Q	Q
1	0	↑	⎍	↓	1	1	1
0	1	↑	⎍	↓	0	0	0
1	1	↑	⎍	↓	TOGGLE	TOGGLE	TOGGLE

70 AND-GATED J-K POSITIVE-EDGE-TRIGGERED FLIP-FLOPS WITH PRESET AND CLEAR

FUNCTION TABLE

INPUTS					OUTPUTS	
PRESET	CLEAR	CLOCK	J	K	Q	$\bar{Q}$
L	H	X	X	X	H	L
H	L	X	X	X	L	H
L	L	X	X	X	H*	H*
H	H	↑	L	L	Q_0	$\bar{Q}_0$
H	H	↑	H	L	H	L
H	H	↑	L	H	L	H
H	H	↑	H	H	TOGGLE	
H	H	L	X	X	Q_0	$\bar{Q}_0$

positive logic: $J = J1 \cdot J2 \cdot \bar{J}$
$K = K1 \cdot K2 \cdot \bar{K}$
If inputs $\bar{J}$ and $\bar{K}$ are not used, they must be grounded.

See page 120

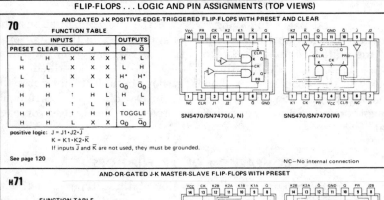

SN5470/SN7470(J, N)

SN5470/SN7470(W)

NC—No internal connection

H71 AND-OR-GATED J-K MASTER-SLAVE FLIP-FLOPS WITH PRESET

FUNCTION TABLE

INPUTS				OUTPUTS	
PRESET	CLOCK	J	K	Q	$\bar{Q}$
L	X	X	X	H	L
H	⊓	L	L	Q_0	$\bar{Q}_0$
H	⊓	H	L	H	L
H	⊓	L	H	L	H
H	⊓	H	H	TOGGLE	

positive logic: $J = (J1A \cdot J1B) + (J2A \cdot J2B)$
$K = (K1A \cdot K1B) + (K2A \cdot K2B)$

See page 124

SN54H71/SN74H71(J, N)

SN54H71/SN74H71(W)

L71 AND-GATED R-S MASTER-SLAVE FLIP-FLOPS WITH PRESET AND CLEAR

FUNCTION TABLE

INPUTS					OUTPUTS	
PRESET	CLEAR	CLOCK	S	R	Q	$\bar{Q}$
L	H	X	X	X	H	L
H	L	X	X	X	L	H
L	L	X	X	X	H*	H*
H	H	⊓	L	L	Q_0	$\bar{Q}_0$
H	H	⊓	H	L	H	L
H	H	⊓	L	H	L	H
H	H	⊓	H	H	INDETERMINATE	

positive logic: $R = R1 \cdot R2 \cdot R3$
$S = S1 \cdot S2 \cdot S3$

See page 128

SN54L71/SN74L71(J, N)

SN54L71/SN74L71(T)

NC—No internal connection

H = high level (steady state), L = low level (steady state), X = irrelevant
↑ = transition from low to high level.
⊓ = high-level pulse; data inputs should be held constant while clock is high; data is transferred to output on the falling edge of the pulse.
Q_0 = the level of Q before the indicated input conditions were established.
TOGGLE: Each output changes to the complement of its previous level on each active transition (pulse) of the clock.
*This configuration is nonstable; that is, it will not persist when preset and clear inputs return to their inactive (high) level.

Courtesy Texas Instruments Incorporated

AND-GATED J-K MASTER-SLAVE FLIP-FLOPS WITH PRESET AND CLEAR

72

FUNCTION TABLE

INPUTS					OUTPUTS	
PRESET	CLEAR	CLOCK	J	K	Q	Q̄
L	H	X	X	X	H	L
H	L	X	X	X	L	H
L	L	X	X	X	H*	H*
H	H	⊓	L	L	Q0	Q̄0
H	H	⊓	H	L	H	L
H	H	⊓	L	H	L	H
H	H	⊓	H	H	TOGGLE	

positive logic: J = J1·J2·J3; K1·K2·K3

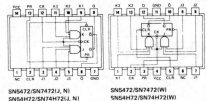

SN5472/SN7472(J, N)
SN54H72/SN74H72(J, N)
SN54L72/SN74L72(J, N)

SN5472/SN7472(W)
SN54H72/SN74H72(W)
SN54L72/SN74L72(T)

See pages 120, 124, and 128

NC—No internal connection

DUAL J-K FLIP-FLOPS WITH CLEAR

73

'73, 'H73, 'L73 FUNCTION TABLE

INPUTS				OUTPUTS	
CLEAR	CLOCK	J	K	Q	Q̄
L	X	X	X	L	H
H	⊓	L	L	Q0	Q̄0
H	⊓	H	L	H	L
H	⊓	L	H	L	H
H	⊓	H	H	TOGGLE	

'LS73 FUNCTION TABLE

INPUTS				OUTPUTS	
CLEAR	CLOCK	J	K	Q	Q̄
L	X	X	X	L	H
H	↓	L	L	Q0	Q̄0
H	↓	H	L	H	L
H	↓	L	H	L	H
H	↓	H	H	TOGGLE	
H	H	X	X	Q0	Q̄0

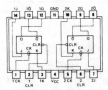

SN5473/SN7473(J, N, W)
SN54H73/SN74H73(J, N, W)
SN54L73/SN74L73(J, N, T)
SN54LS73/SN74LS73(J, N, W)

See pages 120, 124, 128, and 130

DUAL D-TYPE POSITIVE-EDGE-TRIGGERED FLIP-FLOPS WITH PRESET AND CLEAR

74

FUNCTION TABLE

INPUTS				OUTPUTS	
PRESET	CLEAR	CLOCK	D	Q	Q̄
L	H	X	X	H	L
H	L	X	X	L	H
L	L	X	X	H*	H*
H	H	↑	H	H	L
H	H	↑	L	L	H
H	H	L	X	Q0	Q̄0

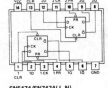

SN5474/SN7474(J, N)
SN54H74/SN74H74(J, N)
SN54L74/SN74L74(J, N)
SN54LS74/SN74LS74(J, N, W)
SN54S74/SN74S74(J, N, W)

SN5474/SN7474(W)
SN54H74/SN74H74(W)
SN54L74/SN74L74(T)

See pages 120, 124, 128, 130, and 132

H = high level (steady state), L = low level (steady state), X = irrelevant
⊓ = high-level pulse; data inputs should be held constant while clock is high; data is transferred to output on the falling edge of the pulse.
↑ = transition from low to high level, ↓ = transition from high to low level
Q0 = the level of Q before the indicated input conditions were established.
TOGGLE: Each output changes to the complement of its previous level on each active transition (pulse) of the clock.
*This configuration is nonstable; that is, it will not persist when preset and clear inputs return to their inactive (high) level.

Courtesy Texas Instruments Incorporated

76

DUAL J-K FLIP-FLOPS WITH PRESET AND CLEAR

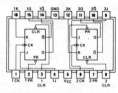

SN5476/SN7476(J, N, W)
SN54H76/SN74H76(J, N, W)
SN54LS76/SN74LS76(J, N, W)

'76, 'H76
FUNCTION TABLE

INPUTS					OUTPUTS	
PRESET	CLEAR	CLOCK	J	K	Q	Q̄
L	H	X	X	X	H	L
H	L	X	X	X	L	H
L	L	X	X	X	H*	H*
H	H	⊓	L	L	Q₀	Q̄₀
H	H	⊓	H	L	H	L
H	H	⊓	L	H	L	H
H	H	⊓	H	H	TOGGLE	

'LS76
FUNCTION TABLE

INPUTS					OUTPUTS	
PRESET	CLEAR	CLOCK	J	K	Q	Q̄
L	H	X	X	X	H	L
H	L	X	X	X	L	H
L	L	X	X	X	H*	H*
H	H	↓	L	L	Q₀	Q̄₀
H	H	↓	H	L	H	L
H	H	↓	L	H	L	H
H	H	↓	H	H	TOGGLE	
H	H	H	X	X	Q₀	Q̄₀

See pages 120, 124, and 130

78

DUAL J-K FLIP-FLOPS WITH PRESET, COMMON CLEAR, AND COMMON CLOCK

SN54H78/SN74H78(J, N, W)

'H78, 'L78
FUNCTION TABLE

INPUTS					OUTPUTS	
PRESET	CLEAR	CLOCK	J	K	Q	Q̄
L	H	X	X	X	H	L
H	L	X	X	X	L	H
L	L	X	X	X	H*	H*
H	H	⊓	L	L	Q₀	Q̄₀
H	H	⊓	H	L	H	L
H	H	⊓	L	H	L	H
H	H	⊓	H	H	TOGGLE	

See pages 124 and 128

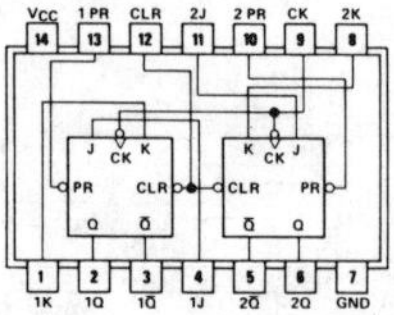

'LS78
FUNCTION TABLE

INPUTS					OUTPUTS	
PRESET	CLEAR	CLOCK	J	K	Q	Q̄
L	H	X	X	X	H	L
H	L	X	X	X	L	H
L	L	X	X	X	H*	H*
H	H	↓	L	L	Q₀	Q̄₀
H	H	↓	H	L	H	L
H	H	↓	L	H	L	H
H	H	↓	H	H	TOGGLE	
H	H	H	X	X	Q₀	Q̄₀

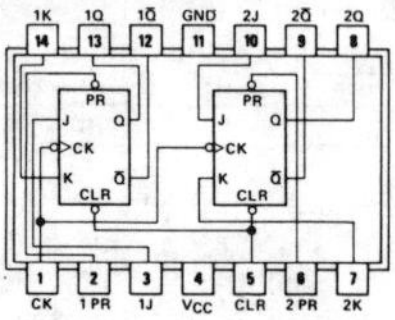

SN54L78/SN74L78(J, N, T)
SN54LS78/SN74LS78(J, N, W)

See page 130

H = high level (steady state), L = low level (steady state), X = irrelevant
⊓ = high-level pulse; data inputs should be held constant while clock is high; data is transferred to output on the falling edge of the pulse.
↓ = transition from high to low level
Q₀ = the level of Q before the indicated input conditions were established.
TOGGLE: Each output changes to the complement of its previous level on each active transition (pulse) of the clock.
*This configuration is nonstable; that is, it will not persist when preset and clear inputs return to their inactive (high) state.

Courtesy Texas Instruments Incorporated

FLIP-FLOPS . . . LOGIC AND PIN ASSIGNMENTS (TOP VIEWS)

101

AND-OR-GATED J-K NEGATIVE-EDGE-TRIGGERED FLIP-FLOPS WITH PRESET

FUNCTION TABLE

INPUTS				OUTPUTS	
PRESET	CLOCK	J	K	Q	Q̄
L	X	X	X	H	L
H	↓	L	L	Q_0	$\bar{Q}_0$
H	↓	H	L	H	L
H	↓	L	H	L	H
H	↓	H	H	TOGGLE	
H	H	X	X	Q_0	$\bar{Q}_0$

positive logic: J = (J1A·J1B)+(J2A·J2B)
K = (K1A·K1B)+(K2A·K2B)

See page 126

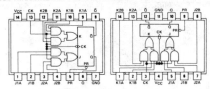

SN54H101/SN74H101(J, N)   SN54H101/SN74H101(W)

102

AND-GATED J-K NEGATIVE-EDGE-TRIGGERED FLIP-FLOPS WITH PRESET AND CLEAR

FUNCTION TABLE

INPUTS					OUTPUTS	
PRESET	CLEAR	CLOCK	J	K	Q	Q̄
L	H	X	X	X	H	L
H	L	X	X	X	L	H
L	L	X	X	X	H*	H*
H	H	↓	L	L	Q_0	$\bar{Q}_0$
H	H	↓	H	L	H	L
H	H	↓	L	H	L	H
H	H	↓	H	H	TOGGLE	
H	H	H	X	X	Q_0	$\bar{Q}_0$

positive logic: J = J1·J2·J3
K = K1·K2·K3

See page 126

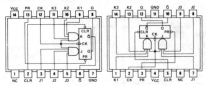

SN54H102/SN74H102(J, N)   SN54H102/SN74H102(W)

NC—No internal connection

103

DUAL J-K NEGATIVE-EDGE-TRIGGERED FLIP-FLOPS WITH CLEAR

FUNCTION TABLE

INPUTS				OUTPUTS	
CLEAR	CLOCK	J	K	Q	Q̄
L	X	X	X	L	H
H	↓	L	L	Q_0	$\bar{Q}_0$
H	↓	H	L	H	L
H	↓	L	H	L	H
H	↓	H	H	TOGGLE	
H	H	X	X	Q_0	$\bar{Q}_0$

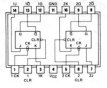

SN54H103/SN74H103(J, N, W)

See page 126

H = high level (steady state), L = low level (steady state), X = irrelevant
↓ = transition from high to low level
Q_0 = the level of Q before the indicated input conditions were established.
TOGGLE: Each output changes to the complement of its previous level on each active transition of the clock.
*This configuration is nonstable; that is, it will not persist when preset and clear inputs return to their inactive (high) level.

Courtesy Texas Instruments Incorporated

FLIP-FLOPS ... LOGIC AND PIN ASSIGNMENTS (TOP VIEWS)

106

DUAL J-K NEGATIVE-EDGE-TRIGGERED FLIP-FLOPS WITH PRESET AND CLEAR

FUNCTION TABLE

INPUTS					OUTPUTS	
PRESET	CLEAR	CLOCK	J	K	Q	Q̄
L	H	X	X	X	H	L
H	L	X	X	X	L	H
L	L	X	X	X	H*	H*
H	H	↓	L	L	Q_0	$\bar{Q}_0$
H	H	↓	H	L	H	L
H	H	↓	L	H	L	H
H	H	↓	H	H	TOGGLE	
H	H	H	X	X	Q_0	$\bar{Q}_0$

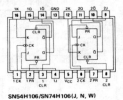

SN54H106/SN74H106(J, N, W)

See page 126

107

DUAL J-K MASTER-SLAVE FLIP-FLOPS WITH CLEAR

FUNCTION TABLE

INPUTS				OUTPUTS	
CLEAR	CLOCK	J	K	Q	Q̄
L	X	X	X	L	H
H	⊓	L	L	Q_0	$\bar{Q}_0$
H	⊓	H	L	H	L
H	⊓	L	H	L	H
H	⊓	H	H	TOGGLE	

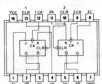

SN54107/SN74107(J, N)

See page 120

108

DUAL J-K NEGATIVE-EDGE-TRIGGERED FLIP-FLOPS WITH PRESET, COMMON CLEAR, AND COMMON CLOCK

FUNCTION TABLE

INPUTS					OUTPUTS	
PRESET	CLEAR	CLOCK	J	K	Q	Q̄
L	H	X	X	X	H	L
H	L	X	X	X	L	H
L	L	X	X	X	H*	H*
H	H	↓	L	L	Q_0	$\bar{Q}_0$
H	H	↓	H	L	H	L
H	H	↓	L	H	L	H
H	H	↓	H	H	TOGGLE	
H	H	H	X	X	Q_0	$\bar{Q}_0$

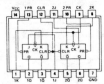

SN54H108/SN74H108(J, N, W)

See page 126

H = high level (steady state), L = low level (steady state), X = irrelevant
↓ = transition from high to low level
⊓ = high-level pulse; data inputs should be held constant while clock is high; data is transferred to output on the falling edge of the pulse.
Q_0 = the level of Q before the indicated input conditions were established.
TOGGLE: Each output changes to the complement of its previous level on each active transition (pulse) of the clock.
*This configuration is nonstable; that is, it will not persist when preset and clear inputs return to their inactive (high) level.

Courtesy Texas Instruments Incorporated

FLIP-FLOPS ... LOGIC AND PIN ASSIGNMENTS (TOP VIEWS)

109

DUAL J-$\bar{K}$ POSITIVE-EDGE-TRIGGERED FLIP-FLOPS WITH PRESET AND CLEAR

FUNCTION TABLE

PRESET	CLEAR	CLOCK	J	$\bar{K}$	Q	$\bar{Q}$
L	H	X	X	X	H	L
H	L	X	X	X	L	H
L	L	X	X	X	H*	H*
H	H	·	L	L	L	H
H	H	↑	H	L	TOGGLE	
H	H	↑	L	H	Q_0	$\bar{Q}_0$
H	H	↑	H	H	H	L
H	H	L	X	X	Q_0	$\bar{Q}_0$

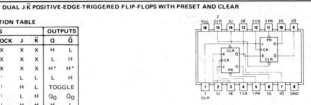

SN54109/SN74109(J, N, W)
SN54LS109/SN74LS109(J, N, W)

See pages 120 and 130

110

AND-GATED J-K MASTER-SLAVE FLIP-FLOPS WITH DATA LOCKOUT

FUNCTION TABLE

PRESET	CLEAR	CLOCK	J	K	Q	$\bar{Q}$
L	H	X	X	X	H	L
H	L	X	X	X	L	H
L	L	X	X	X	H*	H*
H	H	⊓	L	L	Q_0	$\bar{Q}_0$
H	H	⊓	H	L	H	L
H	H	⊓	L	H	L	H
H	H	⊓	H	H	TOGGLE	

positive logic: J = J1·J2·J3
K = K1·K2·K3

See page 120

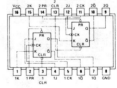

SN54110/SN74110(J, N, W)

NC – No internal connection

111

DUAL J-K MASTER-SLAVE FLIP-FLOPS WITH DATA LOCKOUT

FUNCTION TABLE

PRESET	CLEAR	CLOCK	J	K	Q	$\bar{Q}$
L	H	X	X	X	H	L
H	L	X	X	X	L	H
L	L	X	X	X	H*	H*
H	H	⊓	L	L	Q_0	Q_0
H	H	⊓	H	L	H	L
H	H	⊓	L	H	L	H
H	H	⊓	H	H	TOGGLE	

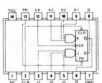

SN54111/SN74111(J, N, W)

See page 120

H = high level (steady state), L = low level (steady state), X = irrelevant, ↑ = transition from low to high level

⊓ = high-level pulse; while the clock is high, changes at the J and K inputs after the specified hold time have no effect. Data is transferred to output on the falling edge of the pulse.

Q_0 = the level of Q before the indicated input conditions were established.

TOGGLE: Each output changes to the complement of its previous level on each active transition (pulse) of the clock.

*This configuration is nonstable; that is, it will not persist when preset and clear inputs return to their inactive (high) level.

FLIP-FLOPS . . . LOGIC AND PIN ASSIGNMENTS (TOP VIEWS)

112

DUAL J-K NEGATIVE-EDGE-TRIGGERED FLIP-FLOPS WITH PRESET AND CLEAR

FUNCTION TABLE

INPUTS					OUTPUTS	
PRESET	CLEAR	CLOCK	J	K	Q	$\bar{Q}$
L	H	X	X	X	H	L
H	L	X	X	X	L	H
L	L	X	X	X	H*	H*
H	H	$\downarrow$	L	L	Q_0	$\bar{Q}_0$
H	H	$\downarrow$	H	L	H	L
H	H	$\downarrow$	L	H	L	H
H	H	$\downarrow$	H	H	TOGGLE	
H	H	H	X	X	Q_0	$\bar{Q}_0$

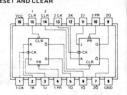

SN54LS112/SN74LS112(J, N, W)
SN54S112/SN74S112(J, N, W)

See pages 130 and 132

113

DUAL J-K NEGATIVE-EDGE-TRIGGERED FLIP-FLOPS WITH PRESET

FUNCTION TABLE

INPUTS				OUTPUTS	
PRESET	CLOCK	J	K	Q	$\bar{Q}$
L	X	X	X	H	L
H	$\downarrow$	L	L	Q_0	$\bar{Q}_0$
H	$\downarrow$	H	L	H	L
H	$\downarrow$	L	H	L	H
H	$\downarrow$	H	H	TOGGLE	
H	H	X	X	Q_0	$\bar{Q}_0$

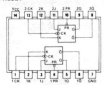

SN54LS113/SN74LS113(J, N, W)
SN54S113/SN74S113(J, N, W)

See pages 130 and 132

114

DUAL J-K NEGATIVE-EDGE-TRIGGERED FLIP-FLOPS WITH PRESET, COMMON CLEAR, AND COMMON CLOCK

FUNCTION TABLE

INPUTS					OUTPUTS	
PRESET	CLEAR	CLOCK	J	K	Q	$\bar{Q}$
L	H	X	X	X	H	L
H	L	X	X	X	L	H
L	L	X	X	X	H*	H*
H	H	$\downarrow$	L	L	Q_0	$\bar{Q}_0$
H	H	$\downarrow$	H	L	H	L
H	H	$\downarrow$	L	H	L	H
H	H	$\downarrow$	H	H	TOGGLE	
H	H	H	X	X	Q_0	$\bar{Q}_0$

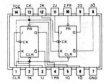

SN54LS114/SN74LS114(J, N, W)
SN54S114/SN74S114(J, N, W)

See pages 130 and 132

H = high level (steady state), L = low level (steady state), X = irrelevant
$\downarrow$ = transition from high to low level
Q_0 = the level of Q before the indicated input conditions were established.
TOGGLE: Each output changes to the complement of its previous level on each active transition of the clock.
*This configuration is nonstable; that is, it will not persist when preset and clear inputs return to their inactive (high) level.

Courtesy Texas Instruments Incorporated

7473, 7476, 74107, and others: Level-triggered flip-flops. Changes in the data present at the J and K inputs while the CLOCK input is at a logic 1 state are sufficient to cause the output, Q, to change logic state at the negative edge of the clock pulse. Lancaster[6] has stated that: "On any level-clocked logic block, the input data or information cannot be changed or altered except immediately after clocking happens. At that time, it can be changed only once." The 7473, 7476, 74107, and related flip-flops are of the master-slave type.

The comparative behavior of the 7470, 7473, 7476, and 74106 flip-flops can best be demonstrated through the use of an experimental circuit in which all four flip-flops are connected to a common CLOCK input, a common J input, and a common K input, as shown in Fig. 8-52. The 7473 and 7476 behave identically. Shown in Figs. 8-53 and 8-54 are two sets of waveforms that apply to the following situations:

$$K = 0 \text{ and } Q = 0 \text{ initially for all four flip-flops}$$
$$J = 0 \text{ and } Q = 1 \text{ initially for all four flip-flops}$$

The sets of waveforms demonstrate the important differences between the three basic types of flip-flops. In Case I (Fig. 8-53), the Q outputs are all initially at logic 0 and, during the first clock pulse, the J input changes state only while the Clock is enabled. Under such conditions, the 7473 and 7476 flip-flops change state. These two flip-flops are level-triggered and change output state at the negative edge of the first clock pulse. The 7470 flip-flop changes logic state at the positive edge of the second clock pulse. Note that the J input is at logic 1 at this positive edge (if J were at a logic 0 at the positive edge, the 7470 flip-flop would remain at $Q = 0$). Finally, the 74106 flip-flop changes at the negative edge of the third clock pulse, at which point in the timing sequence, the J input is at a logic 1 state.

In Case II (Fig. 8-54), all four flip-flops eventually return from $Q = 1$ to $Q = 0$, but they do so at different times. During the first clock pulse, the K input changes state *only* while the Clock is enabled, and not at either edge of the clock pulse. Consequently, only the 7473 and 7476 flip-flops return to a logic 0 state at the negative edge of the first clock pulse. The K input is at a logic 1 at the positive edge of the second clock pulse, and the 7470 flip-flop accordingly returns to $Q = 0$. Finally, the K input is at a logic 1 state at the negative edge of the third clock pulse and, consequently, because of this logic condition, the 74106 flip-flop immediately returns to $Q = 0$.

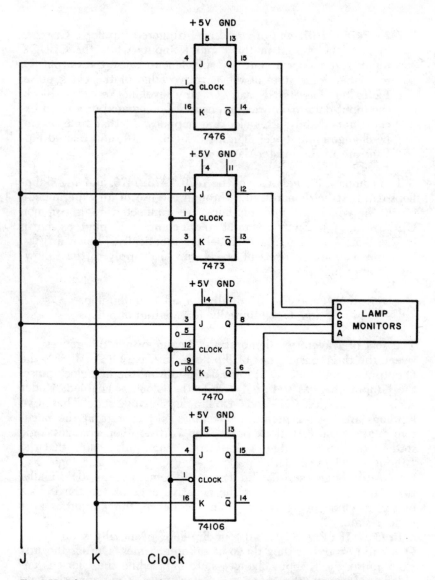

Fig. 8-52. Schematic of circuit that permits comparing three different J-K flip-flop behaviors (7473 and 7476 J-K flip-flops behave the same).

In general, the 7470 and 74106 edge-triggered flip-flops are easier to use when the J and K inputs are rapidly changing. If the 7473, 7476, 74107, and similar flip-flops are employed, the J and K inputs should be held at the desired logic states for a time that is adequate for the flip-flops to function correctly.

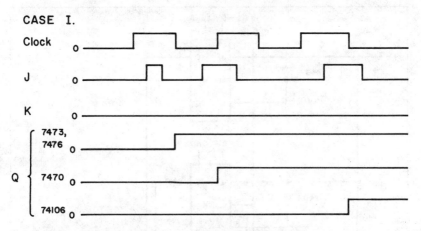

CASE I.

Clock

J

K

Q { 7473, 7476

7470

74106

Fig. 8-53. Case I—timing diagrams showing some differences between three types of J-K flip-flops.

COMPARISON OF LATCHES

We previously indicated that a *latch* is a flip-flop that stores data present at its D input when it receives a clock pulse. Latches can acquire and store data on both the positive and negative edges of a clock pulse. It is useful to compare the behavior of two 7400 series latches—the 7474 and 7475 chips—with three 7400 series of J-K flip-flops—the 7470, 7476, and 4106 chips—that are wired as latches with the aid of a 7404 inverter between the J and K conditioning inputs.

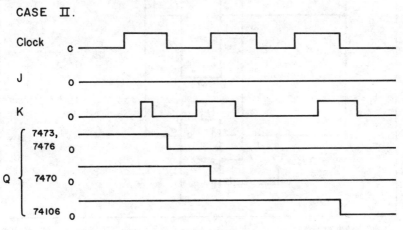

CASE II.

Clock

J

K

Q { 7473, 7476

7470

74106

Fig. 8-54. Case II—timing diagrams showing additional differences between three types of J-K flip-flops.

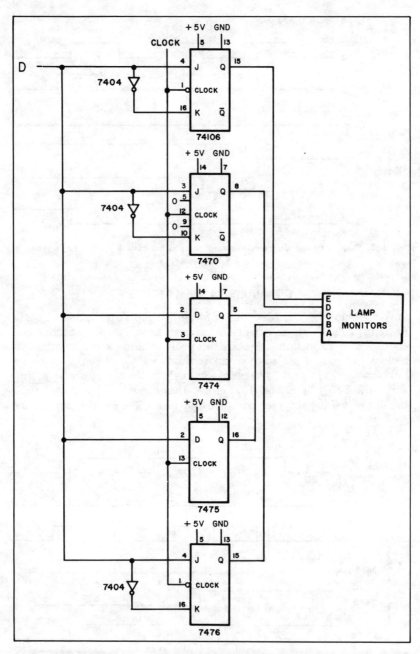

Fig. 8-55. Schematic of circuit that permits comparing behavior of three types of latches (the 7470 and 7474 behave the same).

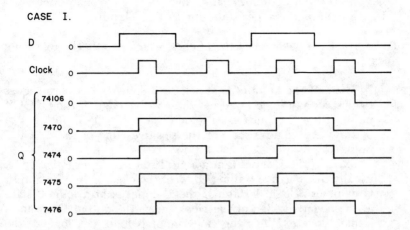

CASE I.

Fig. 8-56. Case I—timing diagrams showing some differences between three types of latches.

As shown in Fig. 8-55, the 7404 inverter converts a J-K flip-flop into a D-type latch by ensuring that the K input is always the complement of the J input, and vice versa. By wiring the five latches together as shown in Fig. 8-55, we ensure that all of the latches receive both the data and clock signals simultaneously.

Shown in Figs. 8-56 and 8-57 are two sets of waveforms that help to distinguish among the behavior of the latches.

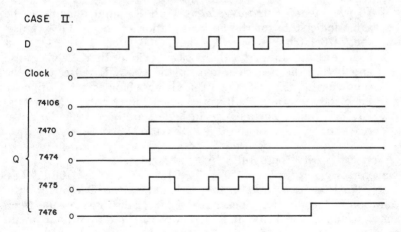

CASE II.

Fig. 8-57. Case II—timing diagrams showing additional differences between three types of latches.

I. The D input does not change state during a clock pulse.
II. The D input changes state during a clock pulse.

To interpret the behavior of the latches, we can apply the following rules:

7474 latch: If the D input is at a logic 1 state, the Q output goes to or stays at a logic 1 state at the positive edge of the CLOCK pulse. If the D input is at a logic 0 state, the Q output goes to or stays at a logic 0 state at the positive edge of the CLOCK pulse.

7475 latch: If the D input is at a logic 1 state at the negative edge, usually the negative trailing edge, of the clock pulse, the output Q assumes a logic 1 state. If the D input is at a logic 0 state at the negative edge of the clock pulse, the output Q assumes a logic 0 state. When the clock input is high, i.e., logic 1, the output Q follows the logic state of the D input.

74106 J-K flip-flop wired as a latch: If the D input is at a logic 1 state at the negative edge of the CLOCK pulse, the output assumes a logic 1 state. If the D input is at a logic 0 state at the negative edge of the CLOCK pulse, the output assumes a logic 0 state.

7470 J-K flip-flop wired as a latch: If the D input is at a logic 1 state at the positive edge of the CLOCK pulse, the Q output goes to or stays at a logic 1 state at the positive edge of the CLOCK pulse. If the D input is at a logic 0 state at the positive edge of the CLOCK pulse, the Q output goes to or stays at the logic 0 state.

7476 J-K flip-flop wired as a latch: If the D input remains at the same logic state for the entire duration of the CLOCK pulse, the 7476 latch behaves like the 74106 latch. If the D input changes logic state after the positive edge of the CLOCK pulse and before the negative edge of the CLOCK pulse, then the following applies: The Q output always changes to the opposite logic state as was initially present on the Q output before the CLOCK pulse. This change in logic state occurs on the negative trailing edge of the CLOCK pulse.

You can verify these rules by studying the two sets of digital waveforms given for the 7470, 7474, 7475, 7476, and 74106 latches. The 7475 latch is unique, in that it "follows" the D input for the duration of the positive clock pulse. Case II distinguishes between the behavior of the 74106 and 7476 latches. We do not recommend that you use the 7473, 7476, or 74107 J-K flip-flops as latches unless you seek the unusual characteristic of such latches.

THE 74279 R-S FLIP-FLOP

The pin configuration and truth table for the 74279 R-S flip-flop, also known as the 74279 R-S latch, are shown in Fig. 8-58. Observe that four simple bistable latches are contained on the integrated

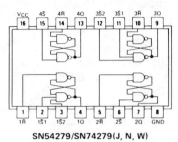

SN54279/SN74279(J, N, W)

FUNCTION TABLE

INPUTS		OUTPUT
$\bar{S}^\dagger$	$\bar{R}$	Q
H	H	Q_0
L	H	H
H	L	L
L	L	H*

H = high level
L = low level
Q_0 = the level of Q before the indicated input conditions were established.
*This output level is pseudo stable; that is, it may not persist when the
$\bar{S}$ and $\bar{R}$ inputs return to their inactive (high) level.
†For latches with double $\bar{S}$ inputs:
   H = both $\bar{S}$ inputs high
   L = one or both $\bar{S}$ inputs low

Fig. 8-58. Pin configuration and truth table for 74279 R-S flip-flop.

circuit. This chip is frequently used to debounce spdt switches. The behavior of the latch circuit has been discussed previously in this chapter.

MONOSTABLE MULTIVIBRATORS

Monostable multivibrator integrated circuits are widely used to generate gating inputs to gated counter circuits. They are considered to be *hybrid* analog-digital chips in that the digital output is determined by the RC time constant of an analog circuit that you wire external to the chip.

A monostable multivibrator is a *monostable element,* that is distinguished from *astable* and *bistable elements* according to the following definitions:

astable element—A two-state element that has no stable states.
bistable element—Another name for a flip-flop. A circuit in which the output has two stable states and can be caused to go to either of these states by input signals, but remains in that state permanently after the input signals are removed.
monostable element, monostable multivibrator—A circuit having only one stable state from which it can be triggered to change the state, but only for a predetermined interval, after which it

returns to the original state. Also called one-shot multivibrator, single-shot multivibrator, or start-stop multivibrator.[1]

Astable elements keep changing from one state to another; they are very useful as clocks or oscillators. Bistable elements can be caused to go from one state to another, and can remain in that state permanently after the input signals have been removed. They are useful as latches and memories. Monostable elements have only a single stable state; such elements can be triggered into such a state, but they remain there only for a limited period of time and soon return to the initial state. The primary use for monostable multivibrators is in *creating pulses of known duration from pulses of shorter, longer, or unknown duration.*

You will encounter four common monostable multivibrator integrated circuits:

- The 555 timer chip wired as a monostable multivibrator
- The 74121 monostable multivibrator with Schmitt trigger inputs
- The 74122 retriggerable monostable multivibrator with clear
- The 74123 dual retriggerable monostable multivibrators with clear

The 555 timer is the best choice for pulse widths ranging from microseconds to hours, and for applications in which the pulse width must be known to better than 0.05%. The 74121, 74122, and 74123 monostables are the preferred choice for pulse widths ranging between 40 ns and 10 μs. If you require 0.05% precision from a 555 timer, keep in mind that you must have passive components that are at least as precise; such components should also have low temperature coefficients. In practice, you should be able to obtain precisions of 0.3%.

THE 74121 MONOSTABLE MULTIVIBRATOR

The 74121 monostable multivibrator chip has the pin configuration and truth table given in Fig. 8-59. The notes apply both to the 74121 chip and to the 74122 and 74123 chips described later. NC means no connection. The Texas Instruments Incorporated *TTL Data Book* provides an excellent description of the 74121 chip, which we have given following this paragraph. An important characteristic of the 74121 chip is that the *input pulse may be of any duration relative to the output pulse.* The repeatability of the output pulses is in the vicinity of ±0.5%. The Schmitt-trigger input at pin 5 permits you to use slowly changing input waveforms with the monostable chip. For further details, consult Chapter 10. The 74121

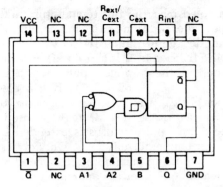

121

FUNCTION TABLE

INPUTS			OUTPUTS	
A1	A2	B	Q	Q̄
L	X	H	L	H
X	L	H	L	H
X	X	L	L	H
H	H	X	L	H
H	↓	H	⎍	⎏
↓	H	H	⎍	⎏
↓	↓	H	⎍	⎏
L	X	↑	⎍	⎏
X	L	↑	⎍	⎏

74121

Fig. 8-59. Pin configuration and truth table for 74121 monostable multivibrator.

is nonretriggerable; once it has started its RC time period, it will continue without being affected by additional trigger inputs.

A description of the 74121 chip follows:

These multivibrators feature dual negative-transistion-triggered inputs and a single positive-transition-triggered input which can be used as an inhibit input. Complementary output pulses are provided.

Pulse triggering occurs at a particular voltage level and is not directly related to the transition time of the input pulse. Schmitt-trigger input circuitry (TTL hysteresis) for the B input allows jitter-free triggering from inputs with transition rates as slow as 1 volt/second, providing the circuit with an excellent noise immunity of typically 1.2 volts. A high immunity to V_{CC} noise of typically 1.5 volts is also provided by interval latching circuitry.

Once fired, the outputs are independent of further transitions of the inputs and are a function only of the timing components. Input pulses may be of any duration relative to the output pulse. Output pulse length may be varied from 40 nanoseconds to 28 seconds by choosing appropriate timing components. With no external timing components (i.e., R_{int} connected to V_{CC}, C_{ext} and R_{ext}/C_{ext} open), an output pulse of typically 30 or 35 nanoseconds is achieved which may be used as a dc triggered reset signal. Output rise and fall times are TTL compatible and independent of pulse length.

Pulse width is achieved through internal compensation and is virtually independent of V_{CC} and temperature. In most applications, pulse stability will only be limited by the accuracy of external timing components.

Jitter-free operation is maintained over the full temperature and V_{CC} ranges for more than six decades of timing capacitance (10 pF to 10 μF) and more than one decade of timing resistance (2 kΩ to 30 kΩ for the SN54121/SN54L121 and 2 kΩ to 40 kΩ for the SN74121/SN74L121). Throughout these ranges, pulse width is defined by the relationship $t_{w(out)} = C_T R_T \text{in} 2 \approx 0.7 \; C_T R_T$. In circuits where pulse cutoff is not critical, timing capacitances up to 1000 μF and timing resistance as low as 1.4 kΩ may be used. Also, the range of jitter-free output pulse widths is extended if V_{CC} is held to 5 volts and free-air temperature is 25°C. Duty cycles as high as 90% are achieved when using maximum recommended R_T. Higher duty cycles are available if a certain amount of pulse-width jitter is allowed.

One way of breadboarding the 74121 chip is shown in Fig. 8-60. You will observe the comment at the $\overline{Q}$ output, "to pin 2 of 555 monostable." The 555 monostable, which we shall discuss shortly, differs from the 74121 chip in that the *input pulse must be of shorter duration than the output pulse.* Thus, if you wish to take advantage of the superior characteristics of the 555 monostable, you may have to drive its input with a 74121 chip.

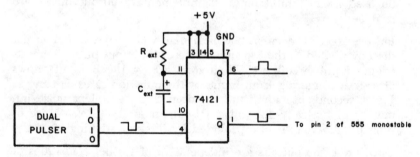

Fig. 8-60. Schematic of circuit that permits generating monostable pulses with pulse widths as low as 40 nanoseconds (no timing restrictions exist on the pulse width applied at pin 4).

The values of R_{ext} and C_{ext} in the above diagram can be obtained from the graphs in Fig. 8-61. Observe that the maximum value for R_{ext} is only 40,000 ohms. The pulse width can be calculated according to the equation

$$t_w = 0.693 \; R_{ext} \; C_{ext}$$

where R_{ext} is in ohms and C_{ext} is in farads. The pulse width, t_w, has units in seconds.

When used as the source of the gating input to a gated counter, the 74121 chip is wired as shown in Fig. 8-62. The output from the

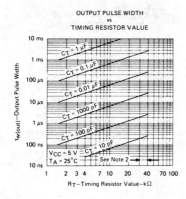

OUTPUT PULSE WIDTH
vs
TIMING RESISTOR VALUE

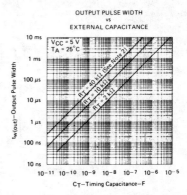

OUTPUT PULSE WIDTH
vs
EXTERNAL CAPACITANCE

§ Data for temperatures below 0°C and above 70°C are applicable for SN54121 and SN54L121 only.
NOTE 2: These values of resistance exceed the maximum recommended for use over the full temperature range of the SN54121 and SN54L121.

Fig. 8-61. Graphs summarizing relationships between output pulse width and external timing resistor and capacitor values.

7400 2-input NAND gate is connected to the input of a cascade of 7490 decade counters.

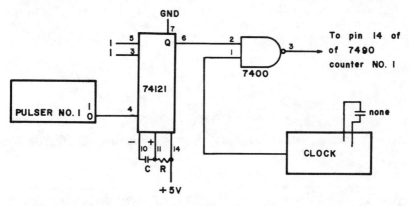

Fig. 8-62. Schematic of circuit that shows how to use 74121 monostable pulse to gate a counter.

THE 74122 RETRIGGERABLE MONOSTABLE MULTIVIBRATOR

The pin configuration and truth table for the 74122 retriggerable monostable multivibrator with clear are given in Fig. 8-63 and Table 8-12, respectively. The term, *retriggerable,* refers to the property that the input can be triggered once again before the output pulse is terminated. The effect is to extend the duration of the output pulse by one additional monostable period; this process can be re-

122 FUNCTION TABLE

	INPUTS				OUTPUTS	
CLEAR	A1	A2	B1	B2	Q	Q̄
L	X	X	X	X	L	H
X	H	H	X	X	L	H
X	X	X	L	X	L	H
X	X	X	X	L	L	H
X	L	X	H	H	L	H
H	L	X	↑	H	⊓	⊔
H	L	X	H	↑	⊓	⊔
H	X	L	H	H	L	H
H	X	L	↑	H	⊓	⊔
H	X	L	H	↑	⊓	⊔
H	H	↓	H	H	⊓	⊔
H	↓	↓	H	H	⊓	⊔
H	↓	H	H	H	⊓	⊔
↑	L	X	H	H	⊓	⊔
↑	X	L	H	H	⊓	⊔

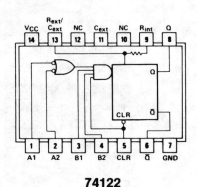

74122

Fig. 8-63. Pin configuration and truth table for 74122 retriggerable monostable multivibrator with clear.

peated indefinitely. Such a capability permits you to generate output pulses of very long durations. The details of the retrigger pulse are described in the Texas Instruments Incorporated *TTL Data Book*, a page of which is shown in Chart 8-1.

Chart 8-1. Details of Retriggerable Monostable Multivibrators

description

The '122, '123, 'L122, and 'L123 multivibrators feature d-c triggering from gated low-level-active (A) and high-level-active (B) inputs, and also provide overriding direct clear inputs. Complementary outputs are provided. The retrigger capability simplifies the generation of output pulses of extremely long duration. By triggering the input before the output pulse is terminated, the output pulse may be extended. The overriding clear capability permits any output pulse to be terminated at a predetermined time independently of the timing components R and C. Figure A below illustrates triggering the one-shot with the high-level-active (B) inputs.

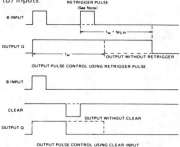

NOTE: Retrigger pulse must not start before 0.22 C_{ext} (in picofarads) nanoseconds after previous trigger pulse.

FIGURE A—TYPICAL INPUT/OUTPUT PULSES

These monostables are designed to provide the system designer with complete flexibility in controlling the pulse width, either to lengthen the pulse by retriggering, or to shorten by clearing. The '122 and 'L122 each has an internal timing resistor which allows the circuit to be operated with only an external capacitor, if so desired. Applications requiring more precise pulse widths (up to 28 seconds) and not requiring the clear feature can best be satisfied with '121 or 'L121.

The output pulse is primarily a function of the external capacitor and resistor. For $C_{ext} > 1000$ pF, the output pulse width (t_w) is defined as:

$$t_w = K \cdot R_T \cdot C_{ext} \left(1 + \frac{0.7}{R_T} \right)$$

where

R_T is in kΩ (either internal or external timing resistor),
C_{ext} is in pF,
t_w is in ns,
K is 0.32 for '122, 0.28 for '123, 0.37 for 'L122, 0.33 for 'L123.

For pulse widths when $C_{ext} \leqslant 1000$ pF, see Figures B and C.

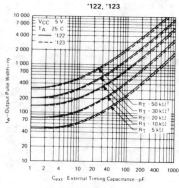

FIGURE B

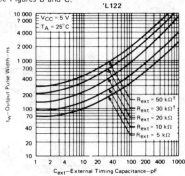

FIGURE C

†These values of resistance exceed the maximum recommended for use over the full temperature range of the SN54' and SN54L' circuits.

Courtesy Texas Instruments Incorporated

171

Retriggerable monostables are used to detect malfunctions in the operation of synchronous, or clocked, digital systems, which operate with the aid of a central source of clock pulses. Computers and digital instruments fit into such a category. The RC time constant of the retriggerable monostable can be adjusted so that the output, Q, will remain at logic 1 for as long as the clock is providing input

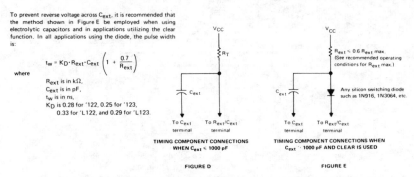

To prevent reverse voltage across C_{ext}, it is recommended that the method shown in Figure E be employed when using electrolytic capacitors and in applications utilizing the clear function. In all applications using the diode, the pulse width is:

$$t_w = K_D \cdot R_{ext} \cdot C_{ext} \left(1 + \frac{0.7}{R_{ext}} \right)$$

where

R_{ext} is in kΩ,
C_{ext} is in pF,
t_w is in ns,
K_D is 0.28 for '122, 0.25 for '123, 0.33 for 'L122, and 0.29 for 'L123.

V_{CC}

R_T

C_{ext}

To C_{ext} terminal   To R_{ext}/C_{ext} terminal

TIMING COMPONENT CONNECTIONS WHEN C_{ext} < 1000 pF

FIGURE D

V_{CC}

R_{ext} < 0.6 R_{ext} max. (See recommended operating conditions for R_{ext} max.)

Any silicon switching diode such as 1N916, 1N3064, etc.

C_{ext}

To C_{ext} terminal   To R_{ext}/C_{ext} terminal

TIMING COMPONENT CONNECTIONS WHEN C_{ext} 1000 pF AND CLEAR IS USED

FIGURE E

Fig. 8-64. Circuitry required when using clear function of electrolytic capacitors with 74122 and 74123 monostable multivibrators.

pulses at a trigger input. If for any reason the clock pulses terminate, the output will go to a logic 0 and a sequence of events initiated to shut the computer or instrument down, or save the contents of memory before a power failure, or remove power from an over-heating machine, etc. While this monostable and the 74123 can be cleared, or brought back to their normal state with a clear pulse, it is also possible for the clear input to trigger the monostable. The last two states in the truth table demonstrate this.

Special precautions must be taken when the timing capacitance is greater than 1000 pF and the clear input is used. A diode is re-

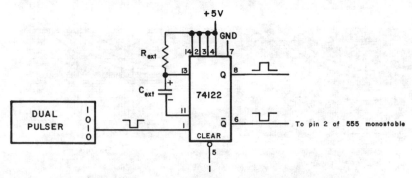

Fig. 8-65. Schematic of simple 74122 monostable multivibrator circuit.

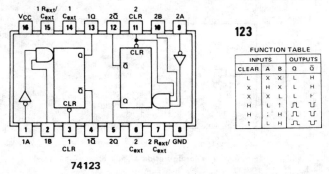

123

| FUNCTION TABLE | | | | |
| INPUTS | | | OUTPUTS | |
CLEAR	A	B	Q	Q̄
L	X	X	L	H
X	H	X	L	H
X	X	L	L	H
H	L	↑	⊓	⊔
H	↓	H	⊓	⊔
↑	L	H	⊓	⊔

74123

Fig. 8-66. Pin configuration and truth table for 74123 dual retriggerable monostable multivibrators with clear.

quired in the circuit, as shown in Fig. 8-64. The diode changes the timing formula.

One way of breadboarding the 74122 chip is shown in Fig. 8-65.

THE 74123 DUAL RETRIGGERABLE MONOSTABLE MULTIVIBRATOR

The pin configuration and the truth table for the 74123 dual retriggerable monostable multivibrator, as shown in Fig. 8-66, contains two independent monostables that behave like the 74122 retriggerable monostable. The 74123 monostable can be breadboarded as shown in Fig. 8-67.

THE 555 MONOSTABLE MULTIVIBRATOR

The 555 timer integrated circuit is a versatile analog-digital hybrid chip that can be operated either as an astable oscillator or as

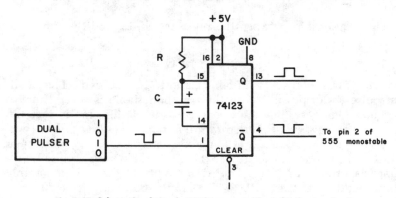

Fig. 8-67. Schematic of simple 74123 monostable multivibrator circuit.

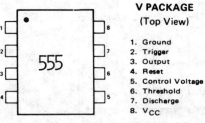

V PACKAGE
(Top View)

1. Ground
2. Trigger
3. Output
4. Reset
5. Control Voltage
6. Threshold
7. Discharge
8. V_{CC}

Courtesy Signetics Corp.

Fig. 8-68. Pin configuration of 555 timer IC.

a monostable multivibrator. The chip contains only eight pins (Fig. 8-68). The 555 timer is wired, as shown in Fig. 8-69, to produce a monostable that has good stability and repeatability. The pulse width at the trigger input (pin 2) must be less than the pulse width of the monostable output.

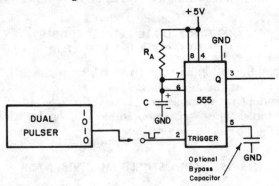

Fig. 8-69. Schematic of simple monostable multivibrator circuit using highly stable 555 timer IC.

The relationship between the pulse width, t_w, and the time constant is

$$t_w = 1.1\ R_A\ C$$

where R_A is in ohms, C is in farads, and t_w is in seconds. The smallest pulse width possible with the 555 monostable is several microseconds. One very important characteristic of this chip is that the *input pulse must be of shorter duration than the output pulse.* Thus, if you wish to produce a 10-microsecond monostable pulse, you must find some means to trigger the monostable with a pulse width that is shorter than 10 μs. The repeatability of the 555 monostable pulse width is at least 0.10%. The graph shown in Fig. 8-70 gives the capacitance required to produce output pulses varying from

10 microseconds to 10 seconds for a series of timing resistors.

Recommended values for the timing capacitor and resistor are:

Timing capacitor: minimum of 500 pF; maximum limited by leakage of capacitor

Timing resistor: minimum of 1000 ohms; maximum of 3.3 megohms

The maximum recommended trigger pulse width is one-fourth that of the output pulse. It should now be clear why we suggest the use

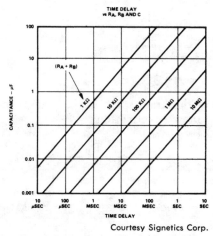

Courtesy Signetics Corp.

Fig. 8-70. Graph summarizing relationships between monostable pulse width from 555 timer and external timing resistor and capacitor values.

of 74121, 74122, or 74123 monostables in conjunction with the 555 monostable. You are able to produce pulse widths of greater repeatability than is possible with the 7400-series monostable chips.

THE 555 ASTABLE MULTIVIBRATOR

The 555 timer chip can also be wired as an astable multivibrator, i.e., clock, as shown in the circuit on the following page. A graph provided in Fig. 8-71 gives the capacitance required to produce a desired output frequency as a function of the sum, $R_A + 2 R_B$. The clock frequency can be calculated according to the following equation,

$$\nu = \frac{1.443}{(R_A + 2 R_B) C}$$

where R_A and R_B are in ohms, C is in farads, and ν is in Hz. The *duty cycle,* in this case the ratio of the time spent in the logic 0

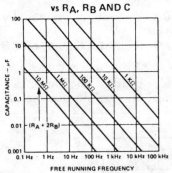

FREE RUNNING FREQUENCY
vs R_A, R_B AND C

Fig. 8-71. Graph summarizing relationship between output frequency from 555 astable multivibrator and external timing resistor and capacitor values.

Courtesy Signetics Corp.

state to the sum of the times spent in the logic 0 and logic 1 states, is given by the following equation:

$$D = \frac{R_B}{(R_A + 2\,R_B)}$$

If you desire a symmetrical square wave output, then $D = 0.50$, or $R_A \ll R_B$. For the clock Outboard, $R_A = 100$ kΩ and $R_B = 1$ MΩ.

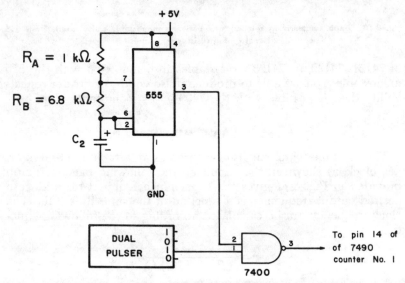

Fig. 8-72. Schematic of circuit that shows how to use 555 astable as source of clock pulses to a gate counter.

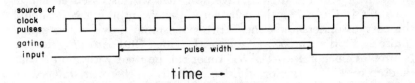

Fig. 8-73. Digital waveforms showing relationship between clock and gating inputs to gated counter.

A typical circuit for the 555 astable is shown in Fig. 8-72, in which $R_A = 1$ kΩ and $R_B = 6.8$ kΩ. The predicted clock frequency is

$$\nu = \frac{1.443}{(14{,}000\ \Omega)(1.5 \cdot 10^{-6}\ \text{F})}$$
$$= 65.89\ \text{Hz}$$

How close you come to this value will depend on the tolerances, i.e., actual values, of the passive components that you use.

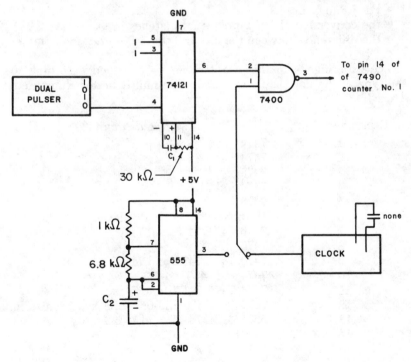

Fig. 8-74. Schematic of circuit using 555 astable and 74121 monostable as sources of clock and gating inputs, respectively, to a gated counter.

Returning to the digital waveform that we discussed earlier in Chapter 4 (Fig. 8-73), the behavior of the circuit in Fig. 8-74 should be easy to understand. The 74121 monostable provides the gating pulse and either the 555 astable or the clock Outboard provides the source of clock pulses. The 555 timer can be used with supply voltage up to +15 volts. For additional details on the many interesting and unusual uses for the 555 chip, we refer you to the *555 Timer Applications Sourcebook, with Experiments,* written by Howard Berlin (Howard W. Sams & Co., Inc., Indianapolis, Indiana, 1978).

INTRODUCTION TO THE EXPERIMENTS

In this chapter, you will study seven flip-flops and four monostable multivibrators. You will observe many of the important characteristics of the integrated-circuits, which include such concepts as these:

- the difference between edge and level triggering
- the PRESET and CLEAR inputs
- the J and K inputs
- the conversion of J-K flip-flops into latches
- the difference between the 555 and the 7400-series monostables

The experiments in this chapter can be classified according to the type of flip-flop, latch, or monostable multivibrator chips used. Thus:

Experiment No.	Integrated circuit
1	7474
2	7474
3	7475
4	7474 and 7475
5	7475
6	HP 5082-7300 latch/display
7	7470, 7474, 7475, and 74106
8	7476
9	7470, 7473, 7476, and 74106
10	7474 and 7475
11	7474, 7475, 74175, and 74193
12	7474 in a one-and-only-one synchronizer
13	555, 74121, 74122, and 74123
14	74121
15	74121
16	555 and 74121
17	555 and 74123

EXPERIMENT NO. 1

Purpose

The purpose of this experiment is to demonstrate the operation of a simple 7474 D-type positive-edge–triggered flip-flop that is used as a latch.

Pin Configuration of Integrated Circuit (Fig. 8-75)

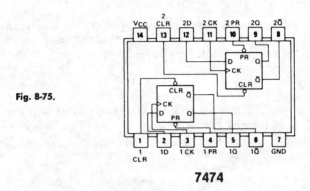

Fig. 8-75.

7474

Schematic Diagram of Circuit (Fig. 8-76)

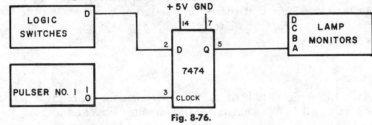

Fig. 8-76.

Step 1

Wire the circuit shown in Fig. 8-76.

Step 2

Apply power to the solderless breadboard. Place the D logic switch input in the logic 1 position. Now press and release the clock input pulser No. 1. The lamp monitor should be lighted after these operations. Now return logic switch D to logic 0. The timing diagrams for these operations are shown in Fig. 8-77. The D input first changed to a logic 1 state and remained at that state while the clock input went from logic 0 to logic 1 and back to logic 0. Finally, the D input returned to logic 0. The flip-flop output, Q, latched at the positive edge of the clock pulse.

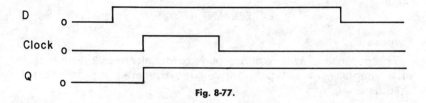

Fig. 8-77.

Step 3

Press and release the clock input pulser No. 1. Since the D input is now at logic 0, you should observe that the lamp monitor becomes unlit and remains unlit. You have latched a logic 0 state.

Step 4

Press the clock input pulser No. 1 and keep it pressed. Actuate the D input logic switch several times. What do you observe on the lamp monitor?

You can now release pulser No. 1. In our case, we observed that the lamp monitor remained unlighted. The reason was that the D input was at a logic 0 at the positive edge of the clock input. This is the logic state that was latched. What the D input did thereafter was unimportant.

Step 5

Place the logic switch in the logic 1 position. Now press pulser No. 1 in and observe that the lamp monitor changes to a logic 1 state. With pulser No. 1 pressed in, repeatedly actuate the logic switch. *You should observe no change in the lamp monitor logic state, which is at logic 1, despite the fact that you are changing the D input.*

All of the above experiments are consistent with the conclusion that the 7474 flip-flop latches at the positive edge of the clock pulse.

EXPERIMENT NO. 2

Purpose

The purpose of this experiment is to demonstrate the operation of the CLEAR and PRESET asynchronous inputs on the 7474 D-type flip-flop.

Pin Configuration of Integrated Circuit (Fig. 8-78)

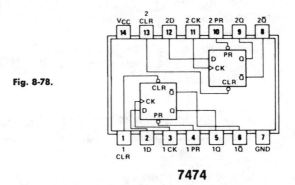

Fig. 8-78.

7474

Schematic Diagram of Circuit (Fig. 8-79)

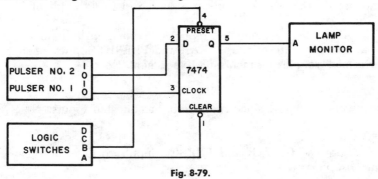

Fig. 8-79.

Step 1

Wire the circuit shown in Fig. 8-79. Do not forget the +5 volts power to pin 14 and the ground connection to pin 7 on the 7474 chip. Apply power to the solderless breadboard.

Step 2

Set the CLEAR input to logic 1 and the PRESET input to logic 0 and observe that the lamp monitor is lighted. This means that the output, Q, of the 7474 flip-flop is at a logic 1 state.

Now push and release pulser No. 1 and switch D in various ways and try to obtain a logic 0 for the output of the 7474. Can you do it?

Your answer should be no. The PRESET asynchronous input overrides the synchronous D and clock inputs.

Step 3

Set the PRESET input to logic 1 and the CLEAR input to logic 0 and observe that the lamp monitor is now unlighted. The output of the 7474 flip-flop is now at a logic 0 state.

Now push and release pulser No. 1 and switch D in various ways and try to obtain a logic 1 for the output from the 7474. Can you do it?

Again, your answer should be no. The CLEAR asynchronous input overrides the D and clock inputs.

Step 4

Set both the CLEAR and PRESET inputs to logic 1. Now push and release pulser No. 1 and switch D in various combinations and demonstrate that the 7474 behaves as it did in Experiment No. 1 in this chapter.

Recall that an unconnected input corresponds to a logic 1 state. What was the state of the CLEAR and PRESET inputs when you performed your experiments in Experiment No. 1?

Both were at logic 1 since they were unconnected inputs.

Step 5

Set both the CLEAR and PRESET inputs to logic 0. What do you observe?

You are on your own here. This is an allowed but ambiguous logic condition for the CLEAR and PRESET inputs.

Questions

1. What would a negative clock pulse, ⊔ , do to a 7474 flip-flop if

   a. Applied at the CLEAR input?

   b. Applied at the PRESET input?

   c. Applied at the D input when the CLOCK input is enabled?

d. Applied at the CLOCK input when the D input is at logic 0?

e. Applied at the CLOCK input when the D input is at logic 1?

2. What would a positive clock pulse, ⌐┐ , do to a 7474 flip-flop if

a. Applied at the CLEAR input?

b. Applied at the PRESET input?

c. Applied at the CLOCK input when the D input is at logic 0?

d. Applied at the CLOCK input when the D input is at logic 1?

EXPERIMENT NO. 3

Purpose

The purpose of this experiment is to demonstrate the operation of a simple 7475 latch.

Pin Configuration of Integrated Circuit (Fig. 8-80)

Fig. 8-80.

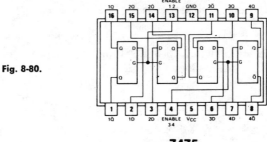

7475

Schematic Diagram of Circuit (Fig. 8-81)

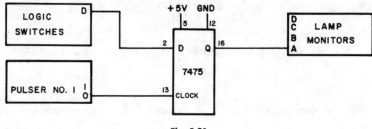

Fig. 8-81.

Step 1

Without removing the 7474 flip-flop, wire the above circuit on your solderless breadboard. Apply power to the breadboard.

Step 2

Perform the following actions *in the order given.*

A. Actuate the logic switch D (i.e., move it between the logic 0 and logic 1 states) and note any changes in the lamp monitor. Did you observe any?

B. With the pulser pressed in, again actuate the logic switch D. What is the relation between the D input and the Q output?

   Must the CLOCK input be at logic 1 to do this?

C. With the logic switch set at logic 1, press and release the CLOCK pulser. Does Q change state?

   What is the relation between the D input and the Q output after the clock pulse between D and Q?

D. Set the logic switch to logic 0 and again press and release the CLOCK pulser. Does Q change state?

   What is the D input-Q output relationship here?

E. Repeat Steps 3 and 4, but after applying the clock pulse (push and release) change the value on the logic switch. Does the Q output change? Can you conclude that the 7475-type latch will "memorize" the data present at D when the clock pulse goes back to logic 0?

Step 3

Sketch a timing diagram for Steps B through D in the following space. Assume that Q starts at logic 0.

You should conclude that the 7475 latch acts as a follower when the clock, or enable, input is at logic 1. By "follower," we mean that the output Q is the same as the input D.

Discussion

The 7475 latch is a very popular one-bit memory. It is found in 8-bit registers in a variety of the newer large-scale integration (LSI) integrated-circuit chips, including the 8080A microprocessor chip, the 2102 read/write memory, and the 8212 eight-bit I/O port chip. Intel Corporation manufactures all of these chips, and clearly they like the latch.

This explains the importance of understanding the characteristics of the different types of flip-flops. When working with microprocessors, we have observed that the two most important flip-flops are the 7475-type latch and the positive-edge–triggered flip-flop.

Question

1. Draw the timing diagram for the output, Q, from the bistable latch based on the given timing diagrams in Fig. 8-82 for the D

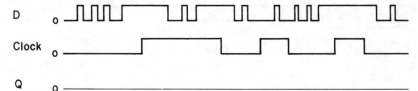

Fig. 8-82.

input and the CLOCK input. What is the final output state, Q, for the latch?

EXPERIMENT NO. 4

Purpose

The purpose of this experiment is to compare the operation of the 7474 D-type flip-flop with the 7475 latch.

Pin Configurations of Integrated Circuits (Fig. 8-83 and 8-84)

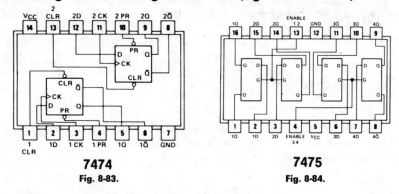

7474

Fig. 8-83.

7475

Fig. 8-84.

Schematic Diagram of Circuit (Fig. 8-85)

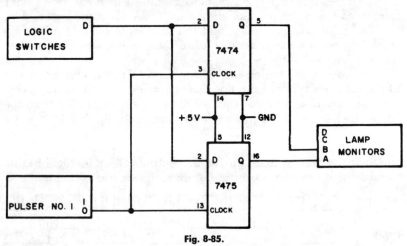

Fig. 8-85.

Step 1

Wire the circuit in Fig. 8-85 on your solderless breadboard. Do not forget the power connections to both the 7474 and 7475 chips.

Both chips are clocked simultaneously by pulser No. 1. Both chips simultaneously receive the D input from logic switch D.

Step 2

Apply power to the broadboard and perform the experiment following the timing diagrams in Fig. 8-86. Observe the outputs from the two latches and determine if they are the same as those shown. We observed that the outputs from both the 7474 and 7475 were the same as above. If you had trouble understanding the timing diagrams, then follow the instructions given in Step 3. Otherwise, skip to Step 4.

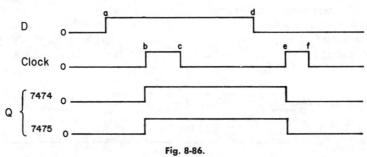

Fig. 8-86.

Step 3

To execute the timing diagrams for the D and clock inputs in Fig. 8-86, perform the following actions:

- Make certain that the outputs of both latches are at logic 0. If one is not, set the logic switch to 0 and press and release pulser No. 2.
- At point *a*, place the logic switch in the logic 1 position and leave it there until you reach point *d*.
- At point *b*, press the clock input pulser No. 1 in for a second and then release it at point *c*.
- Wait several seconds, then switch the D input logic switch back to logic 0.
- Wait an additional second or two, then press the clock input pulser No. 1 in and release it (points *e* and *f*).
- Observe what happens to the 7474 and 7475 outputs at points *b* and *e*. At point *b*, both lamp monitors should light. At point *e*, both should be unlit.

We have described in words the timing diagrams in Step 2. We encourage you to study the above timing diagrams until you can perform a series of actions directly from them. Timing diagrams are widely used in the electronics industry. There now are special scopes that give the timing diagrams for up to fifteen points in a circuit at the same time.

Note that we call pulser No. 2 the "clock" input pulser. Why?

Step 4

The timing diagrams for the second experiment are shown in Fig. 8-87.

Execute the actions given for the D and clock inputs, and demonstrate that both lamp monitors become lit at point *b* and remain lit thereafter. So far, you have not detected any differences in the behavior of the two latches. The reason is that you have not yet performed an experiment that emphasizes their differences. Clear both flip-flops to logic 0.

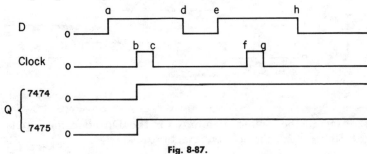

Fig. 8-87.

Step 5

The timing diagrams for the third experiment are shown in Fig. 8-88. You should observe that *the logic state of the 7474 does not change during the entire experiment*. It remains at logic 0. In contrast, the output of the 7475 "follows" the D input while the clock input is at logic 1.

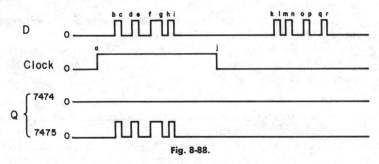

Fig. 8-88.

Why does the 7474 remain at logic 0?

The 7474 output remains at logic 0 because the D input is at logic 0 at the positive edge of the clock pulse. So, the 7474 latches a logic 0 at point *a*.

Step 6

The timing diagrams in Fig. 8-89 are for the fourth and final experiment. You should now observe that both the 7474 and 7475 flip-flops are latched in a logic 1 state. Why?

We will explain why in Step 7.

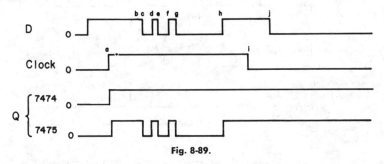

Fig. 8-89.

Step 7

The differences between the two latches can be summarized as follows:

- The 7474 flip-flop latches data present at the D input at the positive edge of the clock pulse.
- The 7475 latch "follows" the data present at the D input whenever the clock input is enabled. It latches the D input at the negative edge of the clock pulse.

In case you forgot what the terms, *positive edge* and *negative edge,* mean, we will refresh your memory with the pulse diagrams in Fig. 8-90.

A positive clock pulse, i.e., a transition from logic 0 to logic 1 and back to logic 0, is given at the top and a negative clock pulse at the bottom.

For the 7474 flip-flop, the logic state of the D input at the positive edge of the clock pulse is the state that is latched. For the 7475 bistable latch, the logic state of the D input at the negative edge of the clock pulse is the state that is latched. In addition, the output of the 7475 follows the logic state excursions of the D input whenever the clock input is at logic 1.

We can now explain all of the different timing diagrams with ease. Consider the timing diagrams in Step 5. At point *a*, the positive edge of the clock pulse, the 7474 latches a logic 0 and, therefore, remains at logic 0. At points *b* through *i*, the output from the 7475 follows the D input since the clock input is at logic 1. At point *j*, the 7475 latches a logic 0 state and remains at logic 0 thereafter. Finally, at points *k* through *r*, nothing happens since the clock input is not at logic 1. The 7475 does not follow these logic excursions.

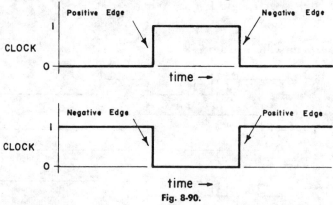

Fig. 8-90.

In Step 6, there exists a similar condition. The 7474 latches a logic 1 since such a logic state was present at the D input during the positive edge of the clock. The 7475 also is latched at logic 1 since such a state was present at the D input during the negative edge of the clock.

EXPERIMENT NO. 5

Purpose

The purpose of this experiment is to latch the output of a 7490 decade counter using four 7475 bistable latches that are enabled together.

Pin Configurations of Integrated Circuits (Figs. 8-91 and 8-92)

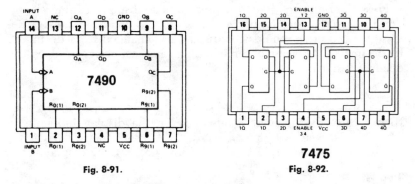

Fig. 8-91.

7475

Fig. 8-92.

Schematic Diagram of Circuit (Fig. 8-93)

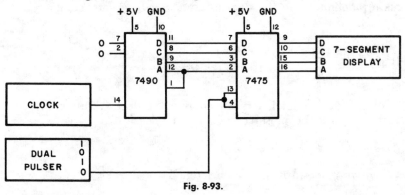

Fig. 8-93.

Step 1

Wire the circuit shown. You will need to use two different clock frequencies, a very low frequency such as 0.1 to 1 Hz, and a very high frequency that exceeds 1000 Hz. Set the clock output to the low-frequency position using either a knob or a suitably chosen capacitor. Our clock consisted of a 555 timer, and we used a 2.0-μF capacitor to keep the frequency extremely low.

Step 2

Apply power to the breadboard. Nothing should happen; you should not see any change in reading on the seven-segment LED display. What number or symbol do you observe on the display?

We observed a zero. You may observe some other number.

Step 3

Press the pulser and keep it pressed. The display reading should jump to some other number and then should count up slowly. Release the pulser as soon as the display has changed from decimal 2 to decimal 3. Do you observe any further counting, or does the decimal 3 remain on the display?

In our case, the decimal 3 remained on the display indefinitely. Thus, we latched a 4-bit bcd word, 0011, using four 7475 latches whose outputs were tied to the seven-segment LED display.

Step 4

Using the pulser, latch the numeral 7 to the display. Does it remain indefinitely on the display after you have latched it?

It should.

Step 5

When does the latch actually latch onto a decimal numeral, when you first press the pulser or when you release it?

When we released it, the latch latched.

Step 6

Now set the clock to a very high frequency. The higher the better, as long as the frequency does not exceed about 10 MHz. Press the pulser and observe that the LED display readings are changing so fast that all you see is a decimal numeral 8. Release the pulser and observe that you have latched one of the ten decimal numerals. The latching action occurs at the instant that the pulser is released, but the process is much too fast for the eye to follow. It is virtually impossible to predict which decimal numeral will be latched when you release the pulser.

Step 7

Press and release the pulser several times and note that different numerals appear. The shorter the time during which you press and release the pulser, the easier it is to see how fast the latching action occurs.

Discussion

Latches are used in computers and in other digital instruments to acquire and latch digital data at extremely fast data rates. Through the use of gates and flip-flops, it becomes possible to latch the precise information that is desired.

Question

1. In this experiment, you latched the DCBA outputs from a 7490 decade counter. Can you suggest other integrated circuits whose inputs or outputs you might desire to latch? This is an open-ended question, so try your best.

EXPERIMENT NO. 6

Purpose

The purpose of this experiment is to demonstrate the operation of the Hewlett-Packard latch/display.

Schematic Diagram of Circuit (Fig. 8-94)

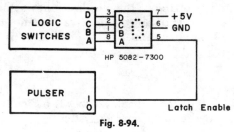

Fig. 8-94.

Step 1

Wire the circuit shown in Fig. 8-94. Make certain that the proper power connections are made. If you accidentally reverse them, you will destroy the display.

Step 2

Set the logic switches to A = 0, B = 1, C = 1, and D = 0. Do you observe any change on the display?

Your answer should be no.

Step 3

Now press and release the pulser. What number appears on the display?

Six.

Step 4

Set the logic switches to A = 1, B = 1, C = 0, and D = 0. Press and release the pulse. A three should appear on the display.

Step 5

Now connect the latch enable input at pin 5 on the display to the "0" output of the pulser. Vary the logic switch settings between DCBA = 0000 and DCBA = 1001. What do you observe on the latch/display?

Our display followed all changes in the logic switch settings. We observed, in sequence, decimal zero through nine.

Step 6

When the latch is enabled, the display follows the data at the input. When the latch is disabled, the data present at the negative edge of the clock input at pin 5 is latched. Is this latch/display positive-edge triggered?

No, it is a follower-type latch display. Does it basically resemble the 7475 latch in its operational characteristics?

Yes, except that a logic 0 enables the latch/display, whereas a logic 1 enables the 7475 latch.

EXPERIMENT NO. 7

Purpose

The purpose of this experiment is to compare the behavior of the 7470, 7474, 7475, and 74106 flip-flops as latches. An inverter is required for the 7470 and 74106 J-K flip-flops to convert them to latches.

Pin Configuration of Integrated Circuits (Figs. 8-95 through 8-99)

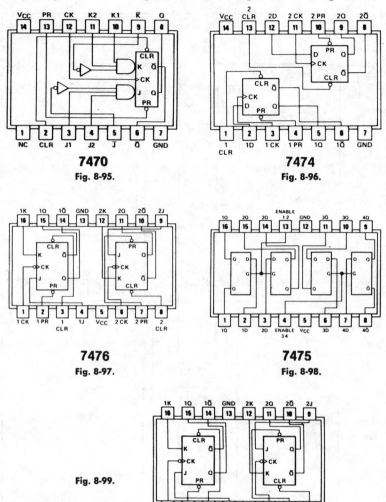

7470

Fig. 8-95.

7474

Fig. 8-96.

7476

Fig. 8-97.

7475

Fig. 8-98.

Fig. 8-99.

74H106

Schematic Diagram of Circuit (Fig. 8-100)

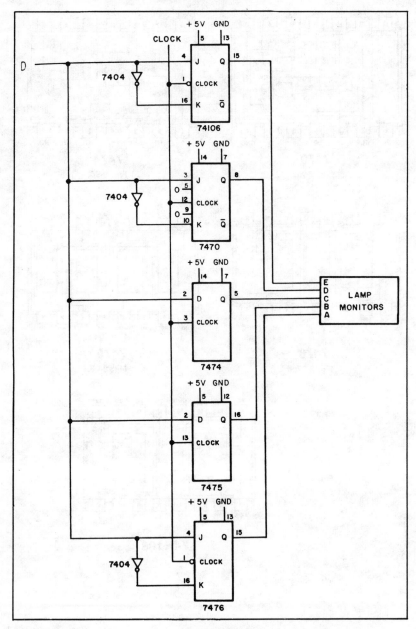

Fig. 8-100.

Step 1

Wire the circuit as shown in Fig. 8-100. Use pulser No. 1 for the CLOCK input and pulser No. 2 for the D input. Observe that you are clocking all four flip-flops simultaneously. In this experiment, your object will be to reproduce the digital waveforms shown in the two sets of digital waveforms in the "Comparison of Latches" section of this chapter.

Step 2

Reproduce the digital waveforms shown in Case I, as shown in Fig. 8-56. Note that there are four CLOCK pulses and two D pulses. Do you observe the predicted behavior?

Yes.

Step 3

Reproduce the digital waveforms shown in Case II in Fig. 8-57. Now there is a single CLOCK input pulse and four D pulses. Is the behavior the same as predicted?

If you have performed this experiment correctly, you should observe results identical to those given in the two sets of digital waveforms. The 74106 flip-flop wired as a latch should change state only on the negative edge of the clock pulse. The other three latches should change state only on the positive edge of the clock pulse. The 7475 is the only latch that should follow the D input while the CLOCK is at logic 1.

Question

1. The first student who performed this experiment used a pair of logic switches instead of two debounced pulsers. The experiment did not work under such conditions. He then substituted the pulsers for the logic switches and observed the correct results. Why did the experiment not work when he employed the logic switches? Use the space below for your answer.

Purpose

The purpose of this experiment is to demonstrate the behavior of a 7476 flip-flop wired as a latch. This type of latch behaves in a very unusual manner. The 7476 flip-flop is level-triggered rather than edge-triggered, so the latching action can occur simply when the CLOCK input is at a logic 1 level.

Pin Configuration of Integrated Circuits (Figs. 8-101 and 8-102)

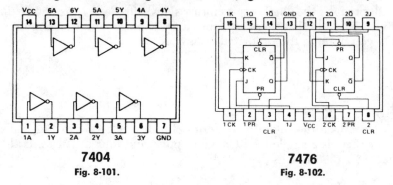

7404

Fig. 8-101.

7476

Fig. 8-102.

Schematic Diagram of Circuit (Fig. 8-103)

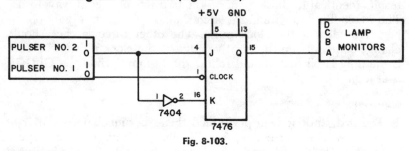

Fig. 8-103.

Step 1

Wire the circuit shown in Fig. 8-103. Apply power to the breadboard. Demonstrate experimentally that each set of the six sets of digital waveforms shown in Fig. 8-104 is correct. The most important of the six sets are the bottom two, in which the D input changes state only when the CLOCK input is at a logic 1 state.

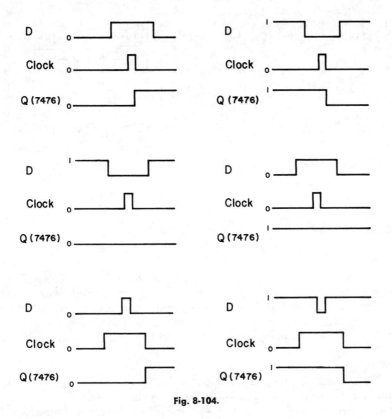

Fig. 8-104.

EXPERIMENT NO. 9

Purpose

The purpose of this experiment is to compare the behavior of three J-K flip-flops: the 7470, 7473, and the 74106.

Pin Configurations of Integrated Circuits (Figs. 8-105 through 8-108)

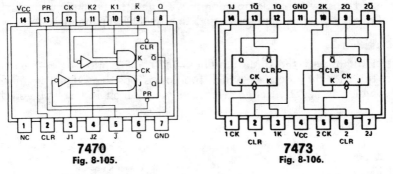

7470
Fig. 8-105.

7473
Fig. 8-106.

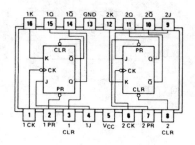

7476

Fig. 8-107.

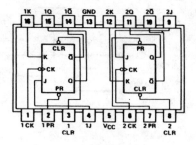

74H106

Fig. 8-108.

Schematic Diagram of Circuit (Fig. 8-109)

Step 1

In the circuit in Fig. 8-109, use pulser No. 1 for the CLOCK input, pulser No. 2 for the J input, and either a third pulser or a logic switch for the K input. Wire the circuit and apply power to the breadboard. Observe that you are clocking all three flip-flops simultaneously. If you wish, you can also add the 7476 flip-flop.

Step 2

Reproduce the digital waveforms shown in Case I in the "Comparison of Flip-Flops" section. There are three CLOCK pulses and three J input pulses. The K input remains at logic 0. Lamp monitors C and D should light first, followed by lamp monitor B, and finally, by lamp monitor A.

Step 3

Reproduce the digital waveforms shown in Case II on the same page. Make certain that the K input has a pulser attached to it. The J input can now be connected to a logic switch. Again, you should observe that lamp monitors C and D become unlit first, followed by lamp monitor B and finally by lamp monitor A.

Question

1. Explain why the three flip-flops—7470, 7473, and 74106—behave the way they do, i.e., which flip-flop is positive edge triggered, which is negative edge triggered, and which is level-triggered.

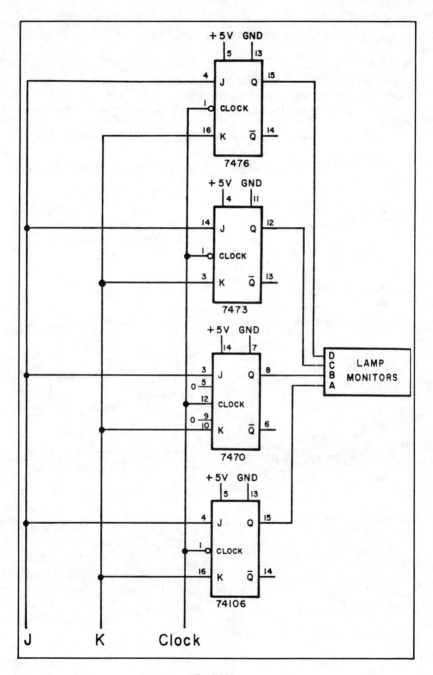

Fig. 8-109.

EXPERIMENT NO. 10

Purpose

The purpose of this experiment is to latch the same decimal numeral output from a 7490 decade counter. The 7490 counter is free running until you latch the output, at which time the counter stops.

Pin Configurations of Integrated Circuits (Figs. 8-110 through 8-113)

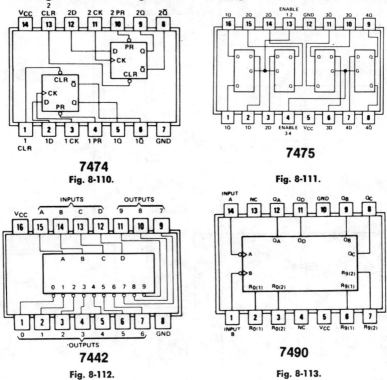

7474

Fig. 8-110.

7475

Fig. 8-111.

7442

Fig. 8-112.

7490

Fig. 8-113.

Schematic Diagram of Circuit (Fig. 8-114)

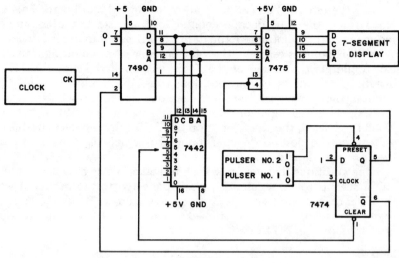

Fig. 8-114.

Step 1

This is a subtle circuit that demonstrates a number of principles:

- Resetting the 7490 decade counter back to decimal 0. This is accomplished when the input at pin 2 of the 7490 chip goes to a logic 1 state.
- Latching the output from the 7490 counter. This occurs when pins 4 and 13 go to a logic 0 state and remain there.
- The use of a D-type positive-edge–triggered flip-flop with preset and clear, the 7474 chip, to accomplish several different functions, including:
    1. Reset the 7490 decade counter back to decimal 0, where it resumes counting until it latches the desired decimal numeral.
    2. Keep the 7490 sequencing between decimal 0 and one digit less than the desired decimal numeral until latching of the desired decimal numeral is desired.
    3. Select which decimal numeral is to be latched.
- The use of a 7442 BCD-to-decimal decoder as both a sequencer and as a chip that allows you to latch any decimal numeral between 0 and 9.

These multiple capabilities are a direct consequence of the use of the 7474 flip-flop, which has four inputs and two outputs that can be used in a wide variety of ways.

Step 2

Wire the circuit. You can fit it all on a single breadboard. Pulser No. 1 resets the 7490 decade counter to 0 and starts the counting sequence to the point where the desired decimal numeral is latched. When this point is reached, the 7490 counter stops counting. Pulser No. 2 inhibits the action of the 7442 decoder and keeps the 7475 bistable latch at its enable position; thus, the latch continues to monitor the output of the 7490 counter. When Pulser No. 2 is pressed, the clock input on the 7475 chip is enabled. When pulser No. 2 is released, the clock input on the 7475 chip becomes disabled only when the desired decimal numeral is reached, at which time the 7475 chip latches it.

Some additions that you may wish to make to this circuit include: (a) a second seven-segment display connected to the output from the 7490 chip; you observe it go to decimal zero as the other seven-segment display shows the latched value; and (b) a LED at the Q output of the 7474 latch.

Step 3

Connect the wire from pin 1 on the 7474 chip to pin 4 on the 7442 chip. Apply power to the breadboard. Set the clock at the input to pin 14 of the 7490 to a low frequency,such as 1 Hz or less. After a few moments, the reading on the seven-segment LED display should be decimal 3. Press and release pulser No. 1. You should observe that the display returns to decimal 0 and resumes counting to decimal 3, where it stops. Press and release pulser No. 1 a second time. The same action occurs for the second time. Thus, you have demonstrated that you can latch the decimal numeral 3 as the decade counter is counting.

Step 4

You will next let the 7490 counter sequence through three states until you decide to latch the decimal numeral 3. To do this, press pulser No. 2 and keep it pressed. The display should read 0, 1, 2, 0, 1, 2, etc. Now release the pulser No. 2 and observe that the display latches numeral 3. Once the numeral is latched, the 7490 counter stops. This is because the output, $\bar{Q}$, from the 7474 chip is at a logic 1 state, which is applied at pin 2 of the 7490 decade counter, causing it to clear to zero and to remain at zero until pulser No. 1 is again pressed.

You should conclude the following:

* When pulser No. 1 is pressed and released, the display counts from numeral 0 to numeral 3 and then latches numeral 3. The 7490 counter is cleared to decimal zero.

• When pulser No. 2 is pressed in and kept pressed, the display sequences between numeral 0 and numeral 2. Only when you release pulser No. 2 does the display proceed to latch decimal 3.

In the next several steps, we ask questions that should challenge your understanding of the circuit. We shall not provide answers, so you are on your own.

Step 5

Why does the application of a positive clock pulse by pulser No. 1 cause the display to count to numeral 3 and then stop?

Step 6

Why does the application of a negative leading edge by pulser No. 2 allow the display to sequence between three states continuously?

Step 7

Why does the sequencing mentioned in Step 6 stop when you release pulser No. 2? Why does the 7490 decade counter stop counting?

Step 8

What happens to the 7490 counter at the time that the 7475 chip latches the decimal numeral 3?

Step 9

What happens to the 7475 4-bit bistable latch chip when the 7490 counter is reset to numeral 0?

Step 10

What logic state is required to reset the 7490 decade counter to numeral 0? This logic state is applied at pin 2 of the 7490 chip.

Step 11

Now connect pin 1 on the 7474 chip to pin 11 on the 7442 rather than pin 4. Press and release pulser No. 1 and observe that the display now latches decimal numeral 9. Explain why in the space below.

When the 7490 counter reaches numeral 9, the 7442 decoder outputs a logic 0 state at pin 11. This logic 0 clears the 7474 flip-flop, which in turn disables the enable inputs to the 7475 latch. The 7475 latches the numeral 9 that is input to it as well as to the 7442 decoder.

Step 12

If you wish to latch the decimal numeral 7, what output pin on the 7442 chip must you use?

Pin 9.

Step 13

If you wish to latch the decimal numeral 5, what output pin on the 7442 chip must you use?

Pin 6.

Step 14

What is the function of pin 4 on the 7474 chip? How does it influence the output, Q, from the chip? What logic state is required to do so?

It permits you to set the 7474 flip-flop output to logic 1, which enables the 7475 latch and permits the 7490 counter to start counting from numeral 0. Pulser No. 2 essentially overrides the action of the 7442 decoder. A logic 0 state is required at pin 4.

Step 15

What is the function of pin 1 on the 7474 chip? How does it influence the output, Q, from the chip? What logic state is required to do so?

It permits you to clear the 7474 flip-flop output to logic 0, which disables the 7475 latch and resets the 7490 counter to 0. A logic 0 state is required.

EXPERIMENT NO. 11

Purpose

The purpose of this experiment is to compare the operation of the 7474, 7475, 74175, and 74193 latches in an attempt to determine which pairs of latches act the same. The 74193 chip is actually a latch/binary counter; you will only be interested in the latch aspect of the chip.

Pin Configurations of Integrated Circuits
(Figs. 8-115 through 8-118)

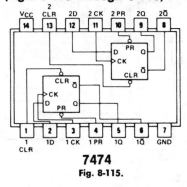

7474

Fig. 8-115.

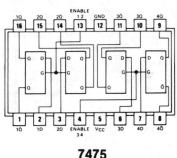

7475

Fig. 8-116.

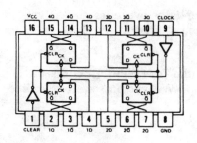

74175

Fig. 8-117.

74192, 74193

Fig. 8-118.

Schematic Diagram of Circuit (Fig. 8-119)

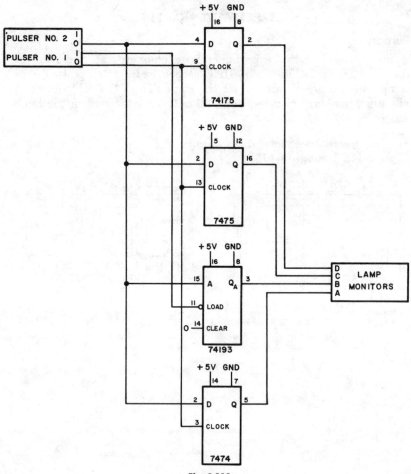

Fig. 8-119.

Step 1

Wire the experiment as shown in Fig. 8-119. Note that all four chips are clocked (gated, in the case of the 7475 chip, and LOAD-ED, in the case of the 74193 chip) simultaneously. Apply power to the breadboard.

Step 2

Pulser No. 1 applies a positive clock pulse to three of the chips and a negative clock pulse to a single chip. In the space below, write down which chip receives a negative clock pulse.

The 74193.

Step 3

Verify that each of the four latches as shown in Fig. 8-120 latch data on the positive edge of the clock pulse of the "0" output from

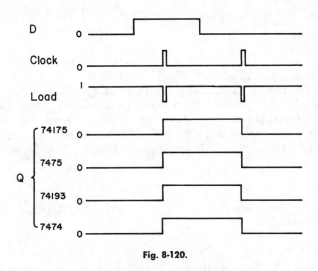

Fig. 8-120.

pulser No. 1. Note that the LOAD waveform is the complement of the CLOCK waveform. For what chip does the LOAD waveform apply? Your answer should be the 74193 chip.

Step 4

Verify that each of the four latches remains latched, despite the use of two clock pulses as shown in the set of digital waveforms

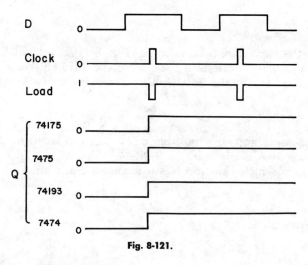

Fig. 8-121.

in Fig. 8-121. Why do the latches remain latched? Give your answer in the following space.

Step 5

Now you come to an experiment that demonstrates differences between the four latches. Using the D and CLOCK pulsers, experimentally reproduce the digital waveforms below and determine the behavior of the 74175 and 74193 chips. Fill in the missing rows in the set of digital waveforms. In the following space, indicate which latches the 74175 and 74193 latches resemble in their behavior.

The 74175 latch resembles the _____ latch.
The 74193 latch resembles the _____ latch.

We shall not give you the answer here; we shall let you determine it experimentally.

Step 6

The final set of waveforms is shown in Figs. 8-122 and 8-123. Predict the digital waveforms for the 74175 and 74193 latches and then perform the experiment to determine whether or not your predictions were correct.

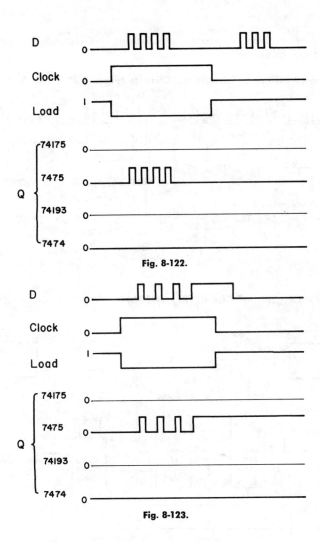

Fig. 8-122.

Fig. 8-123.

EXPERIMENT NO. 12

Purpose

The purpose of this experiment is to construct and demonstrate the operation of a "one-and-only-one" *synchronizer*. A synchronizer is a device that aligns random outside-world commands and gets them to exactly fit a time slot in a timing system. A "one-and-only-one" synchronizer is used to convert a single outside-world command, such as a pulse or a pushed button, into a precise pulse that lasts for one, and exactly one, whole interval between system clock pulses. For further discussion concerning synchronizers, we refer you to D. E. Lancaster.[6]

Pin Configurations of Integrated Circuits (Figs. 8-124 and 8-125)

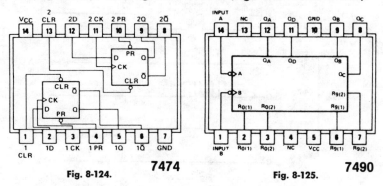

Fig. 8-124.   **7474**   Fig. 8-125.   **7490**

Schematic Diagram of Circuit (Fig. 8-126)

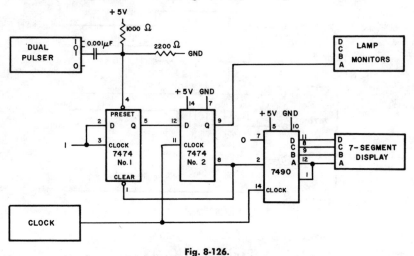

Fig. 8-126.

Step 1

Carefully study the circuit, then wire it on the breadboard. Do not forget the power connections on the 7474 chip.

Step 2

The heart of the circuit is the pulser and two 7474 D-type positive-edge–triggered flip-flops. The 7490 decade counter, seven-segment

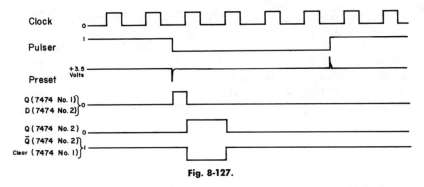

Fig. 8-127.

LED display, and clock is extra "baggage" to help illustrate some of the characteristics of the one-and-only-one synchronizer. Let us first discuss how the synchronizer operates.

Initially, the output Q from 7474 flip-flop No. 1 is at logic 0, as is the output from 7474 flip-flop No. 2. The pulser is at logic 1 and the PRESET input at pin 4 of 7474 No. 1 is at approximately +3.5 volts (note that the two resistors, 1000 ohms and 2200 ohms, serve as a voltage divider), which still corresponds to a logic 1 state. The CLEAR input to 7474 No. 1 is at logic 1. So much for the initial conditions.

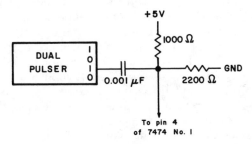

Fig. 8-128.

Now look at the group of digital waveforms shown in Fig. 8-127. We shall use them to explain what happens after you press the pulser. The first question is, what happens when you first press the pulser, thus dropping one side of the 0.001-microfarad capacitor to GROUND potential? As shown in the digital waveform for the PRESET input voltage in Fig. 8-126, you get a sharp negative spike of 2- or 3-microseconds duration. This negative spike occurs as a result of the pulse-forming resistance-capacitance circuit shown in Fig. 8-128 and also in the schematic diagram in Fig. 8-129.

A drop from logic 1 to logic 0 in the pulser (⎍) causes a sharp negative spike to essentially GROUND potential at pin 4,

213

whereas a return from logic 0 to logic 1 in the pulser (_⌐⎯) causes a sharp positive spike to about +5 Volts.

The negative spike causes the 7474 flip-flop No. 1 to preset the output Q to a logic 1 state. This occurs in about 1 microsecond after the pulser drops to logic 0. Since the output Q from flip-flop No. 1 and the input D to flip-flop No. 2 are connected together, the D input goes to logic 1 also 1 microsecond after the pulser drops to logic 0.

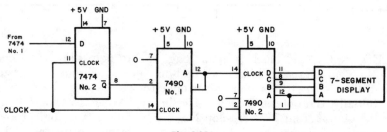

Fig. 8-129.

Nothing else happens until you apply a clock pulse to flip-flop No. 2. This clock pulse can be part of a train of clock pulses, or it can be from a second pulser. Until the clock pulse arrives, Q from flip-flop No. 1 remains at logic 1. Once the clock pulse arrives, the positive edge of the pulse causes the output Q of flip-flop No. 2 to go to a logic 1 state and the complementary output Q of flip-flop No. 2 to go to a logic 0 state. The complementary output of flip-flop No. 2 is attached to the CLEAR input of flip-flop No. 1, and causes flip-flop No. 1 to become cleared, i.e., causes output Q of flip-flop No. 1 to return to logic 0, which means that input D to flip-flop No. 2 also returns to logic 0.

On the next clock pulse to flip-flop No. 2, the Q output returns to logic 0. Nothing further happens either to flip-flop No. 1 or No. 2 until the pulser is pressed again.

The result of the above process, however, is that the output Q from flip-flop No. 2 goes to logic 1 and returns to logic 0 for exactly one full clock cycle. Even at clock frequencies as high as 300 kHz, there will always be only a single output clock pulse from flip-flop No. 2. Actually, the circuit is rather amazing. We have tried it for frequencies up to 10 kHz, and always only a single clock pulse is produced.

Step 3

Set the clock frequency so that it is very low, of the order of 0.1 to 1.0 Hz. Apply power to the breadboard. Press the pulser and keep it pressed. What do you observe on the LED display and the lamp monitor?

The LED display and the lamp monitor briefly make a transition from logic 0 to logic 1 and then back to logic 0. We hope you observed the same behavior.

Step 4

Increase the clock frequency to 10 Hz and repeat the above step. You should observe the same result: the 7490 decade counter counts only to decimal numeral 1 and then returns to 0. This is indicative of the production of a single clock pulse. Also, and more important, this result is indicative of the fact that the single clock pulse has a pulse width that is identical to that of the clock pulse width. Why can we make this second conclusion? Give your answer in the following space; we shall not help you with it.

Step 5

You will now add a second 7490 decade counter and demonstrate that only a single clock pulse is produced in a more dramatic fashion. The reason for doing so is that it becomes very difficult to see the 0-1-0 transition on the LED display with clock frequencies exceeding 30 to 50 Hz. What you will do instead is use this single pulse as the clock input into a second counter.

Take a careful look at the partial schematic shown in Fig. 8-128 and make the necessary changes in Fig. 8-126 to accommodate the changes shown. Apply power to the breadboard. Press the pulser and observe that the seven-segment LED display reading increases by a single digit. Release the pulser and observe that nothing further happens. Press and release the pulser a second time. Note that the display reading again increases by a single digit. Increase and decrease the clock frequency and demonstrate that, in all cases and despite the magnitude of the clock frequency, the LED display increases by only a single count each time the pulser is pressed. As we said before, the circuit is quite amazing in its reliability. If the pulse width of the single output pulse from the pair of flip-flops were several clock pulse widths in length, we would observe more than a single count change each time that we pressed the pulser; however, we do not observe such behavior. Have fun with this circuit. It should never fail.

Questions

1. What do we mean by the term, spike? Guess the answer.

2. What is the difference between a negative spike and a positive spike? Guess the answer here as well.

3. Can you explain why the resistance-capacitance circuit shown in Fig. 8-128 produces a negative spike when the pulser is pressed? Try hard on this question. It is important for you to know how to generate both positive and negative spikes.

4. Why is it necessary for you to produce a negative spike at the PRESET input to 7474 flip-flop No. 1? Why wouldn't a simple transition from logic 1 to logic 0 and then, eventually, back to logic 1 be acceptable in the circuit? This is an equally important question for you to answer. You may wish to employ digital waveforms in your answer to this question.

You now have the ability to press the pulser a single time, and to generate a single pulse of known pulse width. Explain how this capability can be used to gate a counter on and off. How do you determine or set the duration of the gating pulse? How does this type of circuit compare to the behavior of a 74121 monostable multivibrator?

EXPERIMENT NO. 13

Purpose

The purpose of this experiment is to demonstrate the operation of four different monostable multivibrator chips: the 555, 74121, 74122, and 74123. The 555 monostable will be triggered by a pulser and by the 74121, 74122, and 74123 monostables.

Pin Configurations of Integrated Circuits
(Figs. 8-130 through 8-133)

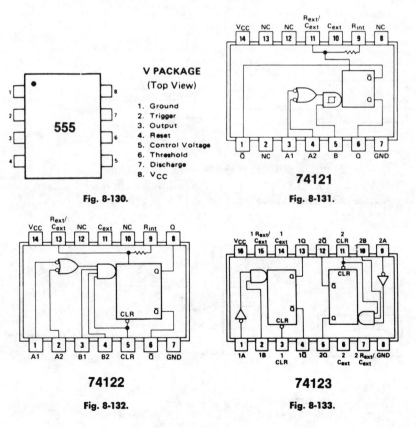

V PACKAGE
(Top View)

1. Ground
2. Trigger
3. Output
4. Reset
5. Control Voltage
6. Threshold
7. Discharge
8. V_{CC}

Fig. 8-130.

74121

Fig. 8-131.

74122

Fig. 8-132.

74123

Fig. 8-133.

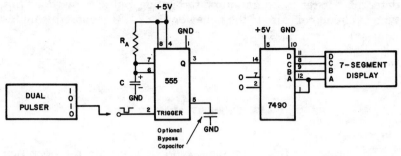

Fig. 8-134.

Step 1

Study the four schematic diagrams in Figs. 8-134 through 8-137. Note that the basic circuit consists of a single 555 monostable that is triggered by one of four different *single pulse-generating circuits:*

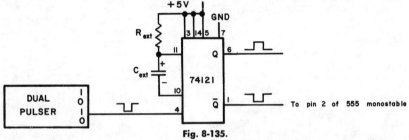

Fig. 8-135.

- A debounced pulser
- A 74121 monostable that is triggered by a debounced pulser
- A 74122 monostable that is triggered by a debounced pulser
- A 74123 monostable that is triggered by a debounced pulser

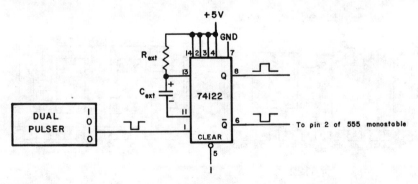

Fig. 8-136.

With the proper choice of timing resistors and capacitors, you can vary the pulse length of each of the four monostables that you will study. You can count the individual pulses that you generate with

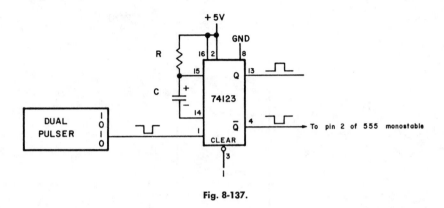

Fig. 8-137.

the aid of a 7490 decade counter and seven-segment LED display. In this manner, if more than a single pulse is generated each time a monostable is triggered, it can be detected with a minimum of difficulty.

Step 2

Wire the 555 monostable, the 7490 counter, and the seven-segment LED display together as shown in the first schematic. Use a pulser to trigger the 555 monostable at pin 2 of the integrated-circuit chip on your breadboard.

Step 3

You will require resistors and capacitors of rather large magnitudes in order to conveniently measure the time duration of the single output pulse. We recommend a 1.0-, 1.5-, or 2.7-megohm resistor, or any resistor of approximate values, to these and several electrolytic capacitors ranging between 1.0 and 10.0 microfarads. Remember to connect the negative terminal of the electrolytic capacitors to ground.

Using either a stopwatch or a wristwatch with a second hand, determine the time duration in seconds of the single output pulses. A 1-megohm resistor and 1-microfarad capacitor will give you a pulse duration of approximately 1.1 seconds. Use large values of the resistors and capacitors to ensure yourself sufficient time to measure the pulse duration. Write your answers in the following space.

Timing Resistor (Megohms)	Timing Capacitor (Microfarads)	Pulse Duration (Seconds)

Step 4

We performed the experiment described in Step 3 above and obtained the following results:

Timing Resistor (Megohms)	Timing Capacitor (Microfarads)	Approximate Pulse Duration (Seconds)
2.7	1.0 (Mylar®)	2.6
2.7	1	2.6
2.7	2	5.5
2.7	5	45.
10.	1.0 (Mylar®)	10.
10.	1	11.
10.	2	23.
22.	1.0 (Mylar®)	21.
22.	1	22.
22.	2	44.

The monostable behaved as expected except for the 5-microfarad capacitor, which was quite out of line. This capacitor was "leaky," with the consequence that it was difficult to charge and required more time. Such a capacitor would be unsuitable in any piece of electronic equipment. Note that the measured pulse duration is approximate, since we only used a stopwatch rather than a digital counting circuit such as that described in the experiments in Chapter 4.

Step 5

In one of our experiments, we obsereved some rather unusual behavior. We held the pulser in the pressed state for too long a time. Use the 2.7-megohm resistor and the 1-microfarad capacitor, press and hold the pulser in while you observe the seven-segment LED display. In the following space, explain what you observe on the display.

In our case, we observed that, after about 3 seconds, the display began to count very rapidly. The count seemed erratic and was not uniform. The numeral 8, which usually appears on the display at very high counting speeds, could not be observed this time. The reason we observed this behavior is because *the time duration of the triggering pulse exceeded the time duration of the output pulse.* In effect, the 555 monostable went "bananas" after precisely 2.6 or 2.7 seconds. This illustrates the importance of a rule stated in the introductory material: *trigger pulses to the 555 monostable must be narrower in pulse width than the output pulses.* You may not observe this kind of behavior on your 555 timer, however. We have found that 555 timers from different manufacturers behave differently.

Step 6

Using a 1-megohm resistor as the timing resistor and capacitors between 0.02 and 1 microfarad, determine how fast you can push and release the pulser. You will determine your limit when the monostable goes "bananas" no matter how fast you try to press and release the pulser. We observed considerable difficulties with a 0.1-microfarad capacitor, which corresponds to a 0.1-second output pulse. Again, owing to manufacturing differences, you may not observe this problem with the 555 timer that you are using.

Step 7

Try a 1-megohm resistor and a 0.001-microfarad capacitor. Repeatedly press and release the pulser as quickly as you can. You should observe that it is impossible to prevent the 555 monostable from acting strange and erratic. In our case, the monostable began to count edges on the single pulser clock pulses. More often than not, two counts were added to the seven-segment LED display each time we pressed and released the pulser. To repeat a third time, your 555 timer may not respond this way. If it does not, it is a better chip than the one we used for this experiment.

Step 8

The object of this step is to demonstrate that the combination of the 74121 monostable plus a pulser can apply very short trigger pulses to the 555 monostable, much shorter in duration than 0.1 second. Follow the circuit in Fig. 8-135. Use a 100-pF capacitor and a 10,000-ohm resistor for C_{ext} and R_{ext}, respectively. According to the manufacturer's specifications for the 74121 monostable, you can expect an output from the 74121 of about 0.7 microsecond in time duration. You may wish to study the manufacturer's specifications and verify that the pulse width will be 0.7 microsecond.

Step 9

Connect the complementary output, $\overline{Q}$, from the 74121 chip to pin 2, the trigger input, of the 555 monostable. Apply power to the breadboard and press and release the pulser. Use $R_A = 1$ megohm and $C = 0.001$ to 1 microfarad on the 555 monostable. For the entire range of C, you should observe that only a single pulse is produced from the 555 monostable.

Step 10

You will now decrease the pulse width from the 555 monostable so that it is similar in magnitude to the pulse width from the 74121 monostable. At some point, you should observe that the 555 monostable becomes erratic.

Use the following timing components in your 555/74121 circuit:

$$R_A = 10,000 \text{ ohms}$$
$$C = 0.001 \text{ microfarad}$$
$$R_{ext} = 10,000 \text{ ohms}$$
$$C_{ext} = 100 \text{ pF} = 0.0001 \text{ microfarad}$$

Press and release the pulser to the 74121 chip and demonstrate that only a single pulse is produced by the 555 monostable. You should observe a change of only one count every time you press and release the pulser.

Step 11

Reduce R_A to 4700 ohms. Do you still observe a single count on the LED display each time you press and release the pulser? Answer yes or no.

In our case, the answer was yes.

Step 12

Reduce R_A to 2200 ohms. Do you still observe a single count on the LED display each time you press and release the pulser? Answer yes or no.

In our case, the answer was no! We observed two counts each time we pressed and released the pulser. The 555 monostable failed when the output pulse width was 1.54 microseconds and the input pulse width was 0.7 microsecond. This is close to the lower operating limit of the 555 monostable, so you can stop at this point.

Step 13

As a final experiment, set the timing components to the following values:

$$R_A = 4700 \text{ ohms}$$
$$C = 0.001 \text{ microfarad}$$
$$R_{ext} = 1000 \text{ ohms}$$
$$C_{ext} = \text{none}$$

Apply power to the breadboard and demonstrate that only a single pulse is produced by the 555 monostable. In this case, the triggering pulse to the 555 monostable is only 30 nanoseconds = 0.000000030 second duration. This pulse width is close to the lower limit of the 74121 monostable.

Step 14

Repeat Steps 8 through 13 with the 74122 monostable substituted for the 74121 monostable, as shown in Fig. 8-136. With $R_A = 10,000$ ohms, $C = 0.001$ microfarad, $R_{ext} = 10,000$ ohms, and $C_{ext} = 0$, we were able to observe only a single pulse on the LED display each time we pressed and released the pulser. The pulse duration from the 74122 was about 100 nanoseconds.

Step 15

Repeat Steps 8 through 13 with the 74123 monostable substituted for the 74121 monostable, as shown in Fig. 8-137. With $R_A = 10,000$ ohms, $C = 0.001$ microfarad, $R_{ext} = 10,000$ ohms, and $C_{ext} = 0$, we were able to observe only a single pulse on the LED display each time we pressed and released the pulser. The pulse duration from the 74123 was about 100 nanoseconds.

EXPERIMENT NO. 14

Purpose

The purpose of this experiment is to measure the pulse width produced by a 74121 monostable chip.

Pin Configuration of Integrated Circuit (Fig. 8-138)

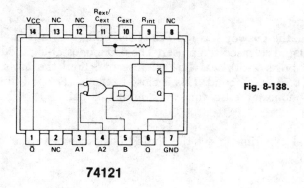

Fig. 8-138.

74121

Schematic Diagram of Circuit (Fig. 8-139)

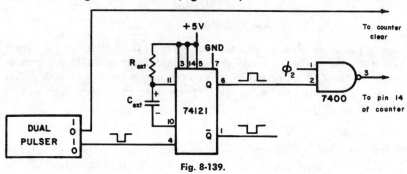

Fig. 8-139.

Step 1

You will require a multidecade counter for this experiment. One that you probably already have wired is the four-decade counter circuit shown in Fig. 8-140. Wire the clear inputs at pin 2 together and attach the connecting wire to logic 0 or to a pulser. You will be making repeated measurements, so you will need a convenient counter clearing mechanism.

You will also require a source of 750-kHz clock pulses. We used a microcomputer clock for this purpose. If you use a lower or higher frequency, your measured results will be different from ours.

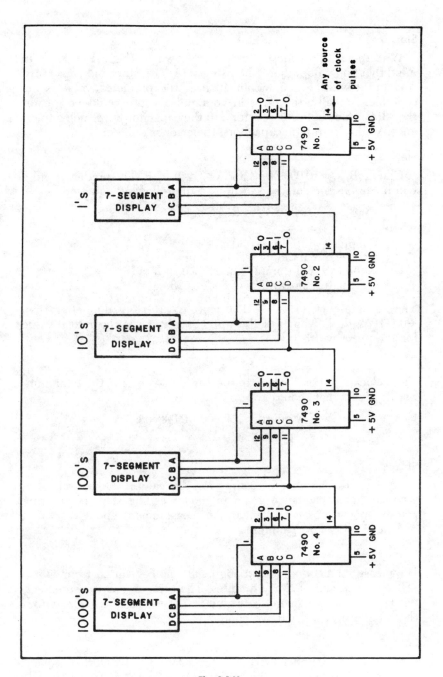

Fig. 8-140.

Step 2

Wire the 74121 monostable circuit shown in Fig. 8-140. Keep in mind that you will probably be using ±10% resistors and capacitors. Any pulse width value within 10% of the predicted value is acceptable. Actually, the error in your pulse width could be greater than 10% since both the resistor and the capacitor have such a tolerance. With electrolytic capacitors, the error may be greater.

Step 3

Choose $R_{ext} = 10,000$ ohms and $C_{ext} = 0.1 \ \mu F$. The predicted pulse width can be calculated according to the following equation,

$$t_w = R_{ext} \ C_{ext} \ln 2$$

where,

t_w is the pulse width in seconds,
R_{ext} is the external timing resistance in ohms,
C_{ext} is the external timing capacitance in farads,
ln 2 is the natural logarithm of 2, or 0.693.

The repeatability of the 74121 chip is probably no better than +0.5%. With the values of R_{ext} and C_{ext} given, the theoretical value for the pulse width is,

$$t_w = 693 \ \mu s$$

For a clock input of 750 kHz to the 2-input NAND gate, the total number of counts that should appear on the counter is,

$$\text{Counts} = 750,000 \cdot 0.000693$$
$$= 519 \pm 1$$

Step 4

Measure the number of counts for the values of the timing resistance and capacitance given in the preceding step. How many counts do you observe? Repeat the measurement about ten times over a period of five minutes.

We measured 481 counts, although this number varied from 475 to 483 over a period of thirty minutes. The error in our measurement, when based on the theoretical value of 519 counts, was 7.3%, within the tolerance of our passive components.

Step 5

Measure the number of counts for a variety of different capacitors, and fill in the following table. Retain R_{ext} at 10 kilohms.

Capacitance (μF)	Theoretical Counts	Measured Counts	Percentage Error
0.02	104		
0.05	260		
1.10	519		
0.33	1716		
1.0	5199		
2.2	11,437		
3.3	17,155		

We obtained the following results. We show several measurements for each timing capacitor to indicate the variations observed.

Capacitance (μF)	Measured Counts
0.02	92, 93, 92, 93, 92, 92, 92
0.05	185, 185, 186, 187, 187, 187
0.10	481, 481, 482, 483, . . . 477, 477, 475
0.33	2545, 2539, 2538, 2527, 2516, 2517, 2523, 2518, 2525
1.0	12,418; 16,909; 17,408; 16,979; 18,618; 19,120; 22,951; 24,101; 24,182
3.3	22,317; 21,994; 21,909; 21,887; 21,893; 21,790; 21,760; 21,788; 21,940

The 1-μF capacitor is considerably in error. This measurement gave us sufficient reason to discard it, which we did.

Step 6

What is your measured pulse width for the 0.10- and 0.33-μF capacitors?

We calculated pulse widths of 0.641 ms and 3.36 ms.

Step 7

What would be the theoretical pulse width if $C_{ext} = 50$ pF and $R_{ext} = 10$ kilohms?

Approximately 347 ns.

If you used such a gating pulse to gate a 750-kHz source of clock pulses into your counter, how many counts would you observe?

Either no counts or one count, depending on whether or not a negative edge appeared at the output of the 2-input NAND gate. With a trial run of 50 pulses, we observed 11 no counts and 39 single counts.

Save this circuit and continue to the following experiment.

Purpose

The purpose of this experiment is to measure the frequency of the clock Outboard with no timing capacitor present.

Pin Configuration of Integrated Circuit (Fig. 8-141)

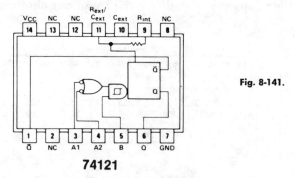

Fig. 8-141.

74121

Schematic Diagram of Circuit (Fig. 8-142)

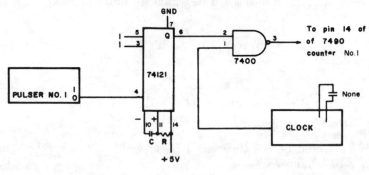

Fig. 8-142.

Step 1

Make the modification in the circuit shown in Fig. 8-142. The only difference is that you are now substituting the clock Outboard for the 750-kHz clock input. The wiring of the 74121 chip remains unchanged.

Step 2

Pick the 0.33-F capacitor and note the pulse width that you measured in Experiment No. 14. Retain $R_{ext} = 10,000$ ohms. Write the appropriate pulse width in the space below.

Our pulse width was 3.36 ms.

Step 3

With this pulse width, determine the number of counts produced by the clock Outboard. Write your results in the following space. Repeat your measurements several times.

We observed the following results: 254 counts, 250, 249, 250, 250, 250, 250, and 247. The mean value was 250 counts.

Step 4

Based on your observation and the known pulse width of the monostable pulse, calculate the frequency of your clock Outboard.

We calculated the following frequency:

$$\text{Frequency} = \text{Number of counts}$$
$$= \text{Pulse width}$$
$$250 \text{ counts}/0.00336 \text{ sec} = 74.4 \text{ kHz}$$

Save this circuit and continue to the following experiment.

EXPERIMENT NO. 16

Purpose

The purpose of this experiment is to wire a 555 timer chip as an astable multivibrator and to measure its frequency.

Schematic Diagram of Circuit (Fig. 8-143)

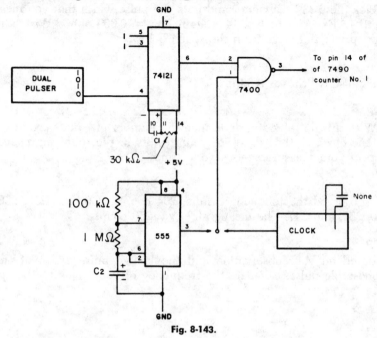

Fig. 8-143.

Pin Configurations of Integrated Circuits (Figs. 8-144 and 8-145)

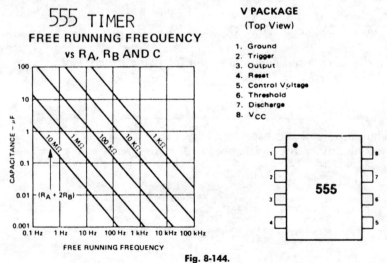

Fig. 8-144.

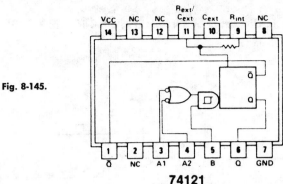

Fig. 8-145.

74121

Step 1

In this experiment, you will wire a clock directly from a 555 timer chip. The timing resistors are identical to those present on the clock Outboard.

Wire the circuit and apply power to the breadboard. Set $C_2 = 0$ (no capacitor).

Step 2

Use the same pulse width for the 74121 chip that you did in Experiment No. 2. With this pulse width, determine the number of counts with your 555 astable multivibrator as a source of clock pulses.

We observed the following results: 291, 289, 289, 288, 289, 288, 288, 289, 287, 288, 288, 288, 287, 288, 288, 287, 288, 288, 287, 287, and 288 counts.

Step 3

Calculate the frequency of the 555 astable multivibrator.

We calculated a frequency of 85.7 kHz. *Save this circuit.*

EXPERIMENT NO. 17

Purpose

The purpose of this experiment is to demonstrate the use of the 555 timer chip as a monostable multivibrator. This experiment is a simpler version of Experiment No. 13.

Schematic Diagrams of Circuits (Figs. 8-146 and 8-147)

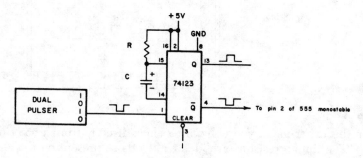

Fig. 8-146.

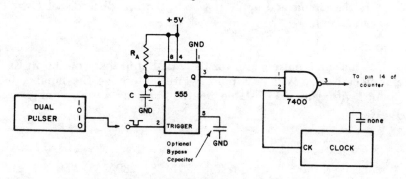

Fig. 8-147.

Pin Configurations of Integrated Circuits (Figs. 8-148 and 8-149)

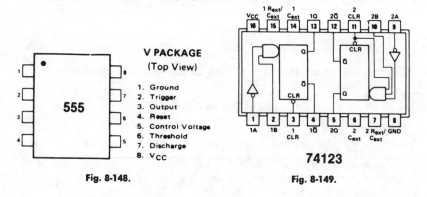

V PACKAGE
(Top View)

1. Ground
2. Trigger
3. Output
4. Reset
5. Control Voltage
6. Threshold
7. Discharge
8. V_{CC}

Fig. 8-148.

74123

Fig. 8-149.

Step 1

The 555 monostable multivibrator requires an input trigger pulse that is shorter than the pulse that it outputs. Valid pulse widths range from approximately 2 μs to several seconds. In this experiment, you will use a 74123 monostable in Fig. 8-149 to trigger the 555 monostable in Fig. 8-148.

Step 2

Wire the circuits shown in Figs. 8-146 and 8-147. Use the following passive components:

74123 monostable: C = none
                   R = 1000 ohms
555 monostable: C = 0.33 μF
                   R_A = 100 kilohms

The clock Outboard should be used as a source of clock pulses. Connect pin 3 of the 74123 chip to pin 2 of the 555 chip; do not use the pulser indicated in the diagram for the 555 monostable circuit. You will use the pulser later.

Step 3

The interesting aspect of this experiment is that you are using a 555 monostable to gate clock pulses from a 555 astable (the clock Outboard) into the multidecade counter. Both the 555 monostable and astable have a very high degree of stability, so you should observe better results than you did in preceding experiments.

Measure the number of counts when you trigger the 74123 monostable. Write your results in the following space. Repeat this experiment several times.

When we performed this experiment, we measured the following: 7089 counts, 6808, 6782, 6682, 6649, 6606, 6584, 6586, 6568, 6550, 6526, and 6639. After waiting several minutes, we obtained counts of 6768, 6680, 6804, 6708, 6639, 6584, and 6600. These values were surprisingly irreproducible. We would expect better from a 555 monostable.

Step 4

Use the clock Outboard frequency that you determined in Experiment No. 2 to calculate the pulse width of your 555 monostable.

Show your calculations in the following space.

Our clock Outboard frequency was 74.4 kHz. The pulse width is, therefore,

$$t_w = \frac{\text{Number of counts}}{\text{Frequency}}$$
$$= 6600 \text{ counts}/74{,}400 \text{ Hz}$$
$$= 88.7 \text{ ms}$$

The theoretical pulse width is

$$t_w = 1.1 \, R_A \, C$$
$$= (1.1)(100{,}000 \text{ ohms})(0.33 \, \mu\text{F})$$
$$= 36.3 \text{ ms}$$

The agreement is poor. The theoretical formula was obtained from the Signetics Corporation digital/linear/MOS Applications Manual.

Step 5

Now eliminate the 74123 circuit and use a pulser to trigger the 555 monostable. Clear the counter. Now press the trigger pulse and keep it pressed. You should observe that the counter continues to count. The reason? The trigger pulse width is greater than the desired output pulse width. This phenomenon will always occur when such is the case.

WHAT HAVE YOU ACCOMPLISHED IN THIS CHAPTER?

Review of Objectives

We have stated in the Introduction to this chapter that when finished you would be able to do the following:

- Define bistable element, flip-flop, synchronous input, asynchronous input, D-type flip-flop, latch, preset, clear, and digital waveform.

The definitions have been provided at the beginning of the chapter.

- Distinguish between a positive edge and a negative edge on a clock pulse.

This has been discussed in the section on positive and negative edges.

- Explain how a simple latch circuit, composed of two 2-input NAND gates, can be used to debounce an spdt mechanical switch.

We have discussed this example of a simple bistable latch in considerable detail.

- Explain the differences between rise time, fall time, and propagation delay.

All three concepts have been discussed in the chapter.

- Describe what inversion circle means when applied to clocked devices.

An entire section has been devoted to the subject of inversion circles. Examples of their use at the inputs and outputs of integrated circuits have been given.

- Describe the operation characteristics of the 7474 D-type positive-edge–triggered flip-flop.

Since this type of flip-flop is one of the most important ones available, we have devoted several sections and numerous experiments to it.

- Describe the operation characteristics of the 7475 latch.

This is an equally important latch, and we have devoted considerable discussion and several experiments to it as well.

- Explain how the preset and clear inputs function in a typical flip-flop.

We have discussed these inputs in a separate section.

- Describe three types of flip-flop clock actions.

The three types of clock actions have been discussed carefully in the text. Comparative experiments have been provided to demonstrate the differences in behavior that can be observed with such clock actions.

- Demonstrate the operation and behavior of the 7470, 7473, 7474, 7475, 7476, 74106, and 74175 flip-flops as either flip-flops or latches, or both.

  You have done this in Experiment Nos. 1 through 5 and 7 through 12.

- Demonstrate the operation of four different monostable multivibrators, the 555, 74121, 74122, and 74123 integrated-circuit chips.

  You have done this in Experiment Nos. 13 through 17.

- Construct a one-and-only-one synchronizer.

  You have done this in Experiment No. 12.

- Latch four binary coded decimal bits from a 7490 decade counter using a 7475 latch.

  You have done this in Experiment No. 5.

- Definite astable element, monostable element, and bistable element.

  We have done this in the definitions section at the beginning of the chapter.

- Describe the operation characteristics of the 74121, 74122, and 74123 monostable chips.

  We have done this in some detail in several sections in this chapter.

- Explain the differences in the operation of the 555 chip as a monostable and an astable multivibrator.

  We have explained such differences in two sections in this chapter.

- Measure the frequency of a clock, given a suitable monostable multivibrator chip.

  You have done this in Experiment No. 15.

- Measure the pulse width from a monostable multivibrator, given a clock of known frequency.

You have done this in Experiment No. 14.

9

Semiconductor Memories

INTRODUCTION

Welcome to what we believe is the most exciting chapter in this text. The experiments are interesting in their own right, but the implications of the integrated circuits that you will use—random access memories and erasable programmable read-only memories—are even more important. Semiconductor manufacturers are currently marketing 4K static read/write memories, 16K dynamic read/write memories, 64K dynamic read/write memories, 16K EPROMs, and 32K ROMs, and are in the process of introducing memory chips that have bit densities that are multiples of two or four of such figures. Newer types of semiconductor memories, including the CCD memory and the bubble memory, are available commercially. Clearly, the area of semiconductor memories is one of the most important and dynamic areas in the entire field of microelectronics. We hope to give you some hint of the excitement in the area through the text and experiments contained in this chapter. You will perform experiments with readily available 1024-bit static random access memories and 2048-bit erasable programmable read-only memories.

OBJECTIVES

At the completion of this chapter, you will be able to do the following:

- Demonstrate the operation of the 7489, 2102A, and 2111A static read/write random access memory integrated circuits.

- Demonstrate the operation of the 1702A erasable programmable read-only memory integrated circuit.
- Construct a simple nonsequential decoder and also a programmable nonsequential decoder.
- Construct the basic feedback loop circuit for a programmable controller.
- Provide an example of the decoding of a 16-bit memory address.

DEFINITIONS

central processing unit—Abbreviated CPU. Also called central processor. Part of a computer system which contains the main storage, arithmetic unit, and special register groups. Performs arithmetic operations, controls instruction processing, and provides timing signals and other housekeeping operations.[1]

dynamic memory—A memory that uses a capacitive element for storing a data bit.

erasable programmable read-only memory—Abbreviated EPROM. A read-only memory that can be erased by exposure to UV radiation and then electrically reprogrammed.

input-output—A general term applied to the equipment used in communicating with a computer and the data involved in the computer.[1]

magnetic core storage—A type of computer storage which employs a core of magnetic material with wires threaded through it. The core can be magnetized to represent a binary 1 or 0.

magnetic disc—A flat circular plate with a magnetic surface on which data can be stored by selective magnetization of portions of the flat surface.[1]

magnetic drum—A storage device consisting of a rapidly rotating cylinder, the surface of which can be easily magnetized and which will retain the data. Information is stored in the form of magnetized spots (or no spots) on the drum surface.[1]

magnetic tape storage—A storage system based on the use of magnetic spots (bits) on metal or coated-plastic tape. The spots are arranged so that the desired code is read out as the tape travels past the read-write head.[1]

memory—Any device that can store logic 1 and logic 0 bits in such a manner that a single bit or group of bits can be accessed and retrieved.[2]

memory access time—The time required to obtain valid output data from a memory once a memory address has been specified.

microprogram—A computer program written in the most basic instructions or subcommands that can be executed by the computer. Frequently, it is stored in a read-only memory.[1]

nonvolatile—A semiconductor memory device in which the stored digital data is not lost when the power is removed.

programmable ROM—Abbreviated PROM. A read-only memory that is field programmable by the user.[2]

random access memory—Abbreviated RAM. A semiconductor memory in which a memory location is addressed randomly by the input of a multibit memory address that is decoded internally. Any memory location can be addressed directly, without sequencing through any other memory location. May be read/write, read-only, or erasable programmable read-only memory. Commonly used to mean read/write memory, which is an incorrect and unnecessarily restrictive use of the term.

read—In semiconductors: To transmit data from a semiconductor memory to some other digital electronic device. The term "read" also applies to computers and other memory devices.

read-only memory—Abbreviated ROM. A semiconductor memory from which digital data can be repeatedly read out, but cannot be written into, as is the case for a random access memory.[2]

read/write memory—Memory that exhibits both the read and write memory operations. Can be either random access or serial access.

static memory—A memory that uses a flip-flop for storing a data bit.

semiconductor memory—A digital electronic memory device in which logic 0 and logic 1 bits are stored in the form of electronic signals in a semiconductor matrix.

serial access memory—A semiconductor memory in which a memory location is addressed sequentially starting from memory location 0 or a known memory location.

volatile memory—A semiconductor memory device in which the stored digital data is lost when the power is removed.

write—In semiconductors: To transmit data into a semiconductor memory from some other digital electronic device or integrated circuit chip. The term "write" also applies to computers and other types of memory devices. A synonym is *store*.

WHAT IS MEMORY?

In digital electronics, a *memory* is any device that can store logic 1 and logic 0 bits in such a manner that a single bit or group of bits can be accessed and retrieved.[2] The main use for memories is in computers, which basically can be considered to consist of three elements,

1. A central processing unit (CPU) or arithmetic unit, which performs arithmetic calculations and a variety of other operations,

2. Memories, both permanent and temporary, and
3. Input/output devices, that allow the computer to interact and communicate with the "outside world" in terms that the "outside world" can readily understand and interpret.

Enormous amounts of memory are required to store computer programs, data, special computer languages, operating procedures for the computer, and temporary information generated while making a computation. Some common computer memory devices include:

- Punched paper card and tape, where a hole represents a logic 1 bit and the absence of a hole represents a logic 0 bit.
- Magnetic tape, including tape cassettes, where logic 0 and logic 1 bits are recorded as domains of magnetization.
- Magnetic disc, where the medium, rather than being tape, is a rigid or flexible magnetic disc.
- Magnetic drums, where the medium, rather than being tape or disc, is a rotating drum.
- Magnetic core, where a logic 0 or logic 1 bit is stored in a tiny donut-shaped magnet.
- Bubble memories, where logic 0 and logic 1 bits are stored in small circular domains of magnetization called bubbles.
- Semiconductor memories, which will be discussed shortly.
- Other memory devices that will not be discussed.

The field of digital memory devices is so large that a reasonable description of the more important kinds of memories could easily occupy another book that is the size of this one. We have, at best, only a single chapter to give you a feeling for what semiconductor memories are and how they can be used. Our treatment, consequently, will be abbreviated, and we can only recommend that you consult recent popular journals in electronics for a more detailed view of the excitement that currently exists in the area of memory technology.

WHAT IS A SEMICONDUCTOR MEMORY?

A *semiconductor memory* is a digital electronic memory device in which logic 0 and logic 1 bits are stored in the form of electronic signals in a semiconductor matrix. Semiconductor memories are known by various names, including read/write memories, random access memories, read-only memories, scratch-pad memories, shift registers, holding registers, memory buffers, FIFOs, programmable read-only memories, charge-coupled devices, etc. In this book, we shall primarily be interested in random access read/

write memories, read-only memories, and erasable programmable read-only memories, abbreviated R/W RAM, ROM, and EPROM, respectively.

SERIAL ACCESS VS. RANDOM ACCESS MEMORY

In a *serial access memory*, a given memory location is addressed sequentially starting from a known memory location. For example, if you wish to address memory location 989 in a 1024-location serial access memory, you will have to start at memory location 0 and count up to location 989, or else start at memory location 1024 and count down to memory location 989. In either case, valuable time is consumed while you are attempting to locate the desired memory cell. In contrast, a *random access memory* permits you to address any location directly, without passing through the address of any other location. Thus, the time to address location 0 is the same as the time to address location 989, or location 1023 in a 1024-location random access memory. A random access memory uses decoder circuits internally to provide the immediate access to any given memory cell. A serial access memory does not provide any decoders; instead, an external counter circuit must be employed to clock through the succession of memory cells.

The term, "random access memory (RAM)," has been greatly abused in the electronics literature, where it has been widely used to denote a specific kind of random access memory, viz., the *read/write random access memory*. It is too late to do anything about the matter, but we shall not persist with the error in terminology in this text. The "RAM" of the electronics literature will be called either a red/write random access memory (R/W RAM) or else a read/write memory, where the context of the paragraph or the chip identification will clearly indicate a random access rather than serial access memory.

Typical examples of read/write random access memories are the 7489, 2102A, and 2111A integrated circuits. Examples of erasable programmable read-only memories that are random access include the 1702A and 2708 integrated circuits. In general, the majority of the semiconductor memories that you will encounter will be random access.

READ/WRITE RANDOM ACCESS MEMORY

A *read/write random access memory* can be defined as a semiconductor memory that exhibits both the read and write memory operations as well as random access to any memory location. A typical R/W RAM has the following inputs and outputs:

INPUTS:

- Memory address—Also known as the memory cell select inputs. This group of input pins on the integrated circuit select the specific memory bit, or group of memory bits, desired for a read or write operation.
- Chip enable—This input is a strobe input that enables or disables the output, or outputs, from the memory integrated circuit. When the chip is disabled, both the read and write operations are disabled.
- Read and write, or read/write—Either a single read/write input or separate read and write inputs determine whether data is input (write) to or output (read) from the memory.
- Data—One or more input pins provide a path or paths for the actual data to be stored in the memory.

OUTPUTS:

- Data—One or more output pins provide the stored data to other digital devices on the receipt of a read input while the chip is enabled.

To repeat a comment made in the previous section, this kind of memory has been widely called a "RAM" in electronics literature. Such terminology is incorrect.

STATIC VS. DYNAMIC MEMORY

There exist two types of read/write memories, *static memories* and *dynamic memories*. Their definitions are as follows:

static memory—A read/write memory in which flip-flops are used for storage. The primary advantage of this technique is that information is retained as long as power is supplied to the device. A minimum clock rate is not required and, in fact, the device can be unclocked.

dynamic memory—A read/write memory in which information is stored by means of temporary charge storage techniques. The major disadvantage of this method is that loss of the stored information occurs if the clock repetition rate is reduced below a minimum value.

Current dynamic RAMs have about four times the memory density as do current static RAMs. The concepts of static and dynamic do not apply to read-only memories, since there is no danger of losing the memory data in a ROM.

READ-ONLY MEMORY

A *read-only memory* (*ROM*) is a semiconductor memory from which digital data can be repeatedly read out, but cannot be written into, as is the case for a read/write memory.[2] When we talk about writing into an R/W RAM, we are thinking of time scales in the 30-nanosecond to 1-microsecond range. It is possible to "re-program" certain types of read-only memories, but the reprogramming operation takes as long as seconds to complete. When we include both the traditional ROMs, which cannot be altered short of destroying the integrated circuit, and the programmable ROMs, we can characterize the available types in the following ways:

- Read-only memory (ROM)—This memory is programmed by the manufacturer during the manufacturing step. Once programmed in such a manner, there is no way to alter the memory contents.
- Programmable read-only memory (PROM)—This memory is specially fabricated so that it can be subjected to a once-only programming operation by the purchaser of the integrated circuit. Once the memory has been programmed, it cannot be altered further. You either do the programming right the first time, or else throw away the chip.
- Erasable programmable read-only memory (EPROM)—This memory is truly programmable; it can be reprogrammed repeatedly. The most common type of EPROM is one in which the memory contents are "erased" by the application of ultraviolet light for a period of about twenty minutes. The erasing process can return the memory data bit either to a logic 0 state or to a logic 1 state, depending on the technology associated with the memory chip.

EPROMs have become very popular in the mid and late 1970s. They possess the advantages of permanence, i.e., they are true read-only memories, coupled with the potential for occasional reprogramming.

HOW DO WE USE READ-ONLY MEMORIES?

Read-only memories are used wherever permanent or near-permanent memory is required in a digital computer, digital instrument, or digital telecommunications device. For example, ROMs

- Store computer programs in computers and other types of devices that incorporate small computers. Some of the jargon words that are used in this category are microcomputers, minicomputers, intelligent terminals, intelligent control systems, and the like.

• Substitute for *combinatorial logic networks*. In other words, instead of using a large number of gates to make a complicated truth table, a single ROM can be used to generate the entire truth table. This kind of activity comes under the heading of "advanced logic design."

VOLATILE VS. NONVOLATILE MEMORY

The terms, *volatile memory* and *nonvolatile memory*, are defined as follows:

volatile memory—A semiconductor memory device in which the stored digital data is lost when power is removed.

nonvolatile memory—A semiconductor memory device in which the stored digital data is not lost when the power is removed.

A random access memory is a volatile memory, whereas read-only memory, programmable read-only memory, and erasable programmable read-only memory are nonvolatile memories.

TYPICAL R/W RAM: THE 7489 INTEGRATED CIRCUIT

An inexpensive and popular random access memory in the 7400-series of chips is the 7489 64-bit read/write memory, which is also known as the Signetics 8225 64-bit bipolar scratch-pad memory (16×4 RAM). These two integrated circuits are identical in their operating characteristics and are small enough to permit easy experimentation.

The pin configuration of the Texas Instruments Incorporated 7489 R/W RAM is shown in Fig. 9-1.

It is more useful to show the logic symbol for the chip, in which the inputs, outputs, and power connections have been segregated

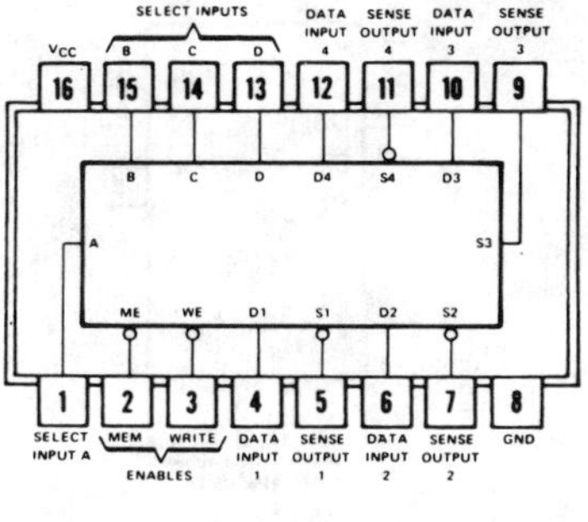

Fig. 9-1. Pin configuration for 7489 IC.

7489

on different sides of the box. We have done so for both the 7489 and the 8225 chips in order to show the comparison between them (Figs. 9-2 and 9-3).

It should first be noted that these two chips have an identical pin layout. The data inputs for both chips are at pins 4, 6, 10, and 12; the inverted data outputs are at pins 5, 7, 9, and 11; the four address lines (memory cell selects) are at pins 1, 15, 14, and 13; and the remaining pins correspond as well.

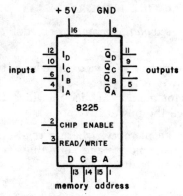

Fig. 9-2. Logic symbol for 7489 IC.

As a second point, we note that the two different manufacturers—Texas Instruments (7489) and Signetics (8225)—label their inputs and outputs differently. Texas Instruments calls the inputs D4, D3, D2, and D1, for which the D stands for "data," whereas Signetics calls them I_D, I_C, I_B, and I_A, for which the I stands for "input." The same can be said for the outputs, which Texas Instruments calls S4, S3, S2, and S1, for which the S stands for "sense," whereas Signetics uses the more standard output letter $\overline{Q}$ and writes $\overline{Q}_D$, $\overline{Q}_C$, Q_B, and Q_A. The bar over the letter Q indicates that the outputs are the complements of the data actually read into memory.

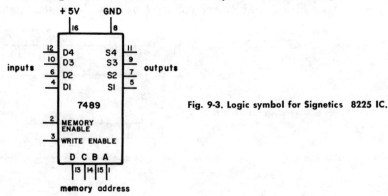

Fig. 9-3. Logic symbol for Signetics 8225 IC.

By his point, you should be able to carefully study the pin configuration of any integrated-circuit chip and write your own schematic representation, in which the inputs are on the left side of the box, the outputs are on the right side of the box, the select inputs are at the bottom, and the power connections are at the top.

Block diagrams—diagrams in which the essential units of the system are drawn in the form of blocks, and their relationship to each other is indicated by appropriately connected lines—of the 7489 and the 8225 are shown in Figs. 9-4 and 9-5, respectively. The 7489 block diagram is more detailed, but both provide the same kind of information.

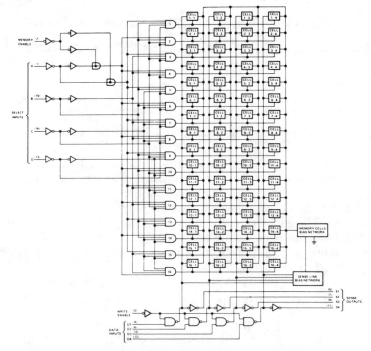

Fig. 9-4. Block diagram for 7489 IC.

It can be observed that the four memory select inputs go to a series of sixteen 4-input AND gates that serve as the address decoding section of the memory. The data bits enter through 2-input NAND gates, which can be disabled by the WRITE ENABLE input. The input data is stored in sixteen sets of four memory cells, which can be accessed four at a time.

A truth table for the 7489 chip, one that also applies to the 8225 chip, is provided in Table 9-1. The fact that the outputs are always

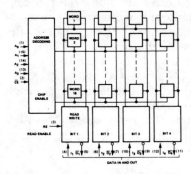

Fig. 9-5. Block diagram for 8225 IC.

Table 9-1. Truth Table for 7489 or 8225 Integrated Circuits

Memory Enable	Read/Write Enable	Operation	Condition of Outputs
0	0	Write	Complement of data inputs
0	1	Read	Complement of selected word
1	0	Inhibit storage	Complement of data inputs
1	1	Do nothing	All at logic 1 state

the complement of the data inputs or the stored data is not as much a nuisance as it might initially seem. You can always provide an inverter on each output line to obtain the normal output.

As a final point, we point out that the outputs from both the 7489 and the 8225 memories are open-collector outputs. This means that a 1000-ohm pull-up resistor is required on each of the four output lines. The outputs from the two chips can, thus, be better represented as shown in Fig. 9-6.

EXAMPLE: STORAGE OF DATA IN THE 7489 RAM

It is appropriate to briefly demonstrate how you would use either the 7489 or 8225 integrated circuit. For purposes of illustration, let us assume that you would like to load 16 decimal numbers, in the order given in Table 9-2, into the 16 memory locations of the RAM.

To load the data into the chip, you set the MEMORY ENABLE input to logic 0 and the READ/WRITE ENABLE input also to logic 0. Then sequence the MEMORY CELL SELECT inputs from 0000 = DCBA to 1111 = DCBA and load the following binary information given in Table 9-3 at the four inputs at pins 4, 6, 10, and 12. The data inputs are the binary coded decimal forms of the sixteen stored decimal numbers.

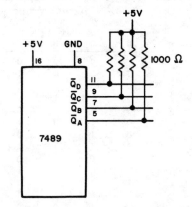

Fig. 9-6. Four outputs of 7489 chip are open-collector outputs.

Table 9-2. Some Data To Store in 7489 Random Access Memory

Memory Cell	Stored Number
0	8
1	2
2	5
3	6
4	0
5	9
6	7
7	7
8	3
9	2
10	4
11	0
12	1
13	8
14	9
15	5

Now you come to the read operation. While maintaining the MEMORY ENABLE input at logic 0, set the READ/WRITE ENABLE input to logic 1. You then sequence the MEMORY CELL SELECT inputs from 0000 to 1111 and observe the outputs both on a series of four lamp monitors as well as on a seven-segment LED display. The observed results, put in the form of a truth table, would be as shown in Table 9-4. Observe that each input data bit has been inverted. This is not at all the data that you placed into memory! On reflection, it should be clear why such data is observed: the output data is the complement of any input or stored data. This is the point that we have tried to make in his section. Either you must apply the complement of the desired output data as input data

Table 9-3. Truth Table for Data Stored in 7489 R/W Random Access Memory (See Table 9-2)

Address				Data			
D	C	B	A	I_D	I_C	I_B	I_A
0	0	0	0	1	0	0	0
0	0	0	1	0	0	1	0
0	0	1	0	0	1	0	1
0	0	1	1	0	1	1	0
0	1	0	0	0	0	0	0
0	1	0	1	1	0	0	1
0	1	1	0	0	1	1	1
0	1	1	1	0	1	1	1
1	0	0	0	0	0	1	1
1	0	0	1	0	0	1	0
1	0	1	0	0	1	0	0
1	0	1	1	0	0	0	0
1	1	0	0	0	0	0	1
1	1	0	1	1	0	0	0
1	1	1	0	1	0	0	1
1	1	1	1	0	1	0	1

to the 7489 or 8225 memory, or else you must supply inverters at the output lines.

THE 74200 AND 74206 256-BIT READ/WRITE MEMORIES

The 74200 and/or 74206 read/write memories have 256 words of 1-bit length. The pin configurations of these two chips are the same

Table 9-4. Actual Output Corresponding to Input Data in Tables 9-3 and 9-4

Address				Lamp Monitor Outputs				LED Display Reading
D	C	B	A	Q_D	Q_C	Q_B	Q_A	
0	0	0	0	0	1	1	1	7
0	0	0	1	1	1	0	1	E
0	0	1	0	1	0	1	0	C
0	0	1	1	1	0	0	1	9
0	1	0	0	1	1	1	1	blank
0	1	0	1	0	1	1	0	6
0	1	1	0	1	0	0	0	8
0	1	1	1	1	0	0	0	8
1	0	0	0	1	1	0	0	U
1	0	0	1	1	1	0	1	E
1	0	1	0	1	0	1	1	J
1	0	1	1	1	1	1	1	blank
1	1	0	0	1	1	1	0	F
1	1	0	1	0	1	1	1	7
1	1	1	0	0	1	1	0	6
1	1	1	1	1	0	1	0	C

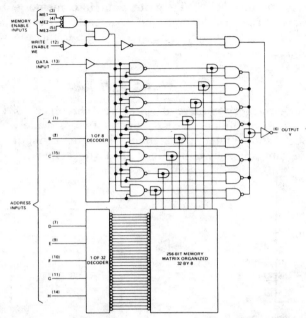

Fig. 9-7. Pin configuration and block diagram for 74200/74206 ICs.

(Fig. 9-7). The 74200 has three-state outputs, whereas the 74206 has open-collector outputs.

The 74200 or 74206 256-bit read/write memories can be schematically represented as shown in Fig. 9-8.

It should be observed that there are eight memory address input pins that can select one memory location among $2^8 = 256$. Pins 3, 4, and 5 are three negated inputs into a 3-input AND gate that serves as a memory enable input into the RAM. When the memory enable output from the AND gate is at logic 1, reading or writing from memory is inhibited and the output from the chip is either a very high impedance, as is the case for the 74200, or a logic 1 state, as

Fig. 9-8. Logic symbol for 74200 or 74206 random access memory.

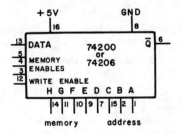

is the case for the 74206. To write data into memory, both the memory and write enables must be at logic 0. To read data from memory, the memory enable must be at logic 0 and the write enable at logic 1.

THE 2102 STATIC R/W RAM

A popular memory is the 2102 integrated circuit, a 1024×1-bit static read/write random access memory that is widely available from hobby and commercial sources. The pin configuration and block diagram are shown in Fig. 9-9. Two versions of the logic

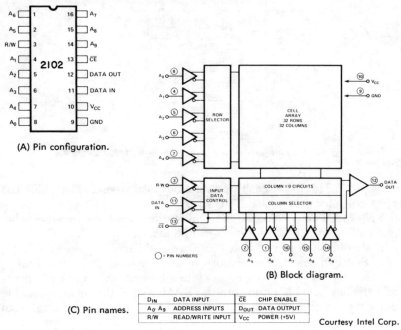

(A) Pin configuration.

(B) Block diagram.

(C) Pin names.

D_{IN}	DATA INPUT	$\overline{CE}$	CHIP ENABLE
A_0-A_9	ADDRESS INPUTS	D_{OUT}	DATA OUTPUT
R/W	READ/WRITE INPUT	V_{CC}	POWER (+5V)

Courtesy Intel Corp.

Fig. 9-9. Pin configuration and block diagram for 2102 static read/write random access memory.

symbol, one by Intel and another which we have drawn, are shown in Fig. 9-10. There are ten memory address inputs, a single data input, and a single three-state data output. The chip requires only a +5-volt supply.

A logic 0 at the chip enable input, pin 13, selects the 2102 chip for either reading or writing. A logic 1 at pin 13 disables the chip, permitting the output to go into its high impedance state. A logic 0 at the read/write, R/W, input at pin 3 causes the 1-bit value at the

252

LOGIC SYMBOL

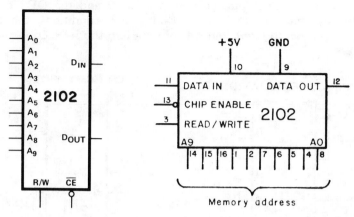

Courtesy Intel Corp.

Fig. 9-10. Two different logic symbol versions for 2102 read/write random access memory.

data input to be written into the location selected by the 10-bit memory address. A logic 1 at the R/W input permits the reading of this data bit at the data output pin.

The 2102 integrated circuit appears in a number of different forms, including the 2102, 8102-2, and 8102A-4, to mention only a few. Such chips differ primarily in the speed of memory access, the 8102A-4 being one of the fastest with a memory access time of 450 nanoseconds maximum.

THE 2111 STATIC RAM

The 2111 integrated circuit is similar to the 2102 memory, but has the 1024 bits arranged as 256×4 bit rather than 1024×1 bit. Like the 2102, the 2111 memory is a static read/write random access memory with three-state outputs. The pin configuration, logic symbol, and block diagram are shown in Figs. 9-11 and 9-12. There are eight memory address inputs and four bidirectional input/output pins. The chip requires only a +5-volt supply. A typical memory access time is 850 nanoseconds.

Both chip enable inputs, at pins 10 and 15, must be at logic 0 for either reading or writing. The most unusual feature of this chip is the group of bidirectional input/output pins. When you read data from the chip, the R/W input at pin 16 must be at logic 1 and the output disable pin, OD, must be at logic 0. Under such conditions, you observe output data from the memory location selected by the eight memory address inputs. When you write data into the chip, the R/W input pin must be at logic 0 and the OD output disable pin must be at logic 1. Under such conditions, the I/O pins permit you to input four bits of data into the selected memory address.

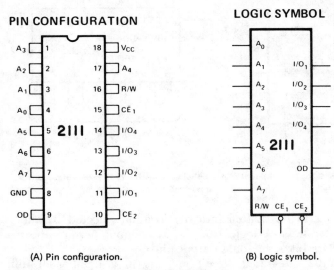

PIN CONFIGURATION

LOGIC SYMBOL

(A) Pin configuration.

(B) Logic symbol.

PIN NAMES

A_0-A_7	ADDRESS INPUTS
OD	OUTPUT DISABLE
R/W	READ/WRITE INPUT
$\overline{CE}_1$	CHIP ENABLE 1
CE_2	CHIP ENABLE 2
I/O_1- I/O_4	DATA INPUT/OUTPUT

(C) Pin names.

Courtesy Intel Corp.

Fig. 9-11. Pin configuration and logic symbol for 2111 static read/write random access memory.

The term, *bidirectional,* indicates that data can flow in either direction, input or output. This concept permits a reduction in the number of pins on a memory integrated circuit.

THE 7400-SERIES ROMs

There are several different ROMs or PROMs, none of which are erasable, that are included in the 7400-series of integrated-circuit chips.

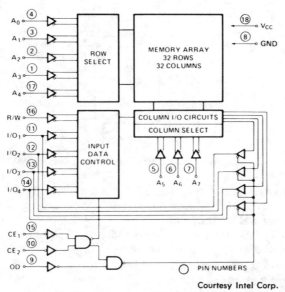

Courtesy Intel Corp.

Fig. 9-12. Block diagram for 2111 IC.

- The 7488 256-bit read-only memory, which contains 32 words of 8 bits each.
- The 74186 512-bit programmable ROM, which contains 64 words of 8 bits each. This ROM is programmable by the user, but it is not erasable.
- The 74187 1024-bit read-only memory, which contains 256 words of 8 bits each.
- The 74188A 256-bit programmable read-only memory, which contains 32 words of 8 bits each and is erasable.

It is useful to show the schematic representations of several ROMs to show how they differ from read/write memories. For example, both the 7488 ROM and the 74188A programmable ROM have the same pin configuration (Fig. 9-13).

As can be seen from Fig. 9-13, there are only four types of inputs or outputs,

- Memory cell select inputs
- Power inputs
- Memory outputs
- A single enable input, which, when at a logic 1, inhibits all of the outputs and sets them each at a logic 1 state.

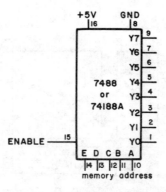

Fig. 9-13. Logic symbol for 7488 ROM and 74188A programmable ROM.

In contrast, a read/write memory has separate data inputs and outputs or, alternatively, permits the reading or writing of data from a single set of data input/outputs.

The 74187 1024-bit read-only memory is a simple chip, having the representation shown in Fig. 9-14. There are 256 words of 4-bits each, so we must have the ability to address 2^8 different memory locations. We require an 8-bit memory address word to address each of these memory locations; a conventional 8-bit binary code is used.

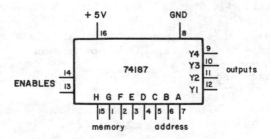

Fig. 9-14. Logic symbol for 74187 read-only memory.

Perhaps the simplest commonly available read-only memory, one that is not erasable, is the 112-bit ROM, which has 16 words of 7-bits each and is represented in the manner shown in Fig. 9-15. This chip is so widely used that it has been programmed by the manufacturer to give a single truth table (Table 9-5). When the ENABLE input is at a logic 0, all of the outputs are also at a logic 0.

Does the truth table in Table 9-5 look familiar? It should. It is the truth table for the 7447 BCD-to-seven-segment decoder/driver! In our opinion, this is a very interesting fact: *all decoders are ROMs!* The clearest example of a ROM among the 7400-series decoders is

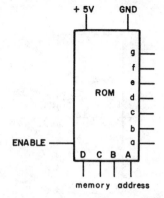

Fig. 9-15. Logic symbol for 7447 read-only memory, also known as 7447 decoder/driver.

Table 9-5. Truth Table for 7447 Read-Only Memory

Memory Address				Outputs						
D	C	B	A	a	b	c	d	e	f	g
0	0	0	0	0	0	0	0	0	0	1
0	0	0	1	1	0	0	1	1	1	1
0	0	1	0	0	0	1	0	0	1	0
0	0	1	1	0	0	0	0	1	1	0
0	1	0	0	1	0	0	1	1	0	0
0	1	0	1	0	1	0	0	1	0	0
0	1	1	0	1	1	0	0	0	0	0
0	1	1	1	0	0	0	1	1	1	1
1	0	0	0	0	0	0	0	0	0	0
1	0	0	1	0	0	0	1	1	0	0
1	0	1	0	1	1	1	0	0	1	0
1	0	1	1	1	1	0	0	1	1	0
1	1	0	0	1	0	1	1	1	0	0
1	1	0	1	0	1	1	0	1	0	0
1	1	1	0	1	1	1	0	0	0	0
1	1	1	1	1	1	1	1	1	1	1

the seven-segment decoder, among which the 7447 and 7448 chips are prime examples.

THE 1702A/8702A ERASABLE PROGRAMMABLE ROM

The 1702A integrated circuit is a 256 × 8-bit electrically reprogrammable and ultraviolet-erasable read-only memory with three-state outputs. The pin configuration, block diagram, and logic symbol are shown in Figs. 9-16 and 9-17. During normal read operation, the chip requires both +5-volt and −9-volt power supplies. The access time depends upon the type of chip used, and is in the range of 650 nanoseconds for the 1702A-2 to 1.5 microseconds for the 1702A-6. Although widely available from hobby sources, the

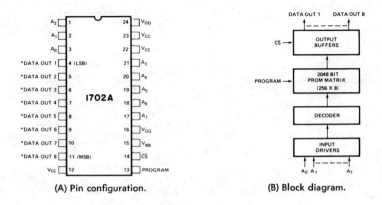

(A) Pin configuration.

(B) Block diagram.

A_0-A_7	ADDRESS INPUTS
$\overline{CS}$	CHIP SELECT INPUT
DO_1- DO_2	DATA OUTPUTS

(C) Pin names.

Courtesy Intel Corp.

Fig. 9-16. Pin configuration and block diagram for 1702A electrically reprogrammable and ultraviolet-erasable read-only memory.

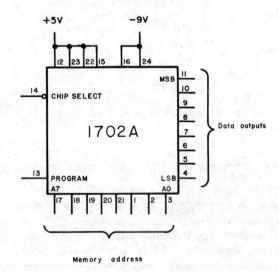

Courtesy Intel Corp.

Fig. 9-17. Logic symbol for 1702A IC.

chip is obsolete, having been replaced by the faster and easier-to-program 2708 and 2716 EPROMs.

The operation of the 1702A in the read mode is very easy. You apply a logic 0 state at the chip select input, $\overline{CS}$, at pin 14 along with an 8-bit memory address. The 8-bit data output corresponding to the chosen memory location then becomes available at output pins 4 through 11.

It is considerably more difficult to program the 1702A; however, we shall not discuss the details of the programming operation here. If you are interested in using EPROMs in your digital circuit or computer, we recommend that you avoid the 1702A in favor of the newer and larger EPROMs, all of which are easier to reprogram.

THE 2708 ELECTRICALLY PROGRAMMABLE ROM

The 2708 integrated circuit is a 1024 × 8-bit electrically reprogrammable and ultraviolet-erasable read-only memory with three-state outputs. The pin configuration and block diagram are shown

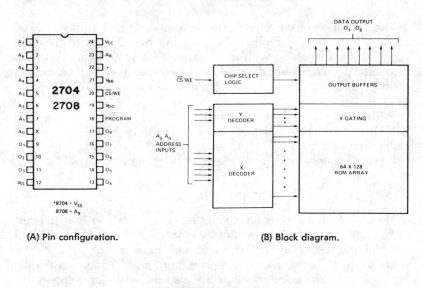

(A) Pin configuration.   (B) Block diagram.

A_0-A_9	ADDRESS INPUTS
O_1 O_8	DATA OUTPUTS
$\overline{CS}$/WE	CHIP SELECT/WRITE ENABLE INPUT

(C) Pin names.

Courtesy Tychon, Inc.

Fig. 9-18. Pin configuration and block diagram for 2704 and 2708 electrically reprogrammable and ultraviolet-erasable read-only memories.

in Fig. 9-18, and a logic symbol is shown in Fig. 9-19. The chip requires +5-volt, −5-volt, and +12-volt power supplies, but is considerably faster and easier to program than the smaller 1702A EPROM. The memory access time for the 2708-1 is fast, 350 nanoseconds.

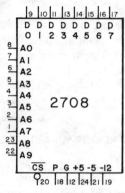

Fig. 9-19. Logic symbol for 2708 memory IC.

Courtesy Tychon, Inc.

The operation of the 2708 in the read mode is also very easy. You apply a logic 0 state both to the program pin, P, and to the chip select input, $\overline{CS}$, along with a 10-bit address at address inputs A0 through A9. The 8-bit data output corresponding to the chosen memory location then becomes available at outputs D0 through D7 (Fig. 9-19).

Within a year or so of the writing of this paragraph, the 2708 EPROM should be obsolete in favor of the 2716 EPROM, which is configured as a 2048 × 8-bit memory. The 2716 requires only a +5-volt power supply, and is still easier to program than the 2708.

OTHER MEMORIES

Memory technology is advancing extremely fast, so it is difficult to keep this chapter about memories current. In Table 9-6, are listed some of the memories that you may encounter in the next several years as they become less expensive and more widely available. Some of the older memory chips are also included for comparative purposes.

MEMORY ACCESS TIME

The term, *memory access time,* refers to the time required to obtain valid data output from a memory chip once you input the

Table 9-6. Partial Listing of Memory Chips

Chip Number	Type	Organization	Outputs	Other Characteristics
7489	R/W RAM	16 × 4	three-state	static
74189	R/W RAM	16 × 4	open-collector	static
74200	R/W RAM	256 × 1	three-state	static
74S206	R/W RAM	256 × 1	open-collector	static
1101A	R/W RAM	256 × 4	three-state	static
2101A	R/W RAM	1024 × 1	three-state	static
2102A	R/W RAM	256 × 4	three-state	static
2111A	R/W RAM	256 × 4	three-state	static
2112A	R/W RAM	1024 × 4	three-state	static
2114	R/W RAM	1024 × 1	three-state	static
2115A	R/W RAM	1024 × 1	three-state	static
2125A	R/W RAM	4096 × 1	three-state	static
2147	R/W RAM	256 × 1	three-state	static
1103A	R/W RAM	1024 × 1	open-collector	dynamic
2107A	R/W RAM	4096 × 1	three-state	dynamic
2108	R/W RAM	8192 × 1	three-state	dynamic
2116	R/W RAM	16384 × 1	three-state	dynamic
7488	ROM	32 × 8	open-collector	static
74187	ROM	256 × 4	open-collector	static
2308	ROM	1024 × 8	three-state	static
2316	ROM	2048 × 8	three-state	static
2332	ROM	4096 × 8	three-state	static
2364	ROM	8192 × 8	three-state	static
74186	PROM	64 × 8	open-collector	static
74188	PROM	32 × 8	open-collector	static
74287	PROM	256 × 4	three-state	static
74288	PROM	32 × 8	three-state	static
74387	PROM	256 × 4	open-collector	static
74470	PROM	256 × 8	open-collector	static
74471	PROM	256 × 8	three-state	static
74472	PROM	512 × 8	three-state	static
74473	PROM	512 × 8	open-collector	static
74474	PROM	512 × 8	three-state	static
74475	PROM	512 × 8	open-collector	static
1702A	EPROM	256 × 8	three-state	static
2704	EPROM	512 × 8	three-state	static
2708	EPROM	1024 × 8	three-state	static
2716	EPROM	2048 × 8	three-state	static
2732	EPROM	4096 × 8	three-state	static
2764	EPROM	8192 × 8	three-state	static

proper memory address and strobe the chip enable and read inputs. The term can also apply to the writing of data into a selected memory address. Some typical memory access times are listed in Table 9-7.

Table 9-7. Memory Access Times for Typical Memory Integrated Circuits

Integrated Circuit	Type	Memory Access Time (Nanoseconds)
7489	R/W RAM (static)	33
74200	R/W RAM (static)	17 (memory enable input)
74200	R/W RAM (static)	42 (address input)
2102A	R/W RAM (static)	350
2111A	R/W RAM (static)	350
2114	R/W RAM (static)	450
2114-2	R/W RAM (static)	200
2115	R/W RAM (static)	75
2115A	R/W RAM (static)	45
2107A	R/W RAM (dynamic)	300
2116-3	R/W RAM (dynamic)	250
1702A-2	EPROM	650
1702A	EPROM	1000
1702A-6	EPROM	1500
2708	EPROM	450
2708-1	EPROM	350
2716 (Intel)	EPROM	450
7488	ROM	25
74186	PROM	50
74187	ROM	40
74188A	PROM	30

MEMORY ADDRESS DECODING

The memory chips that we have discussed have a wide variety of uses in small digital circuits, including decoding, character generation, and small data memories. However, the predominant use for the chips described is in memory banks for microcomputers and minicomputers. Such memory banks, which range in size from 256 × 8 bits to 1,048,576 × 16 bits, take advantage of the busing characteristics of the R/W RAMs, ROMs, and EPROMs that we have described. The open collector busing technique was popular in the late 1960 s and early 1970 s, and is still widely used with the Digital Equipment Corporation PDP-8 and PDP-11 minicomputers. However, the busing technology used today is the three-state approach first developed by National Semiconductor Corporation. Using this technology, you can bus as many as 128 three-state outputs together.

A typical memory address decoder circuit is shown in Fig. 9-20. The circuit was used in the Tychon, Inc. MD-1 microcomputer, one of the very early hobby microcomputers based on the Intel 8080 microprocessor chip. The 16-bit memory address, A0 through A15, was decoded via the use of three common decoder chips, the 7442,

74L42, and 74L154. The 74L versions were used to minimize the load that the chips placed on the address bus. The memory board for the MD-1 microcomputer contained both 2102 RAM integrated circuits and 1702A EPROM integrated circuits.

If you were to use the memory board, you would first specify the 16K block of memory in which the board would reside. This would require a jumper connection between point E in Fig. 9-20 and either the 0, 16, 32, or 48 jumper positions. The relationship between these jumper positions and memory address bits A14 and A15 is provided in Fig. 9-21.

Each memory board would reside completely within one of the 16K blocks defined by the jumper connection to point E. However, individual 1K memory sections on each memory board would be

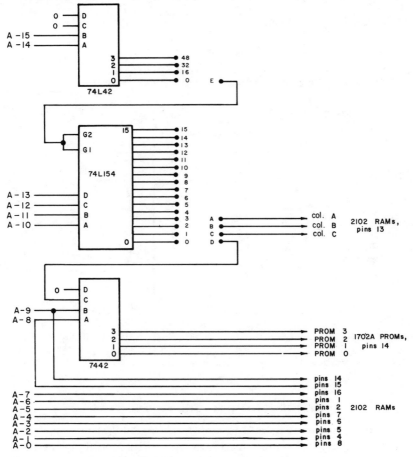

Fig. 9-20. Typical 16-bit memory address decoder circuit.

Address Bits		Block
A15	A14	
0	0	0
0	1	16
1	0	32
1	1	48

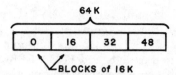

Fig. 9-21. Schematic and truth table for selection of one of four different 16K memory blocks in Fig. 9-20.

placed anywhere within this 16K block. The assignment of the 1K (or 1024-byte) sections would be done via jumper connections from points A, B, C, and D to the sixteen outputs from the 74L154 decoder. The relationship between the address bits A10 through A13 and the outputs from the 74L154 decoder is provided in Fig. 9-22.

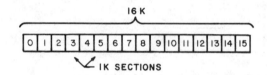

Address Bits				Section
A13	A12	A11	A10	
0	0	0	0	0
0	0	0	1	1
0	0	1	0	2
0	0	1	1	3
0	1	0	0	4
0	1	0	1	5
0	1	1	0	6
0	1	1	1	7
1	0	0	0	8
1	0	0	1	9
1	0	1	0	10
1	0	1	1	11
1	1	0	0	12
1	1	0	1	13
1	1	1	0	14
1	1	1	1	15

Fig. 9-22. Schematic and truth table for selection of one of sixteen 1K memory sections in a given 16K memory block.

INTRODUCTION TO THE EXPERIMENTS

In this chapter, you will demonstrate the digital characteristics of both read/write random access memories and erasable programmable read-only memories. You will also use a commonly available 64-bit R/W RAM, the 7489 integrated circuit, to construct several interesting circuits that permit you to control sequencing operations through the successive 4-bit contents of the random access memory.

The experiments in this chapter can be classified as follows:

Experiment No.	Type of Experiment
1	Demonstrates how to read data from and write data into the 7489 read/write random access memory.
2	Demonstrates the operation of a nonsequential decoder based upon the 7489 R/W RAM and a 7442 decoder.
3	Demonstrates the operation of a programmable nonsequential decoder based upon the 7489 R/W RAM, a 7442 decoder, and a single 7404 inverter. With the addition of the inverter to the circuit of Experiment No. 2, you are able to program the number of states among which you sequence.
4	Simulates the operation of the MAN-2A alphanumeric display through the use of two 7489 read/write random access memories.
5	Demonstrates the operation of a closed-loop feedback circuit based on the 7489 R/W RAM and the 74175 positive-edge–triggered latch.
6	Adds a 7483 full adder to the closed loop feedback circuit of Experiment No. 5.
7	Determines the type of flip-flop contained in the 2102A random access memory.
8	Demonstrates the read/write behavior of the 2102A read/write random access memory.
9	Demonstrates the read/write behavior of the 2111A read/write random access memory with bidirectional input/output pins.
10	Demonstrates the read behavior of the 1702A erasable programmable read-only memory.

EXPERIMENT NO. 1

Purpose

The purpose of this experiment is to demonstrate how you can write data into, and read data from, the 7489 (or 8225) read/write memory.

Pin Configurations of Integrated Circuits (Figs. 9-23 through 9-25)

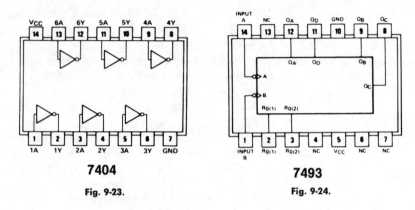

7404

Fig. 9-23.

7493

Fig. 9-24.

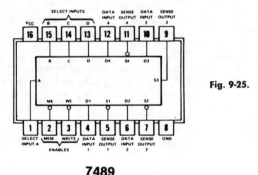

Fig. 9-25.

7489

Step 1

Wire the circuit as shown in Fig. 9-26. Either the 7489 or the 8225 integrated circuit is acceptable; both behave in a similar manner. The read/write memory employed in this experiment has 16 memory locations with 4 bits in each location.

Pulser No. 1 is the "read/write" pulser. When pressed, it causes data from the four logic switches to be loaded into memory. Pulser No. 2 is the "memory address" pulser. It sequences all sixteen memory locations with the aid of a 7493 binary counter.

Step 2

Apply power to the breadboard. You may initially be at any memory location. Cycle through all sixteen memory locations and, in the following space, write the numbers or symbols that you observe.

Schematic Diagram of Circuit (Fig. 9-26)

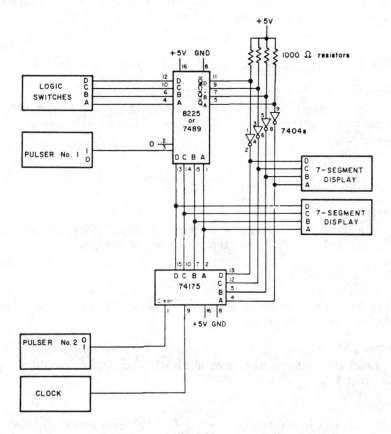

Fig. 9-26.

When we performed this experiment, our 7489 and 8225 chips behaved differently. The 7489 gave fourteen decimal 4 readings, one 5, and one 6. In contrast, the 8225 gave eleven blank readings (corresponding to decimal 15), three ⅂ symbols, and one ⊑ symbol. We concluded that the two chips reached their final memory states in different ways. *Your chips will be different.*

Step 3

Set the four logic switches, DCBA, to 1111 and then press and release pulser No. 1. What number finally appears on the display?

A decimal 0 should appear on the display! Now set the four logic switches to 0000 and again press and release pulser No. 1. What number appears on the display after you release the pulser?

The display should be blank, which corresponds to decimal 15.

Step 4

What decimal numeral would you predict for the display if the logic switches were set at 1100 and pulser No. 1 were pressed and released?

The correct answer should be decimal 3.

Step 5

The letters for the outputs from the 8225 or 7489 chips are Q_A, $\overline{Q}_B$, $\overline{Q}_C$, and $\overline{Q}_D$. What does the bar on top of the Q mean?

The bar on top means that the output data is the complement of the data originally input.

Step 6

Load 1001 into memory location 0001. The display should show decimal 6.

Step 7

Load data into memory location 13 (1101) so that a decimal 5 appears on the display after you release pulser No. 1.

Step 8

Load data into memory locations 1000, 1001, 1010, 1011, and 1100 so that decimal 0, 1, 2, 3, and 4 appear on the display for each indicated memory location, respectively.

Step 9

Load the complements of decimal 0, 1, 2, 3, 4, 5, 6, 7, 8, and 9 in memory locations 0 through 9 (1001) so that the numbers 0 through 9 appear on the display when you cycle through the memory.

Step 10

Load the complement of decimal 0 into all sixteen memory locations so that 0 appears on the seven-segment display for all sixteen memory locations.

Siep 11

In case you are having trouble with the above, keep in mind the following procedure to load information into memory:

(a) Repeatedly press and release pulser No. 2 until the correct memory location appears on the four lamp monitors.
(b) Set the logic switches to the complement of the number or symbol that you desire on the display.
(c) Press and release pulser No. 1 to load the information from the logic switches into the desired memory location.
(d) To load information into a different memory location, repeat steps a, b, and c. You can fill the memory by repeating steps a through c sixteen times.

Step 12

By performing the above experiments, you should have observed the following:

- Sixteen different memory cells can be addressed via the 7493 binary counter and pulser No. 2. The cells are addressed sequentially.
- In each memory cell, it is possible to store one of sixteen different binary words between 0000 and 1111.

Step 13

Briefly remove power from the breadboard and re-apply it. You should observe that all previous information in the R/W memory has been erased by the action of removing the power. An R/W RAM is a volatile memory. If power goes off for any reason, the information in memory is lost. *Save the circuit and continue to the following experiment.*

Question

1. Give several different uses for a small 16 word by 4-bit/word memory such as the 7489 or 8225. Do not put a computer as a

possible use. It is not practical these days to construct a computer out of such small memories.

EXPERIMENT NO. 2

Purpose

The purpose of this experiment is to construct and demonstrate a nonsequential decoder using the 7442 BCD-to-decimal decoder and the R/W RAM circuit constructed in the preceding experiment.

Pin Configurations of Integrated Circuits (Figs. 9-27 through 9-29)

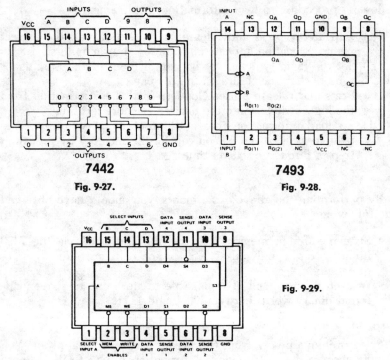

7442

Fig. 9-27.

7493

Fig. 9-28.

Fig. 9-29.

7489

Schematic Diagram of Circuit (Fig. 9-30)

The circuit is almost identical to that given in the preceding experiment. The outputs from the 7489 or 8225 R/W RAM are provided as the DCBA inputs to a 7442 decoder, as shown in Fig. 9-30. A lamp monitor is used to determine which of the ten output states are decoded.

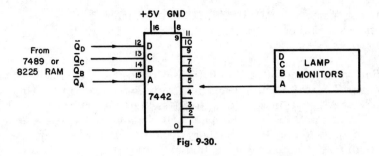

Fig. 9-30.

Step 1

Make the additional wire connections shown in the schematic.

Step 2

What do we mean by a sequential decoder?

The outputs of the decoder go to logic 0 according to the channel sequence, i.e., channel 0, then channel 1, channel 2, etc.

Step 3

What do we mean, then, by a nonsequential decoder?

The outputs of the decoder do not go to logic 0 according to the channel sequence.

Step 4

Apply power to the breadboard and load 1111 into all sixteen memory locations of the 7489 or 8225 integrated circuit. Connect the lamp monitor to pin 1 of the 7442 chip and demonstrate that the lamp monitor remains unlit for all sixteen memory locations.

Step 5

Return to memory location 0001 and deposit 1110, the complement of decimal 1, into memory. Remember, the output from memory location 0001 must read decimal 1 on the seven-segment LED display. This means that you must deposit a 1110 into memory, which then becomes complemented and appears as 0001 at the four outputs from the RAM.

Now demonstrate that pin 1 becomes lit only for memory location 0001. Correspondingly, pin 2 of the 7442 chip goes to a logic 0 only for memory location 0001. Attach the lamp monitor to pin 2 of the 7442 chip and demonstrate that such indeed is the case.

Step 6

Return to memory location 0100 and deposit the complement of decimal 7 into it. This means that you must read into memory DCBA = 1000 from the four logic switches. Connect the lamp monitor to pin 9 on the 7442 chip and demonstrate that the lamp monitor goes out only at memory location 0100 when you cycle through all sixteen memory locations.

You have just demonstrated a nonsequential decoder, which decodes decimal outputs 0, 1, and then 7, in the order given. A three-state sequential decoder would decode decimal outputs 0, 1, and 2 in sequence. By storing the appropriate decimal number into each of the sixteen words of memory, you should be able to sequence the ten outputs from the 7442 chip in any order that you desire.

Step 7

Provide the following 16-state sequence at the outputs of the 7442 decoder:

0, 1, 7, 3, 5, 6, 2, 9, 3, 0, 1, 8, 5, 4, 9, and 4.

Test the sequence with the aid of the lamp monitor. This is certainly a nonsequential decoder. *Save this circuit for the next experiment.*

Questions

1. Can you suggest any uses for a nonsequential decoder?

2. Is the nonsequential decoder that you have constructed in this experiment programmable or not?

EXPERIMENT NO. 3

Purpose

The purpose of this experiment is to use the circuit of the preceding experiment to construct a nonsequential decoder that sequences among any number of different states between two and sixteen.

Pin Configurations of Integrated Circuits (Figs. 9-31 through 9-33)

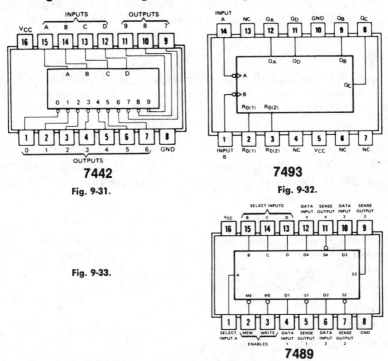

7442

Fig. 9-31.

7493

Fig. 9-32.

Fig. 9-33.

7489

Schematic Diagram of Circuit (Fig. 9-34)

The circuit used in this experiment is almost identical to that given in the preceding experiment. The only change required is a connection between one of the ten output pins on the 7442 chip, through a 7404 inverter, to pin 2 of the 7493 chip. When the proper decimal numeral appears in the output of the memory, the 7493 binary counter is reset and the nonsequential decoder starts again at memory location 0000. The additional circuit connections are shown in Fig. 9-34.

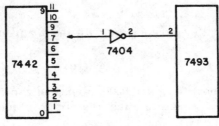

Fig. 9-34.

Step 1

Make the additional wire connections shown. You will require an additional integrated circuit, the 7404 hex inverter. There is enough space on the breadboard to add this chip.

Step 2

Connect pin 11 on the 7442 chip to pin 1 on the 7404 chip. Such a connection indicates that only when decimal 9 appears on the seven-segment display and at the input to the 7442 chip will the 7493 counter reset to memory location 0000.

Step 3

Apply power to the breadboard. Starting at memory location 0000, load the 16-word memory with the *complement* of the following numbers:

$$0, 0, 0, 0, 0, 0, 0, 0, 1, 1, 1, 1, 1, 1, 1, \text{and } 1$$

Note that you can cycle through all 16 memory locations by repeatedly pressing and releasing pulser No. 2. When you cycle through the memory, the above numbers should appear on the seven-segment display.

Step 4

Now load the 16-word memory with the *complement* of the following numbers:

$$0, 0, 0, 0, 0, 0, 0, 0, 9, 1, 1, 1, 1, 1, 1, \text{and } 1$$

Simply go to memory location 1000 and deposit the complement of decimal 9 into the memory. As soon as you do so, a decimal 0 will appear on the seven-segment display. Now repeatedly press and release pulser No. 2 and demonstrate that it is impossible to go past memory location 1000, as shown on the lamp monitors. Actually, you do reach memory location 1000, but the 7493 counter is reset to 0000 so quickly that you are unable to see the decimal 9 on the display.

Step 5

Now load the 16-word memory with the *complement* of the following numbers:

$$0, 1, 2, 3, 4, 9$$

starting at memory location 0000. Repeatedly press and release pulser No. 2 and demonstrate that the display sequences among

$$0, 1, 2, 3, 4, 0, 1, 2, 3, 4, 0, \text{etc.}$$

Step 6

In case you make a mistake in loading the decimal 9 into memory, keep in mind that you have two ways whereby you can help correct any errors in programming:

1. To reset the 7493 counter to memory location 0000, simply disconnect the wire input to pin 2 of the 7493 chip.
2. To allow the 7493 counter to sequence all sixteen memory locations, simply ground the input to pin 2 of the 7493 chip.

In this way, you can relocate the decimal 9 at any memory location between 0000 and 1111.

Step 7

In the above steps, you have used decimal 9 and a wire connection to pin 11 of the 7442 chip as the number that dictates the length of the sequence. In effect, you have constructed a programmable nonsequential decoder. In the experiments below, you use other decimal numbers to terminate the sequence.

(a) Sequence between the output numbers 0, 1, 2, 3, 5, and 7 and use decimal 8 to terminate the sequence and reset the 7493 counter to 0000.
(b) Sequence between the output numbers 0, 2, 4, 8, and blank, and use decimal 1 to terminate the sequence and reset the 7493 counter to 0000.
(c) Sequence between the output numbers 1, 2, 3, 4, 5, 6, 7, and use decimal 0 to terminate the sequence and reset the 7493 counter to 0000.

In these three experiments, the first number in the sequence is located in memory location 0000. The sequence-terminating number is, in effect, the last number in the sequence. This should be a sufficiently strong hint for you now to perform the experiments correctly.

Question

1. Define the term, "programmable nonsequential decoder."

EXPERIMENT NO. 4

Purpose

The purpose of this experiment is to simulate the operation of the MAN-2A alphanumeric display by sequencing two 4-bit 7489 read/write random access memories as inputs into the seven rows of the display.

Pin Configurations of Integrated Circuits (Figs. 9-35 through 9-38)

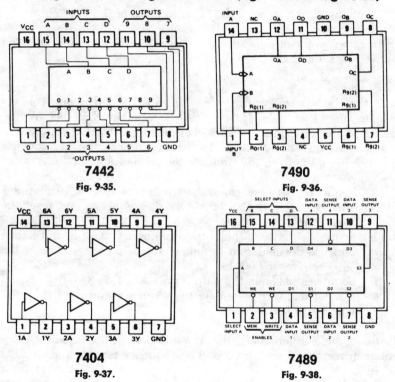

7442

Fig. 9-35.

7490

Fig. 9-36.

7404

Fig. 9-37.

7489

Fig. 9-38.

Schematic Diagram of Circuit (Fig. 9-39)

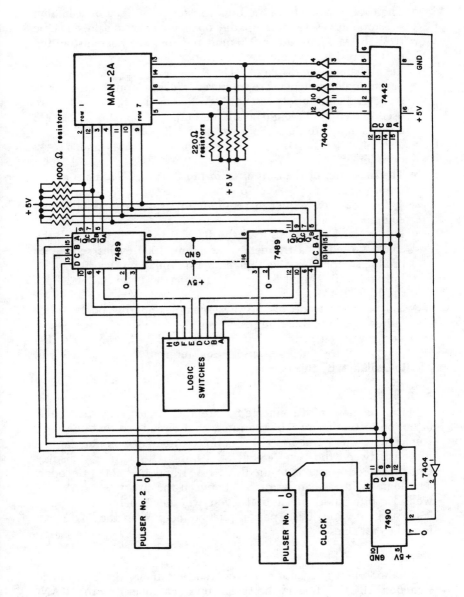

Fig. 9-39.

Step 1

Carefully study the schematic diagram in Fig. 9-39. Note the following points.

- There are two sets of pull-up resistors. One set of 1-kilohm resistors serves to pull up the open collector outputs of the R/W RAMs. The other 220-ohm resistors are current-limiting pull-up resistors to ensure the proper flow of current through the alphanumeric display LEDs.
- Seven logic switches are required. Seven inputs out of the eight available inputs to the R/W RAMS, I_A, I_B, . . ., etc., are used. Seven of the eight available outputs from the RAMs are used as inputs to the seven rows of the display.
- The 7490 decade counter drives two R/W RAMs and a 7442 decoder.
- The inversion of the output from pin 6 of the 7442 chip at the input pin 2 to the 7490 chip provides the 0, 1, 2, 3, 4, 0, 1, 2, 3, 4, 0, . . ., etc., sequence required to scan five and only five columns.
- Pulser No. 1 is used to load the R/W RAMs. Once loaded, the clock is used at a frequency exceeding 1000 cycles/second to produce a nonflickering alphanumeric symbol on the display.
- Pulser No. 2 is used to load data from the logic switches into the R/W RAMs.
- This circuit is one of the most complex in this book. It requires two breadboarding sockets.
- For any given symbol that appears on the alphanumeric display, all of the dots are not of equal intensity. We shall ask you to explain why this occurs.

Step 2

With the power disconnected, wire the circuit. Pay particular attention to the location of the integrated circuits so that the wire connections can be short. For example, the 7490 counter can be placed between the two 7489 R/W RAMs. The MAN-2A display can be placed adjacent to an R/W RAM and to a 7442 decoder. The logic switches can be placed between the two R/W RAMs as well. Despite these precautions, you will nevertheless develop a "rat's nest" of wires. Use a pair of pliers to help insert the final wires into the "rat's nest."

Step 3

It is important to mention the relationship among the seven logic switches, ABCDEFG, and the seven rows (cathodes) on the MAN-2A alphanumeric display (Fig. 9-40).

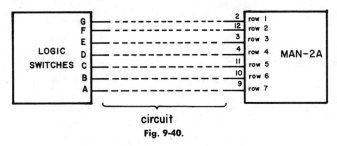

circuit

Fig. 9-40.

- Logic switch A corresponds to row 7, the lowest row of dots
- Logic switch B corresponds to row 6
- Logic switch C corresponds to row 5
- Logic switch D corresponds to row 4
- Logic switch E corresponds to row 3
- Logic switch F corresponds to row 2
- Logic switch G corresponds to row 1, the top row of dots

The statement that ABCDEFG = 1000001 would, therefore, mean that

- Logic switch A is at logic 1 and causes a lot to light up in row 7
- Logic switch G is at logic 1 and causes a dot to light up in row 1
- Logic switches B, C, D, E, and F are all at logic 0 and cause the dots in rows 2 through 6 to remain unlit.

None of the information in the logic switches is conveyed to the R/W RAMs and ultimately to the display until pulser No. 2 is pressed and released.

Step 4

Apply power to the breadboarding sockets. You may see several lit dots in column No. 1 initially. Do not worry about them for the moment. Set ABCDEFG = 1111111.

Step 5

Press and release pulser No. 2. You now should observe a column of seven dots in column No. 1 on the display. If you do not observe this result, you will have to check the wiring of your circuit to find the problem. The circuit is sufficiently complex that we cannot give you much assistance here. Use your accumulated skills in digital electronic circuitry to track down the problem.

Step 6

Press and release pulser No. 1. You are now at column No. 2, which may exhibit one or more lit dots. Press and release pulser No. 2 and observe that seven lit dots now appear in column No. 2.

Step 7

Press and release pulser No. 1. You are now at column No. 3. Press and release pulser No. 2 and observe seven lit dots in column No. 3. Keep in mind that ABCDEFG = 1111111 throughout all of these steps.

Step 8

Press and release pulser No. 1, then press and release pulser No. 2. You now have seven lit dots in column No. 4. Finally, press and release pulser No. 1, and press and release pulser No. 2. You have seven lit dots in column No. 5.

Step 9

Repeatedly press and release pulser No. 1. You should observe that you jump from column to column in the five-column display. When you reach column 5, cycle back to column 1 and repeat the process over again. Each column should contain seven lit dots. If you have observed such results, congratulate yourself on an excellent wiring job of a rather difficult circuit.

Step 10

You are not finished yet; you have more tests to do with the circuit. Set ABCDEFG = 0000000, and alternate between the pressing and releasing of pulser No. 1 and pulser No. 2. If you do a proper job, you should clear out the alphanumeric display of all dots in about five seconds. We were able to do it in slightly under three seconds.

Step 11

Your next task is to create a letter on the display. Press and release pulser No. 1 until you are back at column No. 1. We suggest that you set the logic switches to ABCDEFG = 1000000 so you know where you are in the display. Alternatively, use a logic 1 at pin 2 of the 7490 counter to clear the counter. Once you do this, you should automatically be at column No. 1.

Step 12

You will form the letter "T." Set ABCDEFG = 0000001. Press and release pulser No. 2. Then press and release pulser No. 1 so you can move to column No. 2. Again, press and release pulser No. 2. Now press and release pulser No. 1 two times so that you are set at column No. 4. Press and release pulser No. 2. Finally, press and release pulser No. 1, then press and release pulser No. 2. You now have loaded the proper information into columns 1, 2, 4, and 5.

You must now load a series of seven dots into column No. 3. Proceed to the following step.

Step 13

Press and release pulser No. 1 repeatedly until you are at column No. 3. Set ABCDEFG = 1111111. Press and release pulser No. 2. There, the job is finished. You should have a letter "T" on the display. Check your letter by repeatedly pressing and releasing pulser No. 1. If there are any mistakes, please correct them.

Step 14

Now, switch the connection from pulser No. 1 over to the clock, which should be set to a frequency greater than 1000 cycles/second. When making the connection (remember, do not turn the power to the breadboard off, or you will lose the stored information in the RAMs), you should observe the letter "T" on the display. The only thing wrong with the letter is that the top horizontal bar is more brightly lit than the middle vertical bar of dots. In the following space, try to explain why there is this difference in intensity.

Step 15

You should now be able to make any of the 64 possible alphanumeric letters, numerals, or symbols by modifying the above procedure that you used to make the letter "T." Try making the letter "H," then the letter "L." Both are rather simple to make. Remember the following when you do so:

- Pulser No. 1 is used to select the column on the display. By repeatedly pressing and releasing this pulser, you sequence through columns 1 through 5.
- Pulser No. 2 is used to load information set at the logic switches, This information appears, upon pressing and releasing the pulser, both in the RAMs and on the alphanumeric display.
- You can load the proper information into the RAMs by setting the proper logic states with the logic switches, pressing and releasing pulser No. 2, and then pressing and releasing pulser No. 1 to go to the next column, where this procedure is repeated once again.

This is not a very efficient process for creating letters and numerals on the display, but at least it demonstrates some of the principles involved in using the MAN-2A 7×5 dot matrix alphanumeric display.

Questions

1. Why do you, in Step 14, switch over to the clock from pulser No. 1 as an input to the 7490 counter? What do you accomplish by doing so? You should understand the answer to this question before you terminate this experiment.

2. What do we mean by a "refreshed" alphanumeric display? What does "to refresh" mean?

3. Why do you need the read/write random access memories (R/W RAMs) to produce a letter or number on the alphanumeric display? What purpose do the R/W RAMs serve?

4. Why do you need two R/W RAMs in the circuit?

5. Explain how you sequence among the five columns. What integrated circuits are involved in the sequencing process? What is the critical connection or two that makes the sequencer work among only five states?

EXPERIMENT NO. 5

Purpose

The purpose of this experiment is to examine the operation of a closed-loop circuit consisting of an R/W RAM and a positive-edge–triggered latch.

Pin Configurations of Integrated Circuits (Figs. 9-41 through 9-43)

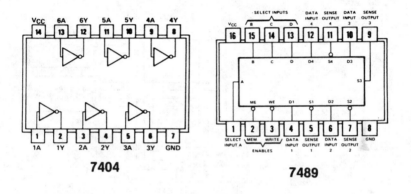

7404

Fig. 9-41.

7489

Fig. 9-42.

Fig. 9-43.

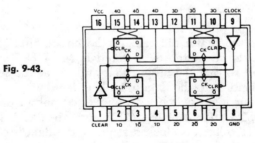

74175

Schematic Diagram of Circuit (Fig. 9-44)

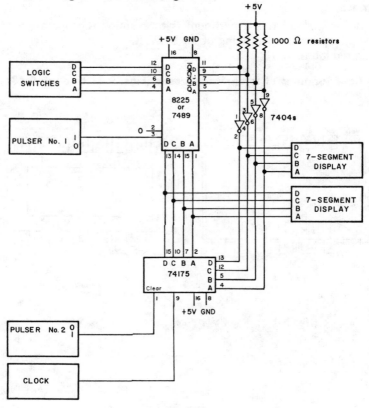

Fig. 9-44.

Step 1

Study the schematic diagram of the circuit in Fig. 9-44. Note that four 7404s invert the data stored in the 7489 (or 8225) integrated circuit so that the output that appears at the seven-segment display is identical to the data initially entered at pins 4, 6, 10, and 12 via the four logic switches. The inverted output data is applied at pins 4, 5, 12, and 13 of the 74175 positive-edge–triggered latch. When the 74175 latch is clocked at pin 9, the data is output at pins 2, 7, 10, and 15 of the 74175 latch, and appears immediately at the address inputs of the 7489 memory. After a time period of approximately 40 nanoseconds, the contents of the memory location is output at pins 5, 7, 9, and 11 of the 7489 memory and the cycle is repeated.

Step 2

Wire the circuit shown in Fig. 9-44. Pay attention to the location of the integrated circuits. In the following experiment, you will add a 7483 integrated circuit, so try to leave space for it on your breadboard.

Step 3

Clear the 74175 latch by flipping the logic switch connected to pin 1 from logic 1 to logic 0 and back to logic 1. A pulser would be preferable for this operation, but you may have only two pulsers available. The two are more important in the locations shown in the schematic diagram.

By clearing the latch, you have output 0000 from the 74175 to the address inputs of the 7489 RAM. You have thus selected memory location 0000 for your first 4-bit data word.

Set the logic switches to DCBA = 0010 and press and release pulser No. 1. You should observe a decimal 2 on the seven-segment display.

Step 4

Now press and release pulser No. 2. The 4-bit word, 0010, should appear on the four lamp monitors. This is your new memory address. Set the logic switches to DCBA = 0001 and press and release pulser No. 1. You should observe a decimal 1 on the seven-segment display.

Step 5

Press and release pulser No. 2. The 4-bit word, 0001, should appear on the four lamp monitors. This is memory address 0001. Set the logic switches to DCBA 0101 and press and release pulser No. 1. You should observe a decimal 5 on the seven-segment display.

Step 6

In the manner described in Steps 3, 4, and 5, try to load as many of the following logic switch data words into the 7489 memory at the indicated memory addresses.

Memory Address				Logic Switch Input Data			
D	C	B	A	D	C	B	A
0	0	0	0	0	0	1	0
0	0	0	1	0	1	0	1
0	0	1	0	0	0	0	1
0	0	1	1	0	1	0	0
0	1	0	0	0	0	1	1
0	1	0	1	0	1	1	1
0	1	1	0	1	0	0	1
0	1	1	1	0	1	0	0
1	0	0	0	1	1	1	1
1	0	0	1	1	1	1	0
1	0	1	0	1	0	0	0
1	0	1	1	0	0	0	0
1	1	0	0	0	0	0	0
1	1	0	1	0	0	0	0
1	1	1	0	1	0	1	0
1	1	1	1	1	1	1	1

Step 7

Which memory addresses can be loaded with the indicated data words?

Memory addresses 0000, 0010, 0001, 0101, 0111, 0100, 0011, and that is about all. Using the circuit shown in the schematic diagram, it is not possible to load the remaining memory addresses with the indicated data words.

Step 8

Clear the 74175 latch once again by applying at least one negative clock pulse at the CLEAR pin 1. The initial reading on the seven-segment display should be 2. Now apply 16 successive clock pulses to pin 9 of the 74175 latch. What sequence of numbers do you observe on the seven-segment display?

We observed the following sequence of numbers: 2, 1, 5, 7, 4, 3, 4, 3, 4, 3, 4, 3, 4, 3, 4, 3, . . ., etc. In the following steps, we shall ask you some questions about the operation of this circuit. You can consider the questions to be a test of your ability to understand the operation of integrated circuits such as the 7489 memory and the 74175 posi-tive-edge–triggered latch. We shall not provide answers.

Step 9

What if the stored data at memory location DCBA = 0011 were changed from DCBA = 0100 to DCBA = 0110? What sequence of numbers or seven-segment display symbols (see Chapter 5 for information on the behavior of the 7447 integrated circuit) would you now observe?

Step 10

Assume that you desire to have the following sequence of numbers appear on the seven-segment display after you clear the 74175 latch and then clock it with 16 clock pulses:

$$7, 3, 5, 8, 4, 6, 2, 1, 1, 1, 1, 1, 1, 1, 1, 1, \ldots \ldots$$

Write a truth table similar to that shown in Step 6 which relates the memory address words to the required logic switch input data. Which memory addresses can be loaded with data words, and which cannot?

Memory Address				Logic Switch Input Data			
D	C	B	A	D	C	B	A
0	0	0	0				
0	0	0	1				
0	0	1	0				
0	0	1	1				
0	1	0	0				
0	1	0	1				
0	1	1	0				
0	1	1	1				
1	0	0	0				
1	0	0	1				
1	0	1	0				
1	0	1	1				
1	1	0	0				
1	1	0	1				
1	1	1	0				
1	1	1	1				

Step 11

Another 4-bit latch that you might use in place of the 74175 latch is the 7475 latch, which contains four separate follower-type D flip-flops that can be clocked together if you connect the inputs at pins 4 and 13 together. If you would replace the 74175 latch by the 7475 latch, would the closed-loop circuit shown in the schematic diagram still perform in the same manner? Explain your answer in detail.

Save your circuit and continue to the following experiment.

EXPERIMENT NO. 6

Purpose

The purpose of this experiment is to examine the operation of a closed-loop circuit consisting of an R/W RAM, a positive-edge–triggered latch, and a full adder.

Pin Configurations of Integrated Circuits (Figs. 9-45 through 9-48)

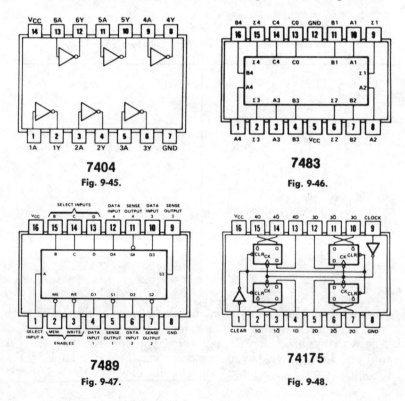

7404

Fig. 9-45.

7483

Fig. 9-46.

7489

Fig. 9-47.

74175

Fig. 9-48.

Schematic Diagram of Circuit (Fig. 9-49)

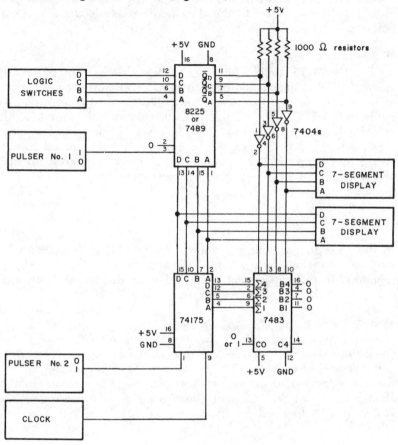

Fig. 9-49.

Step 1

To the circuit of Experiment No. 5, we have now added a 7483 four-bit full adder chip (Fig. 9-49). Please consult Chapter 10 for details on this chip, and perform the experiment given. Keep in mind that the 7483 is a binary full adder, which means that two binary quantities are added together to yield a binary result.

Step 2

Compare this experiment with the preceding one. Observe that the 7483 full adder is inserted in the loop immediately before the inputs to the 74175 latch. Thus, through the use of the CO and four B inputs, B1, B2, B3, and B4, on the full adder, it is possible for you to add a 4-bit quantity to the data leaving the 7489 R/W RAM before it enters the latch.

Step 3

Clear the 74175 latch by flipping the logic switch connected to pin 1 from logic 1 to logic 0 and back to logic 1. You now are at memory address 0000. Set the logic switches to DCBA = 0100 and the CO input to the 7483 chip to logic 1. Press and release pulser No. 1. You should observe a decimal 2 on the seven-segment display. Now press and release pulser No. 2. The 4-bit word, 0011, should appear on the four lamp monitors. How does this result compare with that observed in Step 4 of the preceding experiment?

In the preceding experiment, there was no 7483 full adder in the loop, so the 4-bit data word, 0010, appeared on the four lamp monitors. In this experiment, a logic 1 was added to 0010 to produce the result, 0011. In other words, $2 + 1 = 3$.

Step 4

Set the logic switches to DCBA = 0001 and the CO input to the 7483 chip to logic 0. Press and release pulser No. 1, then press and release pulser No. 2. The data word, 0001, should appear on the seven-segment display after you pressed pulser No. 1, and it should appear at the four lamp monitors after you pressed pulser No. 2. What happened this time, i.e., did the 7483 chip have any effect?

No, the 7483 did not have any effect. All four B inputs to the 7483 chip were at logic 0, and the CO input also was at logic 0. Thus, nothing was added to the 4-bit data word coming from the 7489 memory. In other words, $1 + 0 = 1$.

Step 5

Clear the 74175 latch again. In the manner described in Steps 3 and 4, try to load as many of the following logic switch data words and summed value of input CO to the 7483 chip into the 7489 memory at the indicated memory addresses. Observe that what is actually entered into memory is the sum of the logic switch data and bit CO.

Memory Address				Logic Switch Input Data				7483 CO Input
D	C	B	A	D	C	B	A	CO
0	0	0	0	0	0	0	1	1
0	0	0	1	0	0	1	0	0
0	0	1	0	0	1	0	0	1
0	0	1	1	0	0	0	0	0
0	1	0	0	0	1	1	0	0
0	1	0	1	1	1	1	0	1
0	1	1	0	0	1	1	1	1
0	1	1	1	1	0	0	1	1
1	0	0	0	1	1	0	0	0
1	0	0	1	1	1	0	0	0
1	0	1	0	1	0	1	0	1
1	0	1	0	1	0	0	1	0
1	1	0	0	0	1	0	1	0
1	1	0	1	0	0	1	1	0
1	1	1	0	0	1	1	1	0
1	1	1	1	1	1	1	0	0

Remember, you must properly set both the logic switches and bit CO before you press and release pulser No. 1, then pulser No. 2, in the order given. This procedure must be followed for each memory address.

Step 6

Clear the 74175 latch and apply 16 successive clock pulses to pin 9 of the 74175, changing input CO to its appropriate value corresponding to the address that appears on the seven-segment display (see Step 5). What sequence of numbers do you observe on the seven-segment display?

We observed the following sequence of numbers: 1, 2, 5, blank (15), ⊢ , (14), 7, ⊏ , (10), ⊐ , (11), 9, ⊔ , (12), 5, blank (15), ⊢ , (14), 7, ⊏ , (10), ⊐ , (11), 9, ⊔ , (12), 5, blank (15), ...

In the following steps, we shall ask some questions about the operation of this circuit. You can consider the questions to be a test of your ability to understand how the addition of the 7483 full adder to the loop alters the behavior of the circuit of Experiment No. 5. We shall not provide answers.

Step 7

What influence did bit CO on the 7483 have on the sequence of memory addresses that you observed in Step 6?

Step 8

Assume bit CO were held at a logic 0 state for all 16 sequential pulses. What sequence of numbers would you then observe on the seven-segment display after you cleared the 74175 latch?

Step 9

What influence would data words at input B of the 7483 chip other than 0000 have on the sequence of memory addresses that you observe?

Step 10

Explain how you would employ either the circuit of Experiment No. 5 or the circuit of Experiment No. 6 to loop through five successive memory addresses, starting at 0000.

Step 11

Explain how you would use the circuit in this experiment to remain at memory address 0011 for as long as the CO input bit is at logic 0. In other words what would you store into memory to achieve this result?

Step 12

Explain how you would use the circuit in this experiment to jump to memory address 1000 from address 0011 as soon as bit CO goes from logic 0 to logic 1. As long as the CO bit remains at logic 0, you remain at address 0011, as was the case in the preceding step. What would you store into memory to achieve this result?

Step 13

To the circuit shown in Fig. 9-49, assume that we add a second 7489 R/W RAM whose memory address inputs are connected to the memory address inputs of the first 7489 R/W RAM. Also, we connect four 7404 inverters to the outputs of the second 7489 R/W RAM, and a 74154 four-line-to-sixteen-line decoder to the outputs of the 7404 inverters, similar to what was done with the 7442 chip in Experiment No. 2 in this chapter. We claim that we now have a programmable controller. The outputs from the decoder can be used to turn devices on and off, and we can input bits to the 7483 full adder to change the sequence of operations. Draw the total schematic, with all pins labeled correctly, and explain why such a circuit acts as a programmable controller.

This circuit illustrates the principle of a microprogrammed computer, one based on the Wilkes technique of microprogramming. For further information, please consult the "Design of Microprogrammable Systems" section in *Digital, Linear, and MOS Applications,* copyrighted and published in 1974 by Signetics Corporation.

EXPERIMENT NO. 7

Purpose

The purpose of this experiment is to determine the type of flip-flop contained in the 2102A memory and also to test the operation of the R/W and chip enable inputs.

Pin Configuration of Integrated Circuit (Fig. 9-50)

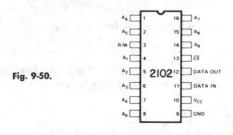

Fig. 9-50.

Schematic Diagram of Circuit (Fig. 9-51)

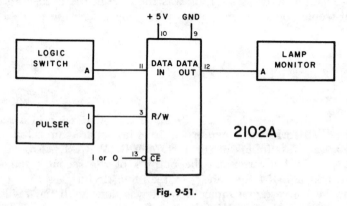

Fig. 9-51.

Step 1

Wire the circuit shown in Fig. 9-51. Set the chip enable input, $\overline{CE}$, at pin 13 to logic 0. Note that none of the memory address inputs is used. What memory address are you selecting?

With TTL logic, an unconnected input is at a logic 1. Thus, the 10-bit memory address is 1111111111.

Step 2

Set logic switch A to a logic 1. Press and release the pulser. What do you observe?

We observed that the lamp monitor became lit.

Step 3

Now set logic switch A to a logic 0 and press and release the pulser. What do you observe this time?

We observed that the lamp monitor became unlit.

Step 4

Press the pulser and keep it pressed. Now flip logic switch A to logic 0 and logic 1 repeatedly. What happens?

The lamp monitor follows the logic state of the logic switch, i.e., when the logic switch is at logic 1, the lamp monitor is at logic 1, and when the logic switch is at logic 0 the lamp monitor is logic 0.

Step 5

What type of flip-flop is contained in the 2102A memory? The results in Step 4 should provide you with the necessary clue.

Each 1-bit memory cell contains a flip-flop of the 7475 type, which is a D-type "follower" latch.

Step 6

Load a logic 1 state into memory address 1111111111. You should observe a lit lamp monitor. Now change the chip enable input, $\overline{CE}$, to logic 1. What happens? Why?

The lamp monitor becomes unlit. The output from the memory is now in the high-impedance state.

Questions

1. If each 1-bit memory cell contained a positive-edge–triggered or negative-edge–triggered D-type latch, how would the cell at memory address 1111111111 behave in Step 4?

2. Does the experiment in Step 6 demonstrate conclusively that the output is three-state? If not, what type of experiment is needed?

EXPERIMENT NO. 8

Purpose

The purpose of this experiment is to observe the read/write behavior of a sequence of 256 memory locations in the 2102A memory chip.

Pin Configurations of Integrated Circuits (Figs. 9-52 and 9-53)

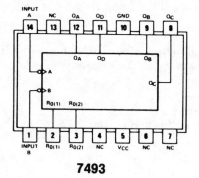

Fig. 9-52.

7493

PIN CONFIGURATION

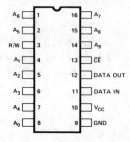

PIN NAMES

D_{IN}	DATA INPUT	$\overline{CE}$	CHIP ENABLE
A_0-A_9	ADDRESS INPUTS	D_{OUT}	DATA OUTPUT
R/W	READ/WRITE INPUT	V_{CC}	POWER (+5V)

Fig. 9-53.

Schematic Diagram of Circuit (Fig. 9-54)

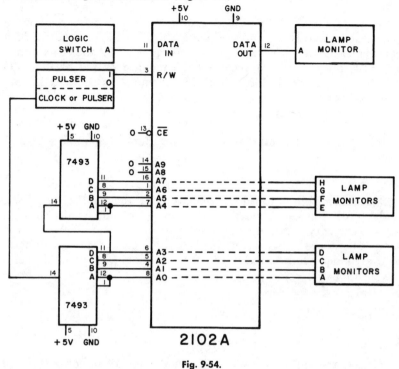

Fig. 9-54.

Step 1

Wire the circuit shown in Fig. 9-54. Note that the 7493 counter outputs are connected to eight lamp monitors, A through H. Apply power to the breadboard. Using a clock set to approximately 20 cycles per second, clock through memory addresses 0000000000 through 0011111111. What do you observe at the lamp monitor, and why?

We observed periodic flickering of the lamp monitor as the 8-bit 7493 counter circuit clocked through 256 successive memory locations. This was random data present in memory; it was created during the powering up of the chip.

Step 2

Set logic switch A to a logic 1 state. Now press the read/write pulser down and keep it pressed while the 20 cycles per second 7493 counter circuit counts through all 256 memory locations. Now release the pulser and observe the lamp monitor output as the 7493 counter circuit counts through all 256 memory locations. What do you observe?

We observed that all 256 memory locations contained a logic 1 state.

Step 3

Set logic switch A to a logic 0 state, press the read/write pulser, and keep it pressed while the 7493 counter circuit counts through all 256 memory locations. Now release the pulser and observe the lamp monitor output as the 7493 counter circuit counts through all 256 memory locations. Do you observe a logic 0 state in all memory locations?

We did.

Step 4

Time how long it takes the 7493 counter circuit to count through all 256 memory locations.

Our counter circuit required 12.4 seconds for 256 memory locations, for a count rate of 20.65 cycles per second.

Step 5

Clear all 256 memory locations, as you did in Step 3. Now set logic switch A to a logic 1 state. As quickly as possible, press and release the read/write pulser. You will now determine how long it took you to operate the pulser.

Step 6

Slow down the clock input to the 7493 counters or else use a pulser. Count to the memory address at which you pressed and released the pulser in Step 4. Note how many memory locations contain a logic 1 state in the following space.

In our case, memory addresses 0000001100 and 0000001101 contained a logic 1 state.

Step 7

Calculate the amount of time during which your pulser was pressed in Step 5.

In our case, 256 counts corresponded to 12.4 seconds, so two counts correspond to 97 milliseconds. This was the duration of our pulse. With a higher clock rate, we could have obtained a more precise figure.

Save the 7493 counter and display ciricuit, and continue to the next experiment.

EXPERIMENT NO. 9

Purpose

The purpose of this experiment is to observe the bidirectional read/write behavior of the 2111A memory chip.

Pin Configuration of Integrated Circuit (Fig. 9-55)

PIN CONFIGURATION

Fig. 9-55.

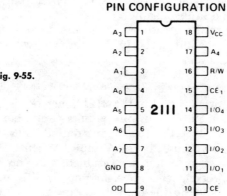

Schematic Diagram of Circuit (Fig. 9-56)

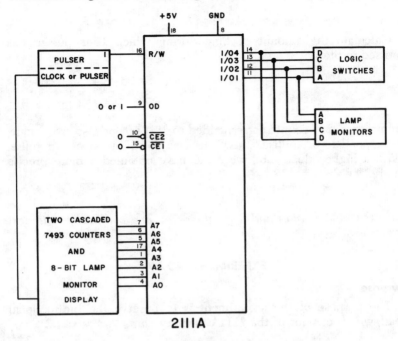

Fig. 9-56.

Step 1

Wire the circuit shown in Fig. 9-56. The "two cascaded 7493 counters and 8-bit lamp monitor display" circuit has been given in Experiment No. 8 in this chapter.

Apply power to the breadboard, and use a clock or pulser to sequence to memory address 11111111, where you will attempt to read and write information.

Step 2

The most important input to the 2111A memory is the output disable input, OD, at pin 9. This pin permits you to control the direction of data flow over the four input/output lines, I/O1 through I/O4, at the time you use the R/W input. When OD is at logic 1, the output three-state buffers are disabled, and you can write new input data by pressing and releasing the R/W pulser. When OD is at logic, you can read the data stored in memory.

Set OD to logic 1, and make certain that the R/W pulser is initially at logic 1.

Step 3

Flip the four logic switches to various 4-bit binary words ranging between 0000 and 1111. You should observe the corresponding words on the four lamp monitors associated with the I/O pins.

Step 4

Now set the four logic switches to 0111. With OD still at logic 1, press and release the R/W pulser. You should observe no change in the lamp monitors.

Step 5

With OD still at logic 1, return the four logic switches to 0000. You should now observe 0000 on the four lamp monitors.

Step 6

Set OD to logic 0, remove the four wires from the logic switches, and observe the output from memory address 1111. What is contained in memory?

In our case, 0111 was contained in memory. This was the data that we loaded into memory address 11111111.

Step 7

With OD at logic 0, reconnect the four wires to the four logic switches. What do you observe at the four lamp monitors and why? The four logic switches should still be at 0000. *Do this experiment quickly and, when finished, remove power from the breadboard.*

We observed that the lamp monitors became 0000. The reason was that the four logic switches overrode the 4-bit output, 0111, from the 2111A memory chip.

Step 8

Remove power from the breadboard. In the following space, explain what you must do to the circuit to permit you to observe both output data from the memory chip and logic switch data independently of each other.

The answer is that you must add a three-state busing circuit between the four logic switches and the lamp monitors. Either a 74125 or 74126 integrated circuit would be fine for such a circuit. The enable/disable pins on the 74125 or 74126 would permit you to eliminate the logic switch output from the four-bit three-state bus and observe only the output from the 2111A memory.

Save the 7493 counter and display circuit and continue to the following experiment.

EXPERIMENT NO. 10

Purpose

The purpose of this experiment is to read the data stored in a 1702A memory chip.

Pin Configuration of Integrated Circuit (Fig. 9-57)

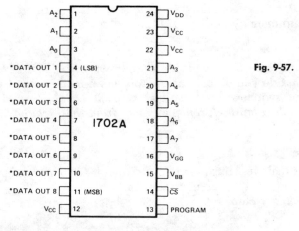

Fig. 9-57.

*THIS PIN IS THE DATA INPUT LEAD DURING PROGRAMMING.

Schematic Diagram of Circuit (Fig. 9-58)

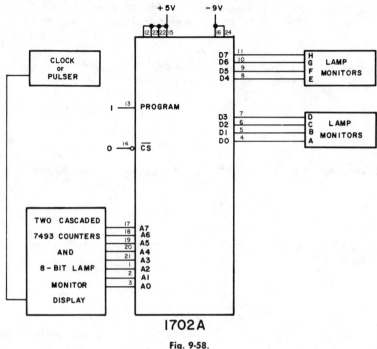

Fig. 9-58.

Step 1

Wire the circuit shown in Fig. 9-58. Your most significant problem probably will be the −9-volt power supply inputs at pins 16 and 24. Do not forget to common the ground terminals of both power supplies.

Step 2

We shall assume that you have a 1702A chip that has valid data stored in it, and also that you know at least some of the data bytes and their corresponding memory addresses. In our case, we used a KEX EPROM from a student microcomputer that had the following data bytes in the first two locations: 11000011 at memory address 00000000, and 00111000 at memory address 00000001. We used these two data bytes to verify our ability to correctly read the EPROM contents.

Step 3

Using the clock or pulser, increment the 7493 counters until you observe the proper memory address. In our case, we cleared the counters so that we could start at memory address 00000000.

Step 4

Observe the output data on the eight lamp monitors, A through H. Does it correspond to what you expected?

In our case we observed 11000011 at memory address 00000000 and 00111000 at memory address 00000001. Thus, our 1702A memory worked properly as a breadboarded memory circuit.

Step 5

Step through memory and verify that it contains the proper memory information.

We did this with most of the KEX program stored in the 1702A chip. At each memory address, we read the correct memory data.

WHAT HAVE YOU ACCOMPLISHED IN THIS CHAPTER?

Review of Objectives

We stated in the Introduction to this chapter that by the end you would be able to do the following:

- Demonstrate the operation of the 7489, 2102A, and 2111A static read/write random access memory integrated circuits.

  You have done this in Experiment Nos. 1, 7, 8, and 9.

- Demonstrate the operation of the 1702A erasable programmable read-only memory integrated circuit.

  You have done this in Experiment No. 10.

- Construct a simple nonsequential decoder and also a programmable nonsequential decoder.

You have done this in Experiment Nos. 2 and 3.

- Construct the basic feedback loop circuit for a programmable controller.

  You have done this in Experiment Nos. 5 and 6. Read the comments in Step 13 of Experiment No. 6.

- Provide an example of the decoding of a 16-bit memory address.

  This has been done in the text in the section entitled, "Memory Address Decoding."

10

Registers, Counters, Arithmetic Elements, and Schmitt Triggers

INTRODUCTION

This is the final chapter in a book that is now almost three times larger than initially planned. We do not have either the available pages or the time to cover the above four topics in a "leisurely" manner, as has been the case in most of the preceding chapters for the respective topics covered. Consequently, you will observe several changes in the way that we have written this chapter, viz.,

- Few schematic representations of integrated-circuit chips are given in the introductory material. In some cases, you will have to deduce the schematic representation directly from the integrated circuit. By now, you should have sufficient experience with the 7400-series of chips to be able to construct the representation yourself. Schematic representations, however, are given in the experiments.
- A considerable number of manufacturer's specifications, including truth tables, block diagrams, and digital waveforms are given. We have done this deliberately to encourage you to become familiar with manufacturers' data books and the wealth of information available therein. Of particular interest are the sets of digital waveforms for shift registers and counters.
- The definitions section is omitted from the introductory material. There is no need to duplicate the long definitions.

If you have come this far in the text and have performed at least 50% of the experiments given in the preceding chapters, a percentage that should include some of the more difficult experiments in the book, then you will not have much trouble with this chapter. Your knowledge of the behavior of flip-flops should help you considerably in your attempts to understand the characteristics of the 7400-series shift registers and counters. The topic of *arithmetic elements* is new to you, but it should not be too difficult to understand.

OBJECTIVES

At the completion of this chapter, you will be able to do the following:

- Define shift register.
- List the different types of shift registers that are available, and describe their individual characteristics.
- Define the following terms associated with integrated-circuit counters: modulo, weighting, count direction, synchronism, presettability, and unit cascadability.
- Define Schmitt trigger.
- List the Boolean algebra symbols for logical addition, logical multiplication, and negation.
- Describe the functions of an arithmetic/logic unit integrated circuit, such as the 74181.
- Test simple arithmetic/logic integrated circuits such as the 7483 and 74181.
- Construct a synchronous receiver/transmitter circuit from a pair of 74194 integrated circuits.

WHAT IS A SHIFT REGISTER?

A *register* is a memory element. Graf has defined the term as follows:
register—A short-term digital electronic storage circuit the capacity of which usually is one computer word.[1]
Computer words range from 8 bits to 32 bits in length, so a typical register must be capable of handling digital words in multiples of 4 or 8 bits. The most common type of register is a *shift register*, which can be defined as:

shift register—A digital storage circuit in which information is shifted from one flip-flop of a chain to the adjacent flip-flop upon application of each clock pulse. Data may be shifted several places to the right or left, depending on additional gating and the number of clock pulses applied to the register. Depending on the number of positions shifted, the rightmost characters are lost in a right shift, and the leftmost characters are lost in a left shift.[1]

static shift register—A shift register in which logic flip-flops are used for storage. This technique, in integrated form, results in greater storage-cell size and, consequently, in shorter shift-register lengths. Its primary advantage is that information is retained as long as power is supplied to the device. A minimum clock rate is not required, and, in fact, the device can be unclocked.[1]

dynamic shift reigster—A shift register in which information is stored by means of temporary charge storage techniques. The major disadvantage of this method is that loss of the information occurs if the clock repetition rate is reduced below a minimum value.[1]

Only static shift registers are available in the 7400-series of integrated circuits. They consist of a series of interconnected flip-flops, usually four, five, or eight in number. Very large metal-oxide-semiconductor (MOS) shift registers are also available from most of the major manufacturers of integrated-circuit chips. For example, the Signetics 2502 chip contains four 256-bit shift registers, the 2503 contains two 512-bit shift registers, and the 2504 contains one 1024-bit shift register. The third chip, the 2504, is only an 8-pin integrated circuit that contains two clock inputs, two power inputs, a serial data input, and a serial data output; as an integrated circuit, it is extremely easy to understand.

While on the subject of shift registers, it is appropriate to define the term *shift*.

shift—The process of moving data from one place to another. Generally many bits are moved at once. Shifting is done synchronously and by command of the clock. An 8-bit word can be shifted sequentially (serially), that is, the first bit goes out, second bit takes first bit's place, third bit takes second bit's place, and so on, in the manner of a bucket brigade. Generally referred to as shifting left or right. It takes eight clock pulses to shift an eight-bit word or all bits of a word can be shifted simultaneously. This is called parallel load or parallel shift.[4]

A slightly different definition for the term is given by Graf:[1]

shift—(1) Displacement of an ordered set of computer characters one or more places to the left or right. If the characters are the digits of a numerical expression, a shift is equivalent to multiplying by a power of the base. (2) The process of moving information from one place to another in a computer; generally, a number of bits are moved at once. A word can be shifted sequentially (generally referred to as shifting left or right), or all bits of a word can be shifted at the same time (called parallel load or parallel shift).[1]

TYPES OF SHIFT REGISTERS

It is useful to distinguish between the terms, *serial* and *parallel*:

serial—This refers to the technique for handling a binary data word which has more than one bit. The bits are acted on *one at a time*. It is like a parade going by a review point.[4] Only a single pair of wires is required for serial data transmission.

parallel—This refers to the technique for handling a binary data word that has more than one bit. All bits are acted on *simultaneously*. It is like the line of a football team. Upon a signal, all line men act.[4] Many wires are required for parallel data transmission.

Of course, we must also distinguish between whether information is going into or out from a shift register. Four possibilities exist:

- serial-in (SI)
- serial-out (SO)
- parallel-in (PI)
- parallel-out (PO)

It is incorrect to characterize a shift register only as a "serial-in" shift register or a "parallel-out" shift register. Information must both enter and leave the shift register as, for example, in the following kind of shift registers,

- serial-in serial-out (SISO)
- serial-in parallel-out (SIPO)
- parallel-in serial-out (PISO)
- parallel-in parallel-out (PIPO)

as well as various combinations of these shift registers.

The terms, *left shift* and *right shift*, or *shift left* and *shift right*, apply to serial shift registers. The "left" refers to the input of the shift register, and the "right" to the output. A shift-right shift register passes information from the input to the output of the register. The most general kind of shift register is one that can acquire data both in serial and in parallel fashion and can transmit such data both in serial and in parallel fashion; it can both shift left and shift right the data.

Shown in Fig. 10-1 are simple schematic diagrams for seven different kinds of shift registers: (1) serial-in serial-out (SISO), (2) parallel-in parallel-out (PIPO), (3) serial-in parallel-out (SIPO),

(4) parallel-in serial-out (PISO), (5) serial-in parallel-out and serial-out (SIPO and SISO), (6) parallel-in serial-out and parallel-out
(PISO and PIPO), and finally, (7) parallel-in parallel-out shift-left
shift-right.

WHERE ARE REGISTERS USED?

The term, register, is usually applied to digital memory devices
that contain more than a single memory element, such as a flip-
flop. You will find them in computers of all sizes: microprocessors,
minicomputers, and main frame computers. For example, in the
popular Digital Equipment Corporation PDP 8 minicomputer, you
will find the following registers:

- Accumulator register, a 12-bit register in which arithmetic and
  logic operations are performed.
- Multiplier quotient register, a 12-bit bidirectional shift register

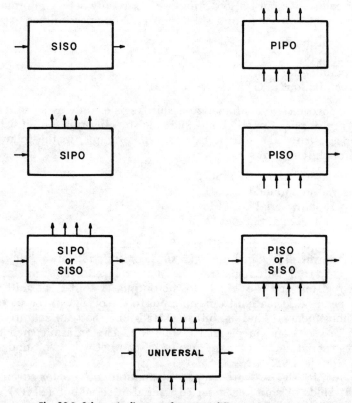

Fig. 10-1. Schematic diagrams for seven different shift registers.

that acts as an extension of the accumulator register during multiplication operations.

- Program counter register, a 12-bit register that is used to control the program sequence.
- Central processor memory address register, a 12-bit register that contains the address in core memory that is currently selected for reading or writing.
- Memory buffer register, a 12-bit register that is used for all information transfers between the central processor registers and the core memory.
- Link register, a 1-bit register that is used as the carry register for 2's complement arithmetic.
- Instruction register, a 3-bit register that contains the operation code of the instruction currently being performed by the machine.

From the above listing, we can deduce that the PDP 8 minicomputer is probably a 12-bit computer.

In Experiment No. 2 in Chapter 8, you created a 4-bit register to store a numeral from a 7490 counter. The 7475 4-bit latch acted as the parallel-in parallel-out register, and the seven-segment LED display indicated the contents of the register.

THE 7400-SERIES SHIFT REGISTERS

The registers in the 7400-series integrated-circuit chips are known by the following numbers:

7491	74172
7494	74173
7495	74178
7496	74179
7498	74194
7499	74195
	74198
74164	74199
74165	74278
74166	74295

To save space, we shall discuss the characteristics of only a few of the more popular shift registers in the series.

The 7491 8-bit shift register is one of the simplest of all the 7400-series integrated-circuit chips. As shown in the pin configuration diagram (Fig. 10-2), it has two power inputs, two data inputs, one clock input, and two complementary data outputs. The truth table for the chip is also shown in Fig. 10-2, as is a functional block diagram that shows the eight serial clocked RS flip-flops in the register.

The correct pin configuration diagram for the 7494 4-bit shift register is shown in Fig. 10-3.

The 74164 8-bit parallel-out serial shift register is quite popular. Given in Fig. 10-4 is the pin configuration and the truth table for the chip as well as a block diagram showing the eight clocked RS flip-flops and a set of digital waveforms that demonstrate the operation of the shift register. In the digital waveforms, note that data is shifted on the positive edge of the CLOCK pulse. When the

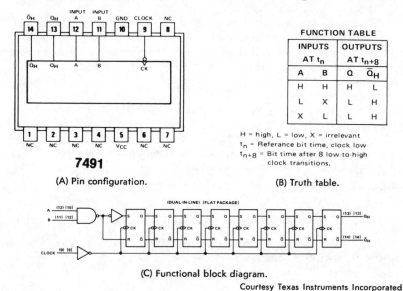

7491

(A) Pin configuration.

FUNCTION TABLE

INPUTS AT t_n		OUTPUTS AT t_{n+8}	
A	B	Q	$\bar{Q}_H$
H	H	H	L
L	X	L	H
X	L	L	H

H = high, L = low, X = irrelevant
t_n = Reference bit time, clock low
t_{n+8} = Bit time after 8 low-to-high clock transitions.

(B) Truth table.

(C) Functional block diagram.

Courtesy Texas Instruments Incorporated

Fig. 10-2. Pin configuration, truth table, and functional block diagram for 7491 8-bit shift register.

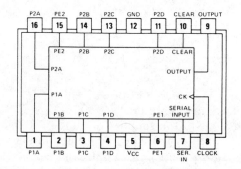

Fig. 10-3.
Pin configuration for 7494 4-bit shift register.

Courtesy Texas Instruments Incorporated

312

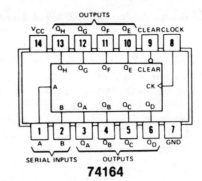

(A) Pin configuration.

74164

SERIAL INPUTS   OUTPUTS

OUTPUTS

FUNCTION TABLE

INPUTS				OUTPUTS		
CLEAR	CLOCK	A	B	Q_A	Q_B ...	Q_H
L	X	X	X	L	L	L
H	L	X	X	Q_{A0}	Q_{B0}	Q_{H0}
H	↑	H	H	H	Q_{An}	Q_{Gn}
H	↑	L	X	L	Q_{An}	Q_{Gn}
H	↑	X	L	L	Q_{An}	Q_{Gn}

H = high level (steady state), L = low level (steady state)
X = irrelevant (any input, including transitions)
↑ = transition from low to high level.
Q_{A0}, Q_{B0}, Q_{H0} = the level of Q_A, Q_B, or Q_H, respectively, before the indicated steady-state input conditions were established.
Q_{An}, Q_{Gn} = the level of Q_A or Q_G before the most-recent ↑ transition of the clock; indicates a one-bit shift.

(B) Truth table.

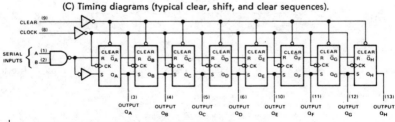

(C) Timing diagrams (typical clear, shift, and clear sequences).

···· dynamic input activated by transition from a high level to a low level

(D) Functional block diagram.

Courtesy Texas Instruments Incorporated

Fig. 10-4. Pin configuration, truth table, timing diagrams, and functional block diagrams for 74164 parallel-out serial shift register.

CLEAR input is at logic 0, all of the eight registers are cleared to logic 0. The 74165 parallel-load 8-bit shift register is a very popular parallel-in serial-out (PISO) shift register that is frequently used in parallel-to-serial data conversion. Shown in Fig. 10-5 are the pin configuration and the truth table.

A related shift register is the 74166 8-bit shift register, whose individual flip-flops can be cleared by a logic 0 input to pin 9. The 74165 register does not have a clear input. The chip is shown in Fig. 10-6.

We defer to Texas Instruments Corporation, the manufacturer of the 74194 4-bit bidirectional universal shift register, for an explanation of why the chip is so useful. They claim that:

> These bidirectional shift registers are designed to incorporate virtually all of the features a system designer may want in a shift register. The circuit contains 46 equivalent gates and features parallel inputs, parallel outputs, right-shift and left-shift serial inputs, operating-mode-control inputs, and a direct overriding clear line. The register has four distinct modes of operation, namely:

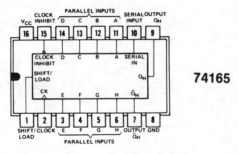

FUNCTION TABLE	INPUTS					INTERNAL OUTPUTS		OUTPUT
	SHIFT/ LOAD	CLOCK INHIBIT	CLOCK	SERIAL	PARALLEL A ... H	Q_A	Q_B	Q_H
	L	X	X	X	a ... h	a	b	h
	H	L	L	X	X	Q_{A0}	Q_{B0}	Q_{H0}
	H	L	↑	H	X	H	Q_{An}	Q_{Gn}
	H	L	↑	L	X	L	Q_{An}	Q_{Gn}
	H	H	↑	X	X	Q_{A0}	Q_{B0}	Q_{H0}

H = high level (steady state), L = low level (steady state)
X = irrelevant (any input, including transitions)
↑ = transition from low to high level
a . . . h = the level of steady-state input at inputs A thru H, respectively.
Q_{A0}, Q_{B0}, Q_{H0} = the level of Q_A, Q_B, or Q_H, respectively, before the indicated steady-state input conditions were established.
Q_{An}, Q_{Gn} = the level of Q_A or Q_G, respectively, before the most recent ↑ transition of the clock.

Courtesy Texas Instruments Incorporated

Fig. 10-5. Pin configuration and truth table for 74165 parallel-load 8-bit shift register.

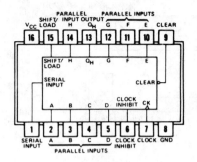

74166

FUNCTION TABLE

| INPUTS | | | | | | INTERNAL OUTPUTS | | OUTPUT |
CLEAR	SHIFT/ LOAD	CLOCK INHIBIT	CLOCK	SERIAL	PARALLEL A...H	Q_A	Q_B	Q_H
L	X	X	X	X	X	L	L	L
H	X	L	L	X	X	Q_{A0}	Q_{B0}	Q_{H0}
H	L	L	↑	X	a...h	a	b	h
H	H	L	↑	H	X	H	Q_{An}	Q_{Gn}
H	H	L	↑	L	X	L	Q_{An}	Q_{Gn}
H	X	H	↑	X	X	Q_{A0}	Q_{B0}	Q_{H0}

H = high level (steady state), L = low level (steady state)

X = irrelevant (any input, including transitions)

↑ = transition from low to high level

a...h = the level of steady-state input.at inputs A thru H, respectively.

Q_{A0}, Q_{B0}, Q_{H0} = the level of Q_A, Q_B, or Q_H, respectively, before the indicated steady-state input conditions were established.

Q_{An}, Q_{Gn} = the level of Q_A or Q_G, respectively, before the most-recent ↑ transition of the clock.

Courtesy Texas Instruments Incorporated

Fig. 10-6. Pin configuration and truth table for 74166 8-bit shift register.

Parallel (Broadside) Load
Shift Right (In the direction Q_A toward Q_D)
Shift Left (In the direction Q_D toward Q_A)
Inhibit Clock (Do nothing)

Synchronous parallel loading is accomplished by applying the four bits of data and taking both mode control inputs, S0 and S1, high. The data is loaded into the associated flip-flop and appears at the outputs after the positive transition of the clock input. During loading, serial data flow is inhibited.

Shift right is accomplished synchronously with the rising edge of the clock pulse when S0 is high and S1 is low. Serial data for this mode is entered at the shift-right data input. When S0 is low and S1 is high, data shifts left synchronously and new data is entered at the shift-left serial input.

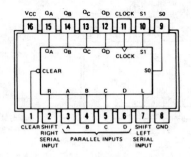

(A) Pin configuration.

74194

FUNCTION TABLE

CLEAR	MODE		CLOCK	SERIAL		PARALLEL				OUTPUTS			
	S_1	S_0		LEFT	RIGHT	A	B	C	D	Q_A	Q_B	Q_C	Q_D
L	X	X	X	X	X	X	X	X	X	L	L	L	L
H	X	X	L	X	X	X	X	X	X	Q_{A0}	Q_{B0}	Q_{C0}	Q_{D0}
H	H	H	↑	X	X	a	b	c	d	a	b	c	d
H	L	H	↑	X	H	X	X	X	X	H	Q_{An}	Q_{Bn}	Q_{Cn}
H	L	H	↑	X	L	X	X	X	X	L	Q_{An}	Q_{Bn}	Q_{Cn}
H	H	L	↑	H	X	X	X	X	X	Q_{Bn}	Q_{Cn}	Q_{Dn}	H
H	H	L	↑	L	X	X	X	X	X	Q_{Bn}	Q_{Cn}	Q_{Dn}	L
H	L	L	X	X	X	X	X	X	X	Q_{A0}	Q_{B0}	Q_{C0}	Q_{D0}

H = high level (steady state)
L = low level (steady state)
X = irrelevant (any input, including transitions)
↑ = transition from low to high level
a, b, c, d = the level of steady-state input at inputs A, B, C, or D, respectively

$Q_{A0}, Q_{B0}, Q_{C0}, Q_{D0}$ = the level of Q_A, Q_B, Q_C, or Q_D, respectively, before the indicated steady-state input conditions were established

$Q_{An}, Q_{Bn}, Q_{Cn}, Q_{Dn}$ = the level of Q_A, Q_B, Q_C, Q_D, respectively, before the most-recent ↑ transition of the clock.

(B) Truth table.

(C) Timing diagrams (typical clear, load, right-shift, left-shift, inhibit, and clear sequences).

Courtesy Texas Instruments Incorporated

Fig. 10-7. Pin configuration, truth table, and timing diagrams for 74194 4-bit bidirectional universal shift register.

Clocking of the flip-flop is inhibited when both mode control inputs are low. The mode controls of the SN54194/ SN74194 should be changed only while the clock input is high.

This description can be better understood with the aid of the pin configuration, truth table, and especially, digital waveforms for the chip (Fig. 10-7).

Finally, there is the 74198 8-bit shift register, which basically is similar to the 74194 register but has 4 additional bits and 8 additional pins. It also has four distinct modes of operation, namely: parallel (broadside) load, shift right (in the direction Q_A toward Q_H), shift left (in the direction Q_H toward Q_A), and inhibit clock (do nothing). The pin configuration, truth table, and digital waveforms are given in Fig. 10-8.

For information on the remaining shift registers in the 7400 series, please consult a manufacturer's handbook, such as the *TTL Data Book for Design Engineers*, Texas Instruments Incorporated, Dallas, Texas 75222). Lancaster[6] has written an excellent chapter on shift registers in *TTL Cookbook* in which he gives circuits for a teletype transmitter, a character generator, an electronic stepper, a walking ring counter, electronic dice, and a pseudo-random sequencer.

COUNTERS

Malmstadt and Enke[4] have defined the terms, *counter* and *binary counter*, as follows:

counter—A device capable of changing states in a specified sequence upon receiving appropriate input signals. *The output of the counter indicates the number of pulses which have been applied* (author's emphasis). (See also Divider) A counter is made from flip-flops and some gates. The output of all flip-flops is accessible to indicate the exact count at all times.[4]

binary counter—An interconnection of flip-flops having a single input so arranged as to enable binary counting. Each time a pulse appears at the input, the counter changes state and tabulates the number of input pulses for readout in binary form. It has 2^n possible counts, where n is the number of flip-flops.[4]

Binary counters are also called *divide-by-n counters* since such devices produce a single output pulse for every n input pulse. They can also be used as *scalers,* or *frequency dividers,* in which an applied input frequency is reduced by a factor of n. *Decade counters* contain logic gates and four flip-flops arranged as to enable decade

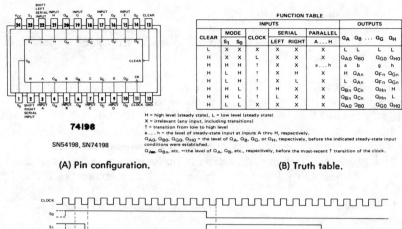

(A) Pin configuration.　　　　　　　　　　　　(B) Truth table.

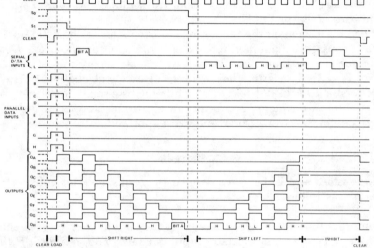

(C) Timing diagrams (typical clear, load, right-shift, left-shift, inhibit, and clear sequences).

Courtesy Texas Instruments Incorporated

Fig. 10-8. Pin configuration, truth table, and timing diagrams for 74198 8-bit bidirectional universal shift register.

counting. They have ten stable states and may be cycled through these states by the application of ten clock or pulse inputs.[1] A decade counter usually counts in a binary sequence from state 0 through state 9 and then cycles back to 0; they are sometimes referred to as *divide-by-10 counters.*

Lancaster[6] has listed a number of features of counters that we have summarized here:

- *Modulo*—The *modulo* of a counter is simply *n*, the number of distinct states the counter goes through before repeating. A 4-

bit binary counter has a modulo of 16; a decade counter has a modulo of 10; and a divide-by-7 counter has a modulo of 7. In a *variable modulo* counter, *n* can be any value within a range of values.

- *Weighting*—Most counters in the 7400 series of integrated-circuit chips are *weighted* counters, that is, we can assign a weighted value to each of the flip-flop outputs in the counter. By summing the product of the logic state times the weighting value for each of the flip-flops, we can compute the counter state. For example, the weighting factors for a 4-bit binary counter are D = weight of 8, C = weight of 4, B = weight of 2, and A = weight of 1. The binary output, DCBA = 1101_2, from a 4-bit binary counter would, therefore, be 13.

$$13 = 8 \times 1 + 4 \times 1 + 2 \times 0 + 1 \times 1$$

- *Count direction*—Most of the counters in the 7400 series of chips are *up counters*, that is, they count only in a direction of increasing states on a weighted basis. The 7490 counter counts from 0 to 9 and cycles back to 0. The 7493 counter counts from 0 to 15 and also cycles back to 0. The 74190, 74192, and 74193 counters are different, however. They are *up/down counters*, and are extremely versatile. They are, however, more expensive than the 7490 and 7493 counters.

- *Synchronism*—Counters can be either *asynchronous* (or *ripple*) or *synchronous*. In an asynchronous counter, a change in the output of one flip-flop initiates a possible change in the next flip-flop, which, in turn, initiates a change in the following flip-flop, and so on. Such counters are not preferred, since they exhibit both *propagation delays* and spurious output spikes called *glitches*. The preferred counter is a synchronous counter, in which the outputs of all flip-flops in the counters change immediately after the clock pulse arrives. They change simultaneously, and propagation delays and glitches do not occur. While the 7490, 7492, and 7493 counters are inexpensive, they are, unfortunately, asynchronous. The 74160, 74161, 74162, 74163, 74190, 74191, 74192, and 74193 counters are all synchronous and more expensive.

- *Presettability*—It can be important both to clear a counter to 0 and also to *preset* it to a certain value within the range of counting states. The 7490 counter can be preset to either 0 or 9, whereas the 7493 counter can be preset only to 0. The remaining counters listed under the "synchronism" heading above can all be preset, or "loaded," to any state within the respective range of each counter.

- *Unit cascadability*—Counters can be connected together in sequence, or *cascaded,* so that the output of the first counter is the input to the second, the output of the second is the input to the third, etc. The modulo of such counters is the product of the modulos of the individual counters in the cascade. Thus, three cascaded decade counters produce a modulo 1000 counter. Asynchronous counters clock on the negative edge of the clock pulse, whereas synchronous counters frequently clock on the positive edge of the clock pulse.

Rather than obtaining modulo counters that are the product of the modulos of the individual counters, it is frequently desirable to create modulo counters that are the sum of the modulos of the individual counters. Such would be the case if a modulo 273 counter would be desired. The 74160 through 74163 and 74190 through 74193 counters are *unit cascadable,* and can be wired in a way whereby unusual modulo counters can be created.

Lancaster[6] has also described some of the pitfalls inherent in the design of counter sequences of special length. Such pitfalls include disallowed states, clearing problems, self-annihilating coincidences, too-short reset pulse, slow reset rise and fall times, and noise.

THE 7400-SERIES COUNTERS

Table 10-1 provides a comparison of eleven 7400-series counters. Again, we shall discuss the characteristics of only a few chips.

You are already familiar with the 7490 decade counter and the 7493 binary counter. Shown in Fig. 10-9 are the truth tables and the functional block diagrams for these two counters and the 7492 counter. Two truth tables per chip are required, one for the count sequence and the other for the reset inputs.

Note how simple the block diagram is for the 7493 counter. It is a 4-stage ripple counter; no special logic gates are required between the stages. The 2-input positive NAND gate resets the counter to DCBA = 0000.

The 74160 through 74163 group of counters are the more sophisticated versions of the 7490 and 7493 counters. The 74160 to 74163 counters are synchronous, and can be preset synchronously to any value between either 0 and 9 or 0 and 15. The one important difference between the 74160 and 74161 counters, when compared to the 74162 and 74163 counters, is that the CLEAR input for the latter pair is synchronous. The distinction between the two pairs of chips is best expressed by the manufacturer, who has stated: "The clear function for the 74160 and 74161 is asynchronous and a low level

'90A, 'L90
BCD COUNT SEQUENCE
(See Note A)

COUNT	OUTPUT			
	Q_D	Q_C	Q_B	Q_A
0	L	L	L	L
1	L	L	L	H
2	L	L	H	L
3	L	L	H	H
4	L	H	L	L
5	L	H	L	H
6	L	H	H	L
7	L	H	H	H
8	H	L	L	L
9	H	L	L	H

'90A, 'L90
BI-QUINARY (5-2)
(See Note B)

COUNT	OUTPUT			
	Q_A	Q_D	Q_C	Q_B
0	L	L	L	L
1	L	L	L	H
2	L	L	H	L
3	L	L	H	H
4	L	H	L	L
5	H	L	L	L
6	H	L	L	H
7	H	L	H	L
8	H	L	H	H
9	H	H	L	L

'90A, 'L90
RESET/COUNT FUNCTION TABLE

RESET INPUTS				OUTPUT			
$R_{0(1)}$	$R_{0(2)}$	$R_{9(1)}$	$R_{9(2)}$	Q_D	Q_C	Q_B	Q_A
H	H	L	X	L	L	L	L
H	H	X	L	L	L	L	L
X	X	H	H	H	L	L	H
X	L	X	L	COUNT			
L	X	L	X	COUNT			
L	X	X	L	COUNT			
X	L	L	X	COUNT			

'92A
COUNT SEQUENCE
(See Note C)

COUNT	OUTPUT			
	Q_D	Q_C	Q_B	Q_A
0	L	L	L	L
1	L	L	L	H
2	L	L	H	L
3	L	L	H	H
4	L	H	L	L
5	L	H	L	H
6	H	L	L	L
7	H	L	L	H
8	H	L	H	L
9	H	L	H	H
10	H	H	L	L
11	H	H	L	H

'92A, '93A, 'L93
RESET/COUNT FUNCTION TABLE

RESET INPUTS		OUTPUT			
$R_{0(1)}$	$R_{0(2)}$	Q_D	Q_C	Q_B	Q_A
H	H	L	L	L	L
L	X	COUNT			
X	L	COUNT			

NOTES: A. Output Q_A is connected to input B for BCD count.
B. Output Q_D is connected to input A for bi-quinary count.
C. Output Q_A is connected to input B.
D. H = high level, L = low level, X = irrelevant

'93A, 'L93
COUNT SEQUENCE
(See Note C)

COUNT	OUTPUT			
	Q_D	Q_C	Q_B	Q_A
0	L	L	L	L
1	L	L	L	H
2	L	L	H	L
3	L	L	H	H
4	L	H	L	L
5	L	H	L	H
6	L	H	H	L
7	L	H	H	H
8	H	L	L	L
9	H	L	L	H
10	H	L	H	L
11	H	L	H	H
12	H	H	L	L
13	H	H	L	H
14	H	H	H	L
15	H	H	H	H

(A) Truth tables.

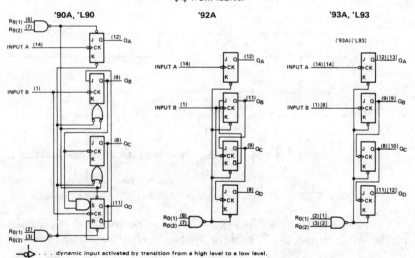

'90A, 'L90 **'92A** **'93A, 'L93**

◁|▷ . . . dynamic input activated by transition from a high level to a low level.

The J and K inputs shown without connection are for reference only and are functionally at a high level.

(B) Functional block diagrams.

Courtesy Texas Instruments Incorporated

Fig. 10-9. Truth tables and functional block diagrams for 7490, 7492, and 7493 counters.

SN54160, SN54162, SN74160, SN74162 SYNCHRONOUS DECADE COUNTERS

typical clear, preset, count, and inhibit sequences

Illustrated below is the following sequence:
1. Clear outputs to zero.
2. Preset to BCD seven.
3. Count to eight, nine, zero, one, two, and three.
4. Inhibit

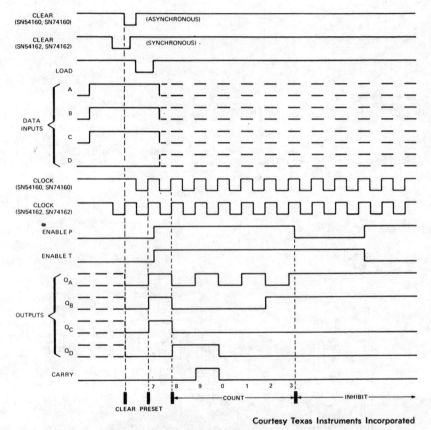

Courtesy Texas Instruments Incorporated

Fig. 10-10. Digital waveforms for 74160 and 74162 synchronous 4-bit counters.

at the clear input sets all four of the flip-flop outputs low regardless of the levels of the clock, load, or enable inputs. The clear function for the 74162 and 74163 is synchronous and a low level at the clear input sets all four of the flip-flop outputs low after the next clock pulse, regardless of the levels of the enable inputs." Shown in Fig. 10-10 are the digital waveforms for the 74160 and 74162 counters. In Fig. 10-11, we give the pin configurations for the 74160 to 74163

Table 10-1. The 7400-Series Counters

Chip	Mod-ulo	Direction	Type	Presets?	Unit Cas-cad-able?	Organi-zation	Clock
7490	10	up	asynchronous	0 and 9	no	2 × 5	negative edge
7492	12	up	asynchronous	0	no	2 × 6	negative edge
7493	16	up	asynchronous	0	no	2 × 8	negative edge
74160	10	up	synchronous	yes	yes	1 × 10	positive edge
74161	16	up	synchronous	yes	yes	1 × 16	positive edge
74162	10	up	synchronous	yes	yes	1 × 10	positive edge
74163	16	up	synchronous	yes	yes	1 × 16	positive edge
74190	10	up/down	synchronous	yes	yes	1 × 10	positive edge
74191	16	up/down	synchronous	yes	yes	1 × 16	positive edge
74192	10	up/down	synchronous	yes	yes	1 × 10	positive edge
74193	16	up/down	synchronous	yes	yes	1 × 16	positive edge

group of counters as well as the functional block diagram for the 74160 counter. You should have sufficient skills in digital electronics to interpret both the digital waveforms and the block diagram.

The pin configurations and digital waveforms for the 74190, 74192, and 74193 counters are given in Figs. 10-12 through 10-15. For a

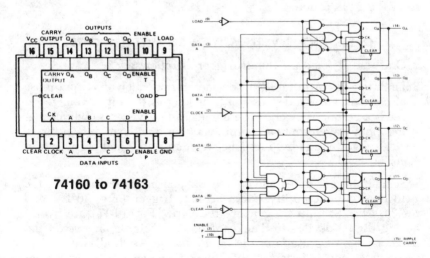

SN54160, SN74160 SYNCHRONOUS DECADE COUNTERS

SN54162, SN74162 synchronous decade counters are similar; however the clear is synchronous as shown for the SN54163, SN74163 binary counters at right.

74160 to 74163

Courtesy Texas Instruments Incorporated

Fig. 10-11. Pin configuration for 74160 to 74163 synchronous 4-bit counters and functional diagram of 74160 counter.

more detailed explanation of the differences between the 74190 and 74192 counters, and between the 74191 and 74193 counters, we refer you to the *TTL Data Book for Design Engineers*. *In the 74192 and 74193 chips, when pin 4 is used as a clock input, pin 5 must be disabled by connecting it to a logic 1 state. When pin 5 is used as a clock input, pin 4 must be disabled by connecting it to a logic 1 state.* We prefer the 74192 and 74193 chips for decade and binary counting, respectively. You will perform an experiment using the

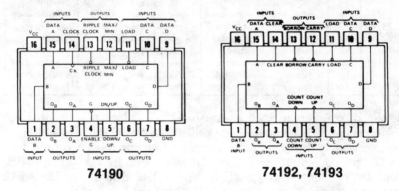

Courtesy Texas Instruments Incorporated

Fig. 10-12. Pin configurations for 74190, 74192, and 74193 synchronous up/down counters.

74193 counter to obtain an indication for how such a chip differs from the 7493 counter.

GATES AND INVERTERS WITH SCHMITT TRIGGERS

Graf[1] has defined a *Schmitt trigger* as follows:

Schmitt trigger—A bistable pulse generator in which an output pulse of constant amplitude exists only as long as the input voltage exceeds a certain dc value. The circuit can convert a slowly changing input waveform to an output waveform with sharp transitions. Normally, there is hysteresis between an upper and a lower triggering level.

Schmitt trigger gates and inverters, such as those found on the 7413 dual 4-input positive-NAND Schmitt trigger (Fig. 10-16) and the 7414 hex Schmitt trigger inverter chips (Fig. 10-17) are hybrid analog/digital devices in that *the action of the gate or inverter depends on the magnitude of the input voltage.* With all other 7400-series gates and inverters, the input voltage can vary over a relatively wide range and not influence the logic state of the output of the gate or inverter. If the supply voltage to the chip is exactly

'190, 'LS190 DECADE COUNTERS

typical load, count, and inhibit sequences

Illustrated below is the following sequence:

1. Load (preset) to BCD seven.
2. Count up to eight, nine (maximum), zero, one, and two.
3. Inhibit.
4. Count down to one, zero (minimum), nine, eight, and seven.

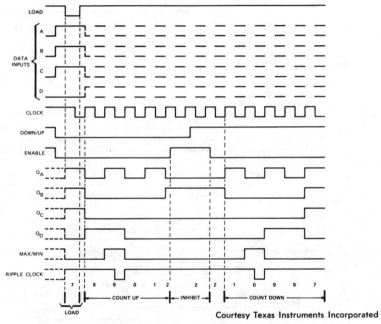

Courtesy Texas Instruments Incorporated

Fig. 10-13. Digital waveforms for 74190 synchronous up/down counter.

+5 volts and the free air temperature is 25°C, then the 7414 Schmitt trigger inverter will change from a logic 1 output state to a logic 0 output state when the input voltage reaches +1.683 volts ±0.005 volt, and will return to a logic 1 output when the input voltage declines back to +0.856 volt ±0.005 volt. This behavior is illustrated by the *hysteresis curve* in Fig. 10-18, in which the output voltage from the 7414 inverter is plotted as a function of the input voltage to the inverter.

The analog voltage level at which the Schmitt trigger causes a change in logic state is dependent both on the magnitude of the supply voltage and on the ambient air temperature surrounding the integrated-circuit chip. The experimental curves that document such behavior are given in Fig. 10-19.

Schmitt trigger integrated-circuit chips can be used as pulse shapers, multivibrators, and threshold detectors, as shown in the application notes from Texas Instruments Incorporated (Fig. 10-20). In these diagrams, V_T+ is the *positive-going threshold voltage*, which is approximately $+1.683$ volts, and V_T- is the *negative-going*

TYPES SN54192, SN54L192, SN54LS192, SN74192, SN74L192, SN74LS192
SYNCHRONOUS 4-BIT UP/DOWN COUNTERS (DUAL CLOCK WITH CLEAR)

'192,'L192, 'LS192 DECADE COUNTERS

typical clear, load, and count sequences

Illustrated below is the following sequence:

1. Clear outputs to zero.
2. Load (preset) to BCD seven.
3. Count up to eight, nine, carry, zero, one, and two.
4. Count down to one, zero, borrow, nine, eight, and seven.

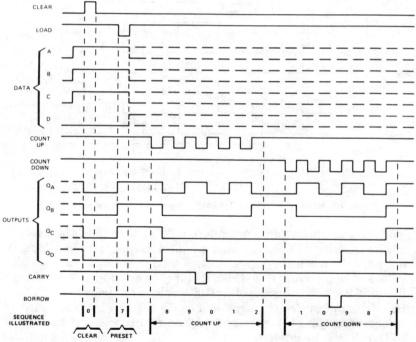

NOTES: A. Clear overrides load, data, and count inputs.
B. When counting up, count-down input must be high; when counting down, count-up input must be high.

Courtesy Texas Instruments Incorporated

Fig. 10-14. Digital waveforms (timing diagrams) for 74192 synchronous up/down counter.

threshold voltage, which has a value close to +0.856 volt. The difference between these two voltages is called the *hysteresis voltage* of the Schmitt trigger; this voltage is equal to +0.800 ±0.005 volt.

TYPES SN54193, SN54L193, SN54LS193, SN74193, SN74L193, SN74LS193 SYNCHRONOUS 4-BIT UP/DOWN COUNTERS (DUAL CLOCK WITH CLEAR)

'193, 'L193, 'LS193 BINARY COUNTERS

typical clear, load, and count sequences

Illustrated below is the following sequence:

1. Clear outputs to zero.
2. Load (preset) to binary thirteen.
3. Count up to fourteen, fifteen, carry, zero, one, and two.
4. Count down to one, zero, borrow, fifteen, fourteen, and thirteen.

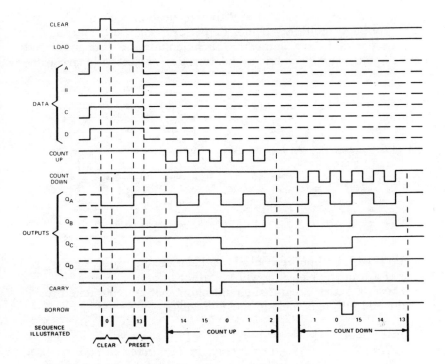

NOTES: A. Clear overrides load, data, and count inputs.

  B. When counting up, count-down input must be high; when counting down, count-up input must be high.

Courtesy Texas Instruments Incorporated

Fig. 10-15. Digital waveforms for 74193 synchronous up/down counter.

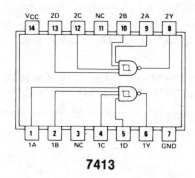

7413

Fig. 10-16. Pin configuration for 7413 dual
4-input positive-NAND Schmitt trigger.

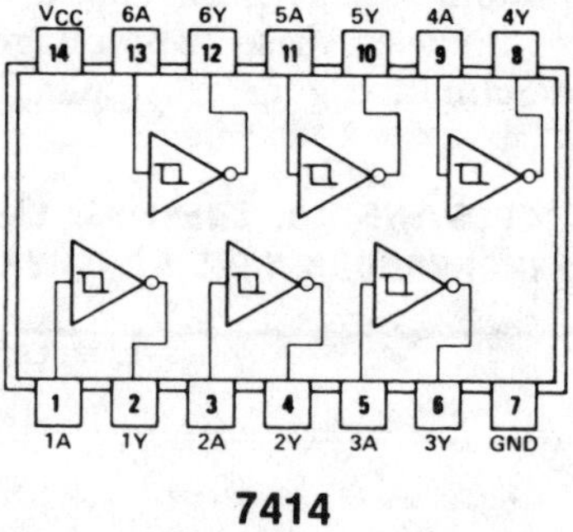

7414

Fig. 10-17. Pin configuration for 7414 hex
Schmitt trigger inverter.

THE 7400-SERIES ARITHMETIC ELEMENTS

An *arithmetic element* is any digital electronic circuit that can add, subtract, multiply, divide, or perform some other arithmetic function with binary numbers.[2] Such circuits are primarily used in computers and electronic calculators. The subject of binary arith-

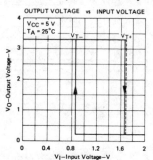

Fig. 10-18. Hysteresis curve for 7414 Schmitt
trigger inverter.

Courtesy Texas Instruments Incorporated

metic is vast, and entire books have been devoted to it. Our coverage of arithmetic elements will be rather brief.

The 7400-series integrated-circuit chips that are considered to be arithmetic elements include the following:

Integrated Circuit	Description of Integrated Circuit
7480	Gated full adder. Adds two 2-bit binary numbers plus a carry bit. Provides sum and complementary sum outputs.
7482	2-Bit binary full adder. Adds 2-bit binary numbers plus a carry bit.

7483	4-Bit binary full adder. Adds two 4-bit binary numbers plus a carry bit. A useful chip.
7485	4-Bit magnitude comparator. Compares the magnitude of two 4-bit binary numbers, A and B, determines whether $A < B$, $A > B$, or $A = B$.
74H87	4-Bit true/complement, zero/one element. This chip is a 4-bit controllable inverter that contains four gated 2-input Exclusive-OR gates.
74180	9-Bit odd/even parity generator/checker. Checks a 9-bit word consisting of 8 data bits and 1 parity bit for parity and provides outputs for both odd and even parity.
74181	Arithmetic logic unit/function generator. A magnificent integrated circuit chip that performs 16 binary arithmetic operations on two 4-bit binary words as well as 16 logic operations, including AND, NAND, OR, NOR, and Exclusive-OR. Also is a 4-bit magnitude comparator.
74182	Look-ahead carry generator. Capable of anticipating a carry across four binary adders or groups of adders. Carry, generate-carry, and propagate-carry functions are provided.
74H183	Dual carry-save full adders.
74S280	9-Bit odd/even parity generator/checker. An improved version of the 74180 chip.
74S281	4-Bit parallel binary accumulator. Performs fifteen arithmetic/logic-type operations, including add, subtract, complement, increment, transfer, and ten other functions. Has full shifting capabilities, including logic shift (left or right), arithmetic shift (left or right) for sign bit protection, hold, and parallel load.
74283	4-Bit binary full adders with fast carry. Improved version of the 7483 chip.
74284, 74285	4-Bit-by-4-bit parallel binary multiplier. Used in high-performance parallel multiplication applications.

The pin configuration and schematic representation of the 7482 2-bit binary full adder is shown in Fig. 10-21. It is a simple chip that performs the arithmetic operation, A plus B plus carry bit $= \Sigma$ plus carry bit in the 2^2 position.

The 7483 4-bit binary full adder integrated-circuit chip is similar to the 7482 chip. It performs the arithmetic operation, A plus B plus carry bit $= \Sigma$ plus carry bit in the 2^4 bit position. The pin configura-

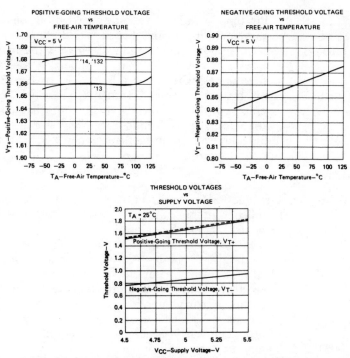

Fig. 10-19. Dependence of Schmitt trigger inverter on free-air temperature and supply voltage.

tion and schematic representation are given in Fig. 10-22 and a truth table and functional block diagram for the chip in Fig. 10-23. The truth table is somewhat difficult to understand; we suggest that you perform the experiment that we have given for the 7483 chip and convince yourself that the chip arithmetically adds two 4-bit numbers and a carry bit.

We defer to the manufacturer, Texas Instruments Incorporated, for a description of the 7485 4-bit magnitude comparator. In Figs. 10-24 and 10-25, we show the pin configuration of the chip, a schematic diagram, a description of the chip, and a typical application for the chip, the comparison of two 24-bit words. In the truth table, H = high level (logic 1), L = low level (logic 0), and X = irrelevant (either logic 0 or logic 1). The three inputs at pins 2, 3, and 4 on the 7485 chip permit the cascading of the chip.

BOOLEAN ALGEBRA

In order to discuss the final arithmetic element, the 74181 arithmetic logic unit/function generator, we must briefly digress to the

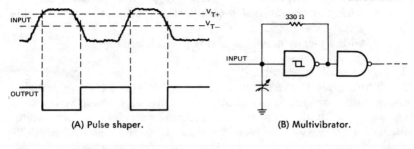

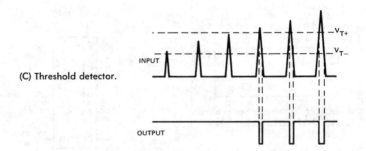

(A) Pulse shaper.

(B) Multivibrator.

(C) Threshold detector.

Fig. 10-20. Three applications for Schmitt trigger devices.

subject of *Boolean algebra*. Boolean algebra is the mathematics of logic systems. Alphabetic symbols such as A, B, C, . . . , Q are used to represent logical variables and 1 and 0 to represent logic states. This particular form of mathematics was originated in England by George Boole in 1847. It did not become widely used until 1938, when Claude Shannon adapted it to analyze multicontact networks.

What we would like you to learn here are the three basic symbols that are employed in Boolean algebra computations. They are:

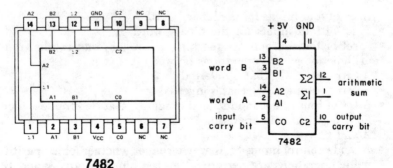

7482

Fig. 10-21. Pin configuration and schematic for 7482 2-bit binary full adder.

- \+ which means *logical addition* and is given the name OR
- • which means *logical multiplication* and is given the name AND
- − which means *negation* and is given the name NOT

Thus, the Boolean statement for a 2-input positive AND gate is $Q = A \cdot B$, or simply $Q = AB$, where the equality symbol, $=$, means that the variables or groups of variables on either side of the symbol are the same, i.e., both are in the same logical state. The Boolean statements for a variety of different types of gates are given in Fig. 10-26. Note the use of the bar, $\overline{}$, for the NAND and NOR gates.

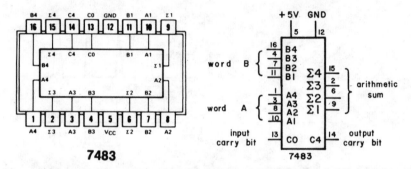

Fig. 10-22. Pin configuration and schematic diagram for 7483 4-bit binary full adder with fast carry.

THE 74181 ARITHMETIC LOGIC UNIT/FUNCTION GENERATOR

The 74181 arithmetic logic unit/function generator is the most complicated arithmetic chip that we shall discuss in this book. It is a 24-pin integrated circuit that has a complexity of 75 equivalent gates. The pin configuration and schematic diagram are shown in Fig. 10-27. The chip consists of:

- • A set of four inputs for the binary word, A
- • A set of four inputs for the binary word, B
- • A set of four outputs for the binary word, F, that results from arithmetic or logic operations between A and B
- • A carry input, C_n, that is inverted
- • A carry output, C_{n+4}, that is inverted
- • A set of four select inputs, S_0 through S_3, that determine which logic or arithmetic operation is performed on the binary words A and B
- • A mode control input, M, that determines whether logic or arithmetic operations are performed on the binary words A and B. When $M = 0$, arithmetic operations are performed.

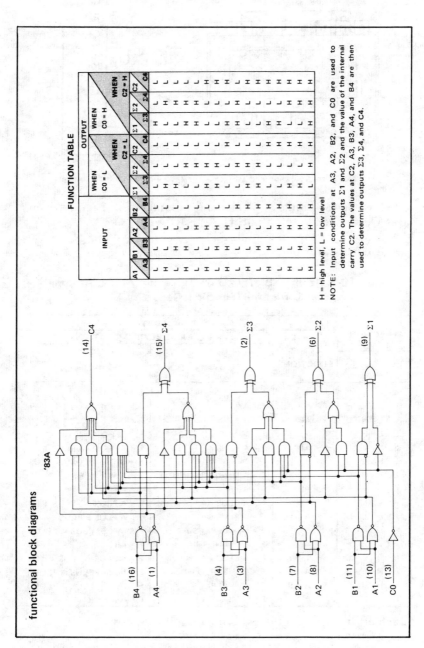

Fig. 10-23. Functional block diagram and truth table for 7483 4-bit binary full adder.

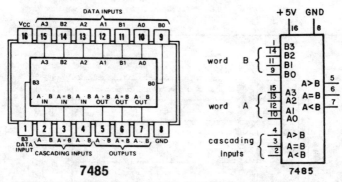

Fig. 10-24. Pin configuration and schematic for 7485 4-bit magnitude comparator.

- Two power inputs, +5 volts and ground
- A carry generate output, G
- A carry propagate output, P
- A comparator output, A = B, that is open collector

Table 10-2. Truth Table/Function Table for 74181 Arithmetic Logic Unit/Function Generator

SELECTION				ACTIVE-HIGH DATA		
				M = H	M = L: ARITHMETIC OPERATIONS	
				LOGIC FUNCTIONS	C_n = H (no carry)	C_n = L (with carry)
S3	S2	S1	S0			
L	L	L	L	$F = \bar{A}$	$F = A$	$F = A \text{ PLUS } 1$
L	L	L	H	$F = \overline{A + B}$	$F = A + B$	$F = (A + B) \text{ PLUS } 1$
L	L	H	L	$F = \bar{A}B$	$F = A + \bar{B}$	$F = (A + \bar{B}) \text{ PLUS } 1$
L	L	H	H	$F = 0$	$F = \text{MINUS } 1 \text{ (2's COMPL)}$	$F = \text{ZERO}$
L	H	L	L	$F = \overline{AB}$	$F = A \text{ PLUS } A\bar{B}$	$F = A \text{ PLUS } A\bar{B} \text{ PLUS } 1$
L	H	L	H	$F = \bar{B}$	$F = (A + B) \text{ PLUS } A\bar{B}$	$F = (A + B) \text{ PLUS } A\bar{B} \text{ PLUS } 1$
L	H	H	L	$F = A \oplus B$	$F = A \text{ MINUS } B \text{ MINUS } 1$	$F = A \text{ MINUS } B$
L	H	H	H	$F = A\bar{B}$	$F = A\bar{B} \text{ MINUS } 1$	$F = A\bar{B}$
H	L	L	L	$F = \bar{A} + B$	$F = A \text{ PLUS } AB$	$F = A \text{ PLUS } AB \text{ PLUS } 1$
H	L	L	H	$F = \overline{A \oplus B}$	$F = A \text{ PLUS } B$	$F = A \text{ PLUS } B \text{ PLUS } 1$
H	L	H	L	$F = B$	$F = (A + \bar{B}) \text{ PLUS } AB$	$F = (A + \bar{B}) \text{ PLUS } AB \text{ PLUS } 1$
H	L	H	H	$F = AB$	$F = AB \text{ MINUS } 1$	$F = AB$
H	H	L	L	$F = 1$	$F = A \text{ PLUS } A^*$	$F = A \text{ PLUS } A \text{ PLUS } 1$
H	H	L	H	$F = A + \bar{B}$	$F = (A + B) \text{ PLUS } A$	$F = (A + B) \text{ PLUS } A \text{ PLUS } 1$
H	H	H	L	$F = A + B$	$F = (A + \bar{B}) \text{ PLUS } A$	$F = (A + \bar{B}) \text{ PLUS } A \text{ PLUS } 1$
H	H	H	H	$F = A$	$F = A \text{ MINUS } 1$	$F = A$

*Each bit is shifted to the next more significant position.

description

These four-bit magnitude comparators perform comparison of straight binary and straight BCD (8-4-2-1) codes. Three fully decoded decisions about two 4-bit words (A, B) are made and are externally available at three outputs. These devices are fully expandable to any number of bits without external gates. Words of greater length may be compared by connecting comparators in cascade. The A > B, A < B, and A = B outputs of a stage handling less-significant bits are connected to the corresponding A > B, A < B, and A = B inputs of the next stage handling more-significant bits. The stage handling the least-significant bits must have a high-level voltage applied to the A = B input and additionally for the 'L85, low-level voltages applied to the A > B and A < B inputs. The cascading paths of the '85 and 'S85 are implemented with only a two-gate-level delay to reduce overall comparison times for long words. An alternate method of cascading which further reduces the comparison time is shown in the typical application data.

FUNCTION TABLES

COMPARING INPUTS				CASCADING INPUTS			OUTPUTS		
A3, B3	A2, B2	A1, B1	A0, B0	A > B	A < B	A = B	A > B	A < B	A = B
A3 > B3	X	X	X	X	X	X	H	L	L
A3 < B3	X	X	X	X	X	X	L	H	L
A3 = B3	A2 > B2	X	X	X	X	X	H	L	L
A3 = B3	A2 < B2	X	X	X	X	X	L	H	L
A3 = B3	A2 = B2	A1 > B1	X	X	X	X	H	L	L
A3 = B3	A2 = B2	A1 < B1	X	X	X	X	L	H	L
A3 = B3	A2 = B2	A1 = B1	A0 > B0	X	X	X	H	L	L
A3 = B3	A2 = B2	A1 = B1	A0 < B0	X	X	X	L	H	L
A3 = B3	A2 = B2	A1 = B1	A0 = B0	H	L	L	H	L	L
A3 = B3	A2 = B2	A1 = B1	A0 = B0	L	H	L	L	H	L
A3 = B3	A2 = B2	A1 = B1	A0 = B0	L	L	H	L	L	H

'85, 'S85

A3 = B3	A2 = B2	A1 = B1	A0 = B0	X	X	H	L	L	H
A3 = B3	A2 = B2	A1 = B1	A0 = B0	H	H	L	L	L	L
A3 = B3	A2 = B2	A1 = B1	A0 = B0	L	L	L	H	H	L

TYPICAL APPLICATION DATA

COMPARISON OF TWO N-BIT WORDS

This application demonstrates how these magnitude comparators can be cascaded to compare longer words. The example illustrated shows the comparison of two 24-bit words; however, the scheme is expandable to n-bits. As an example, one comparator can be used with five of the 24-bit comparators illustrated to expand the word length to 120-bits. Typical comparison times for various word lengths using the '85, 'L85, or 'S85 are:

WORD LENGTH	NUMBER OF PKGS	'85	'L85	'S85
1-4 bits	1	23 ns	90 ns	11 ns
5-24 bits	2-6	46 ns	180 ns	22 ns
25-120 bits	8-31	69 ns	270 ns	33 ns

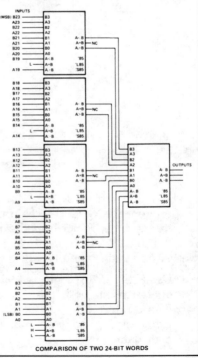

COMPARISON OF TWO 24-BIT WORDS

Courtesy Texas Instruments Incorporated

Fig. 10-25. Description and typical application for 7485 4-bit magnitude comparator.

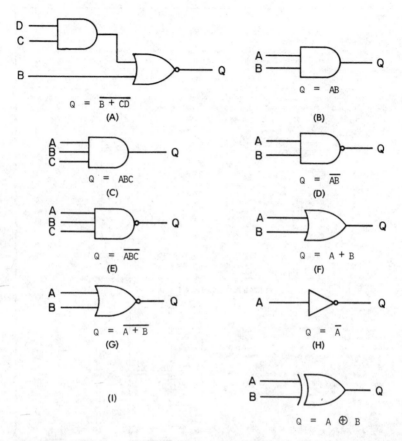

Fig. 10-26. Comparison of Boolean statements and symbolic diagrams for a variety of different gates.

The most important piece of information that you require to properly operate the 74181 chip is the truth table (Table 10-2).

Until we actually performed experiments with the 74181 chip, we found Table 10-2 to be confusing. Here are some of the things that we learned that hopefully will be of use to you.

- Using the 74181 chip, you can perform arithmetic and logic operations in both positive and negative logic. Positive logic data is referred to by Texas Instruments Incorporated, Signetics Corporation, and other manufacturers of the chip as "active-high data."

  In this text, you will only be concerned with the use of 74181 chip with positive logic data, as is shown in the table above.

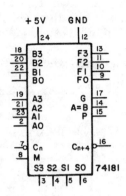

PIN DESIGNATIONS

DESIGNATION	PIN NOS.	FUNCTION
A3, A2, A1, A0	19, 21, 23, 2	WORD A INPUTS
B3, B2, B1, B0	18, 20, 22, 1	WORD B INPUTS
S3, S2, S1, S0	3, 4, 5, 6	FUNCTION-SELECT INPUTS
$\overline{C_n}$	7	INV. CARRY INPUT
M	8	MODE CONTROL INPUT
F3, F2, F1, F0	13, 11, 10, 9	FUNCTION OUTPUTS
A = B	14	COMPARATOR OUTPUT
P	15	CARRY PROPAGATE OUTPUT
$\overline{C_{n+4}}$	16	INV. CARRY OUTPUT
G	17	CARRY GENERATE OUTPUT
V_{CC}	24	SUPPLY VOLTAGE
GND	12	GROUND

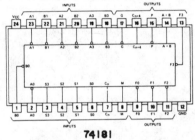

74181

Fig. 10-27. Pin configuration, pin designations, and schematic diagram for 74181 arithmetic logic unit/function generator.

- The 74181 chip performs a total of 32 different arithmetic or logic operations. These operations can be subdivided as follows: 5 arithmetic operations, 16 logic operations, 8 combined arithmetic/logic operations.

These operations total 29; three logic operations are repeated. We conclude that the 74181 is not as powerful an arithmetic chip as we would initially be led to believe. The 74S281 chip can perform only 16 different arithmetic or logic operations on a pair of 4-bit words; however, all of its operations are generally quite useful. The 74181 chip provides a number of operations that are rarely used.

- When you are performing purely arithmetic operations, it is very useful to monitor the four function outputs F0 through F3 with a seven-segment LED display. Keep in mind, though, that the 74181 chip is not a decimal adder and subtracter, *but rather a hexadecimal adder or subtracter.* In decimal addition, 7 plus

7 equals 4 plus a carry in the 10^1 position. In hexadecimal addition, 7 plus 7 equals the symbol for 14, ⊢ , with no carry. A carry is produced when the sum of the two 4-bit binary hexadecimal numbers exceeds 15. Thus, 8 plus the symbol for 10, ⊏ , equals 2 plus a carry in the 16^1 position. We

Table 10-3. Decimal and Hexadecimal Counting Systems

Decimal System	Hexadecimal system	Comments
0	0	
9	9	
10	⊏	On the 74181, the carry bit should be at
11	⊐	a logic 0, but it is inverted so it is at a
12	⊔	logic 1.
13	⊏	
14	⊢	
15	blank	
16	10	
17	11	
18	12	
19	13	
20	14	
21	15	
22	16	On the 74181, the carry bit should be at
23	17	a logic 1, but it is inverted so it is at a
24	18	logic 0.
25	19	
26	1⊏	
27	1⊐	
28	1⊔	
29	1⊏	
30	1⊢	
31	1	The largest sum possible on the 7418.
32	20	
33	21	
34	22	
35	23	
36	24	
48	30	
64	40	
80	50	
96	60	
112	70	
128	80	
144	90	
160	⊏0	
176	⊐0	
192	⊔0	
208	⊏0	
224	⊢0	
240	0	
255	blank	

compare the decimal and hexadecimal counting systems, using the seven-segment LED symbols for the latter system, in Table 10-3.

On the 74181 chip, the largest possible arithmetic sum between two 4-bit binary numbers is the symbol "blank" on the seven-segment display plus a carry bit at pin 16 of logic 0 (remember, this carry bit is inverted), corresponding to the decimal number $31 = 16 + 15$. If you can understand hexadecimal addition and subtraction, you will encounter no problems with the arithmetic operations on the 74181 chip.

- Finally, the logic operations are performed *on corresponding bits on the two 4-bit words A and B*. Thus, a logical multiplication, which is given by the statement $F = AB$ and the name AND, is equivalent to the statement that you have four 2-input positive AND gates that perform the operations shown in Fig. 10-28.

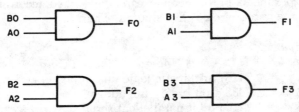

Fig. 10-28. Four 2-input logical AND operations are possible using 74181 arithmetic logic unit/function generator.

Rather than use a seven-segment LED display, *we recommend that you use four lamp monitors to test the logic states of the outputs F0, F1, F2, and F3 when you perform logic operations using the 74181 chip.* Each lamp monitor will be controlled by its own two respective bits in the two 4-bit binary words A and B. We can summarize here by listing the meaning of some of the logic operations performed by the 74181 chip:

Logic Operation	Meaning
$F = \overline{A}$	Four inverters that operate on the four bits of A
$F = \overline{A + B}$	Four 2-input positive NOR gates
$F = \overline{AB}$	Four 2-input positive NAND gates
$F = A \oplus B$	Four 2-input Exclusive-OR gates
$F = AB$	Four 2-input positive AND gates
$F = A + B$	Four 2-input positive OR gates
$F = \overline{B}$	Four inverters that operate on the four bits of B

With the aid of the points outlined above, you should now be able to correctly use the 74181 arithmetic element in an experiment in this chapter.

INTRODUCTION TO THE EXPERIMENTS

The experiments in this chapter are somewhat simpler than those given in several preceding chapters. Our objective is to introduce you to a number of different arithmetic chips, shift registers, and counters. The 74181 arithmetic logic unit/function generator is a fascinatinig chip, certainly one of the most complicated in the 7400 series. It allows you to add and subtract two 4-bit binary words and also to operate on such words using the AND, NAND, OR, NOR, INVERT, Exclusive-OR, and negated Exclusive-OR logic operations. You will study several highly useful shift registers, including the 74164, 74165, 74166, 74194, and 74198 chips. You may enjoy performing the serial transmitter/receiver experiment (Experiment No. 7).

The experiments in this chapter can be classified according to the type of integrated-circuit chip studied. Thus,

Experiment No.	Integrated-Circuit Chip
1	74181 arithmetic logic unit/function generator
2	7483 4-bit binary full adder
3	74164 8-bit parallel-out serial shift register
4	74165 and 74166 parallel-load 8-bit shift registers
5	74194 4-bit bidirectional universal shift register
6	74198 8-bit bidirectional universal shift register
7	74194 4-bit bidirectional universal shift register as a transmitter/receiver
8	74193 synchronous 4-bit up/down counter

EXPERIMENT NO. 1

Purpose

The purpose of this experiment is to demonstrate the operation of the 74181 4-bit arithmetic logic unit/function generator integrated circuit.

Pin Configuration of Integrated Circuit (Fig. 10-29)

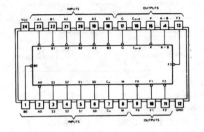

Fig. 10-29.

74181

Schematic Diagram of Circuit (Fig. 10-30)

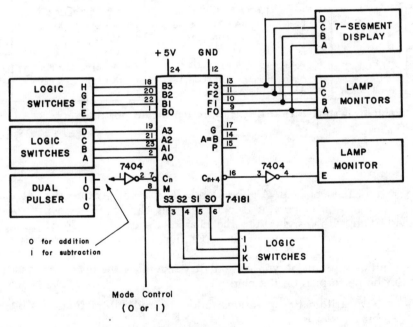

Fig. 10-30.

Summary of Numerals and Symbols on Seven-Digit LED Display

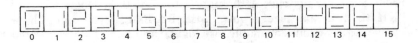

Truth Table (Positive Logic)

SELECTION				M = H LOGIC FUNCTIONS	ACTIVE-HIGH DATA	
					M = L; ARITHMETIC OPERATIONS	
					C_n = H (no carry)	C_n = L (with carry)
S3	S2	S1	S0			
L	L	L	L	F = $\overline{A}$	F = A	F = A PLUS 1
L	L	L	H	F = $\overline{A + B}$	F = A + B	F = (A + B) PLUS 1
L	L	H	L	F = $\overline{A}B$	F = A + $\overline{B}$	F = (A + $\overline{B}$) PLUS 1
L	L	H	H	F = 0	F = MINUS 1 (2's COMPL)	F = ZERO
L	H	L	L	F = $\overline{AB}$	F = A PLUS A$\overline{B}$	F = A PLUS A$\overline{B}$ PLUS 1
L	H	L	H	F = $\overline{B}$	F = (A + B) PLUS A$\overline{B}$	F = (A + B) PLUS A$\overline{B}$ PLUS 1
L	H	H	L	F = A $\oplus$ B	F = A MINUS B MINUS 1	F = A MINUS B
L	H	H	H	F = A$\overline{B}$	F = A$\overline{B}$ MINUS 1	F = A$\overline{B}$
H	L	L	L	F = $\overline{A}$ + B	F = A PLUS AB	F = A PLUS AB PLUS 1
H	L	L	H	F = $\overline{A \oplus B}$	F = A PLUS B	F = A PLUS B PLUS 1
H	L	H	L	F = B	F = (A + $\overline{B}$) PLUS AB	F = (A + $\overline{B}$) PLUS AB PLUS 1
H	L	H	H	F = AB	F = AB MINUS 1	F = AB
H	H	L	L	F = 1	F = A PLUS A*	F = A PLUS A PLUS 1
H	H	L	H	F = A + $\overline{B}$	F = (A + B) PLUS A	F = (A + B) PLUS A PLUS 1
H	H	H	L	F = A + B	F = (A + $\overline{B}$) PLUS A	F = (A + $\overline{B}$) PLUS A PLUS 1
H	H	H	H	F = A	F = A MINUS 1	F = A

*Each bit is shifted to the next more significant position.

Step 1

Study the "Boolean Algebra" and "The 74181 Arithmetic Logic Unit/Function Generator" sections in this chapter. They will provide you with insights into the characteristics of the 74181 chip, especially the meaning of the operations given in the preceding truth table.

In this experiment, you will only try several of the operations that can be performed on the chip, viz.,

- Two arithmetic operations: addition and subtraction of 4-bit binary words
- Five logic operations: AND, NAND, OR, NOR, and Exclusive-OR

Step 2

Wire the experiment as shown in the schematic diagram in Fig. 10-30. Set logic switches A through H to logic 0. Set logic switches LKJI, the function-select inputs, to LKJI = 1001. If you do not have twelve logic switches available, use logic 0 and logic 1 states created by wiring the respective pins to +5 volts and ground. Apply power to the breadboard.

Step 3

For your first operation, you will add two 4-bit binary numbers together to produce sums ranging from 0 to 30 or, if you also add a carry bit, from 0 to 31. Before you start, however, remember the following:

- If you perform a purely arithmetic operation, look at the seven-segment LED display and at lamp monitor E for your output.
- If you perform a purely logic operation, look at the four lamp monitors A through D for your output.
- If you perform a combined arithmetic/logic operation, you are on your own.

The addition of two 4-bit binary numbers is an arithmetic operation, so your sum will be on the seven-segment LED display and on lamp monitor E (the carry bit). Make certain that the mode control input, M, at pin 8 is at logic 0 (corresponding to arithmetic operations) and that logic switches LKJI = 1001 correspond to the selection of the F = A plus B operation in the truth table (remember, H = logic 1 and L = logic 0).

Step 4

You should now be able to perform the following additions:

Binary Word B	Binary Word A	Seven-Segment Display Reading	Lamp Monitor E	A + B = F Decimal Equivalent of Binary Addition
0000	0000	0	0	0 + 0 = 0
0001	0001	2	0	1 + 1 = 2
0010	0010	4	0	2 + 2 = 4
0100	0100	8	0	4 + 4 = 8
1000	1000	0	1	8 + 8 = 0 + 16

Note that when you added 8 plus 8, you obtained a display reading of 0 and one carry bit. The weighting factor of the carry bit is 16, since the carry bit is added to the 16^1 position in the hexadecimal number. Continuing, you should observe the following additions: Note that the display symbol, ⊏ , represents decimal 14, and that $16 + 14 = 30$.

If you desire, you can now add the C_n carry bit at pin 7 on the 74181 chip. When you press the pulser in, you add 1 to whatever sum you have above. The above tests should convince you that the chip is adding two 4-bit binary words plus a carry bit.

Binary Word B	Binary Word A	Seven-Segment Display Reading	Lamp Monitor E	A + B = F Decimal Equivalent of Binary Addition
1001	0111	0	1	9 + 7 = 0 + 16
1100	1100	8	1	12 + 12 = 8 + 16
1001	1001	2	1	9 + 9 = 2 + 16
1111	1111	⌶	1	15 + 15 = 14 + 16

Step 5

To subtract two 4-bit binary numbers, you will have to make one minor adjustment in the circuit and change the logic states of the function select inputs. Connect pin 1 of the 7404 inverter to the "1" output of the pulser, and set logic switches LKJI to LKJI = 0110, corresponding to the arithmetic operation, F = A minus B, in the truth table.

You should now be able to perform the following subtractions:

Binary Word B	Binary Word A	Seven-Segment Display Reading	Lamp Monitor E	A − B = F Decimal Equivalent of Binary Subtraction
0000	0000	0	1	0 − 0 = 0
0001	0100	3	1	4 − 1 = 3
0100	1000	4	1	8 − 4 = 4
1000	1111	7	0	15 − 8 = 7
1111	1000	9	0	8 − 15 = −7 = 9 − 16
0001	0000	blank	0	0 − 1 = −1 = 15 − 16
0010	0000	⌶	0	0 − 2 = −2 = 14 − 16
0011	0000	⊑	0	0 − 3 = −3 = 13 − 16
0110	0000	⊏	0	0 − 6 = −6 = 10 − 16
0111	0000	9	0	0 − 7 = −7 = 9 − 16
1000	0000	8	0	0 − 8 = −8 = 8 − 16
1111	0000	1	0	0 − 15 = −15 = 1 − 16

If you press the pulser in, you will observe that the final seven-segment display reading corresponds to the subtraction of a carry bit from the quantity F = A − B. In the above tabulation, note that the sum of F and the reading on the seven-segment display adds to 16 (or to 0 with a carry bit in the 16^1 position). It should be clear that the chip is performing the subtraction of one 4-bit binary word from another.

Step 6

In the remaining part of this experiment, you will perform a group of logic operations. *You will observe your results on the four lamp monitors, A through D.* The seven-segment display is no longer needed, nor is lamp monitor E. In our experience, the display tends to cause a bit of confusion when one is performing logic operations.

Set the mode control input, M, at pin 8 to logic 1. From this point forward, all operations by the 74181 chip will be logic operations.

Step 7

One of the best experiments that you can perform is to generate the truth tables for all of the sixteen "logic functions." To do this, you will have to set the logic switches A through H to the following values:

$$DCBA = 1010$$
$$HGFE = 1100$$

The four lamp monitors will now represent the correct output, Q, from the following truth table,

B	A	Q
0	0	lamp monitor A
0	1	lamp monitor B
1	0	lamp monitor C
1	1	lamp monitor D

Step 8

You will now be able to generate the proper truth table for any of the logic function operations performed by the 74181. To assist you in your experiments, we summarize some of the more interesting logic functions and the corresponding settings of the function outputs, which are connected to logic switches I through L. Remember, logic switch I = function input S0, logic switch J = function input S1, logic switch K = function input S2, and logic switch K = function input S3.

Select Inputs				
S3	S2	S1	S0	Logic Operation
0	0	0	0	inversion of A inputs
0	0	0	1	2-input positive NOR gate
0	1	0	0	2-input positive NAND gate
0	1	0	1	inversion of B inputs
0	1	1	0	2-input Exclusive-OR
1	0	0	1	negated 2-input Exclusive-OR
1	0	1	1	2-input positive AND gate
1	1	1	0	2-input positive OR gate

We have tried all of the above operations. The 74181 works exactly as expected. Try it yourself.

Step 9

You may now wish to perform the combined arithmetic/logic operations shown when $M = 0$. You will probably have a bit of difficulty in predicting the value of F. These combined operations are not commonly used.

Question

1. How do you interpret a combined arithmetic/logic operation? For example, what does the arithmetic/Boolean expression, $F = A$ plus AB signify? This is not an easy question.

EXPERIMENT NO. 2

Purpose

The purpose of this experiment is to demonstrate the operation of the 7483 4-bit binary full adder integrated circuit.

Pin Configuration of Integrated Circuit (Fig. 10-31)

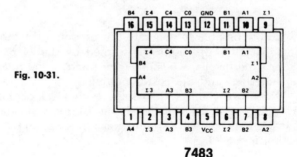

Fig. 10-31.

7483

Schematic Diagram of Circuit (Fig. 10-32)

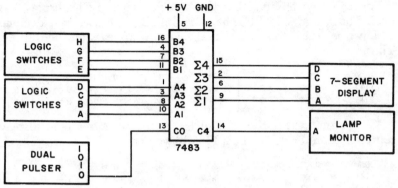

Fig. 10-32.

Step 1

Wire the simple circuit shown in Fig. 10-32. Set the two sets of logic switches to HGFE = 0000 and DCBA = 0000. Apply power to the breadboard. You should observe a decimal 0 on the seven-segment LED display and an unlit lamp monitor. If you do not, check your circuit.

Step 2

You will now add two binary numbers plus a carry bit, C_0, to produce an arithmetic sum plus a carry bit C_2. Remember, you will perform simple binary addition. Perform the additions shown in the far left-hand columns below.

Binary Number B HGFE	Binary Number A DCBA	Carry Bit C_0	Sum Σ $\Sigma_4\Sigma_3\Sigma_2\Sigma_1$	Carry Bit C_4	Seven-Segment Display and Lamp Monitor Decimal Equivalent of Binary Addition
0000	0000	0	0000	0	0 + 0 + 0 = 0
0001	0001	0	0010	0	1 + 1 + 0 = 2
0010	0001	0	0011	0	3 + 1 + 0 = 4
0101	0001	0	0100	0	4 + 4 + 0 = 8
0100	0100	0	1000	0	6 + 6 + 0 = 12
0110	0110	0	1100	0	7 + 7 + 0 = 14
0111	0111	0	1110	0	8 + 7 + 0 = 15
1000	0111	0	1111	0	

You can add any two numbers to give a sum that is less than or equal to decimal 15 and you will not get a logic 1 in the carry bit, C_2. However, when you exceed or equal 16 for your sum, C_2 will go to logic 1. This is shown by the additions given below,

1000	1000	0	0000	1	$8 + 8 + 0 = 0 + 16$

You can now observe that the seven-segment LED display has cycled back to decimal 0. The carry bit, C_2, indicates that decimal 16 must be added to any numeral that now appears on the display. Thus,

1010	1010	0	0100	1	$10 + 10 + 0 = 4 + 16$
1111	1000	0	0111	1	$15 + 8 + 0 = 7 + 16$
1111	1111	0	1110	1	$15 + 15 + 0 = 14 + 16$

Keep in mind that the symbol, ⊏, is the seven-segment display representation for decimal 14. Finally, you can add the carry bit, C_0

0000	0000	1	0001	0	$0 + 0 + 1 = 1$
1111	0000	1	0000	1	$15 + 0 + 1 = 0 + 16$
1111	1111	1	1111	1	$15 + 15 + 1 = 15 + 16$

We have performed this experiment to guide you in the use of the 7483 full adder. Hopefully, you are now convinced that the integrated circuit is performing a true binary addition and yields simple decimal additions. The 7483 full adder is very simple, and results identical to that which you would predict on the basis of the preceding is all that you need to do with it.

Question

1. Explain how you would add two 8-bit binary numbers using a pair of 7483 full adders.

EXPERIMENT NO. 3

Purpose

The purpose of this experiment is to demonstrate the operation of a simple serial-in parallel-out (SIPO) shift register, the 74164 integrated circuit.

Pin Configuration of Integrated Circuit (Fig. 10-33)

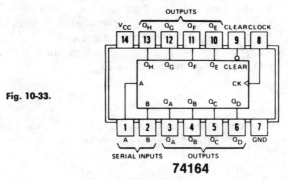

Fig. 10-33.

74164

Schematic Diagram of Circuit (Fig. 10-34)

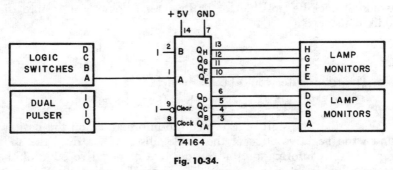

Fig. 10-34.

Step 1

Wire the circuit as shown in Fig. 10-34. Eight lamp monitors will be required for the experiment. Pin 9 is the CLEAR input pin; a logic 0 at this pin will clear all eight shift registers and cause all eight lamp monitors to become unlit.

Step 2

Apply power to the breadboard and touch pin 9 to logic 0 for a moment. Set logic switch A to a logic 1 state and press and release the pulser eight times. All eight lamp monitors should light up. Now set logic switch A to a logic 0 state and clock the shift register eight more times. What happens? Give your answer in the following space.

All eight lamp monitors become unlit, one at a time.

Step 3

Clear the shift register. Set logic switch A to a logic 1 state and clock the shift register only once. Return logic switch A to logic 0 and clock the shift register eight more times. In the following space, explain what you observe. In which direction does the shift register shift, from Q_A to Q_H or from Q_H to Q_A?

A single lit lamp monitor shifts one clock pulse at a time from output Q_A to output Q_H and then disappears.

Step 4

Pins 1 and 2 are the two inputs to a 2-input positive NAND gate. What would happen if pin 2 were always at a logic 0 state, i.e., would it ever be possible for us to enter a logic 1 state into the shift register?

No. The NAND gate would be disabled.

Step 5

When does the shift register acquire information, on the positive or on the negative edge of the clock pulse? When does the shift register shift information, on the positive or negative edge of the clock pulse? Perform experiments to answer these two questions and write your answers in the following space.

Everything happens at the positive edge of the clock pulse.

EXPERIMENT NO. 4

Purpose

The purpose of this experiment is to demonstrate the operation of the 74165 parallel-in serial-out (PISO) or serial-in serial-out (SISO) shift register.

Pin Configuration of Integrated Circuit (Fig. 10-35)

Fig. 10-35.

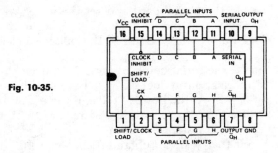

74165

Schematic Diagram of Circuit (Fig. 10-36)

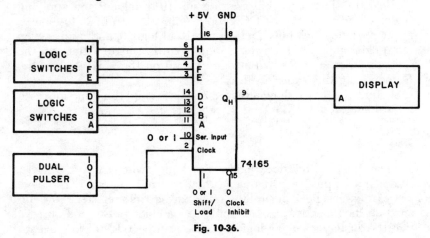

Fig. 10-36.

Step 1

Wire the circuit as shown in Fig. 10-36. In this case, eight logic switches are required. Pin 15 is a CLOCK INHIBIT input; when at logic 1, the CLOCK input at pin 2 will be inhibited and the shift register will not "shift." Data can be entered in parallel fashion at the ABCDEFGH inputs, or in serial fashion at the serial input (pin 10). Pin 1, the SHIFT/LOAD input, controls whether data is parallel loaded or shifted.

Pin 1	Action
0	Load data into the shift register from the ABCDEFG parallel inputs
1	Shift data in the shift register at each clock pulse, unless the clock is inhibited

Step 2

Apply power to the breadboard and set the logic switches ABC-DEFGH = 00000000. Set pin 15 to logic 0 and pin 10 to logic 0. Apply ten clock pulses with the aid of the pulser to clear the shift register.

Now set pin 10, the serial input, to logic 1. At each clock pulse, a single bit of information at logic 1 will be entered into the shift register at flip-flop A. At the positive edge of the eighth clock pulse, the display will go to a logic 1 state and remain there for as long as pin 10 is at a logic 1 state. Perform this experiment and demonstrate to yourself that you can obtain a similar result.

Step 3

Clear the shift register by setting pin 10 to logic 0 and applying ten clock pulses at the CLOCK input (pin 2). Set pin 10 to logic 1, apply a single clock pulse, return pin 10 to logic 0, and apply seven more clock pulses. The display should go to a logic 1 state on the seventh pulse, and then to a logic 0 state on the next clock pulse. Demonstrate this experiment as well.

So far, you have shown that the 74165 chip can function as a serial-in serial-out (SISO) shift register.

Step 4

Clear the register once again. Set logic switch A to a logic 1 state. Ground pin 1 for a moment, then return it to logic 1. You have just loaded a logic 1 bit in flip-flop A in the shift register. To demonstrate that such is the case, apply seven clock pulses and observe that the display goes to a logic 1 on the positive edge of the seventh pulse.

Return logic switch A to logic 0, but now set logic switch C to logic 1. Load the data from the logic switches into the register by applying a negative pulse at pin 1, the SHIFT/LOAD input. Make certain that you return pin 1 to a logic 1 state before you attempt to shift data. Now apply five clock pulses. The display should go to a logic 1 state on the positive edge of the fifth pulse, and return to logic 0 on the positive edge of the sixth clock pulse.

You have now demonstrated to yourself how you can parallel load the 74165 shift register. Keep in mind the fact that the only output possible with this chip is a serial output. Try loading various 8-bit words at the input pins ABCDEFGH. Shift them out of the register with the aid of eight clock pulses. You should not have much difficulty in mastering this chip.

If you connect the output, Q_H, at pin 9 to the serial input at pin 10, you create a *circulating shift register*. Try this with various 8-bit words. In the space below, explain in your own words what a circulating shift register does.

A circulating shift register has the output of the final series flip-flop connected to the input of the first series flip-flop. In doing this, data can never be lost. It is continuously circulated in the shift register.

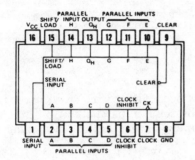

Fig. 10-37.

74166

Step 5

The 74166 shift register is almost identical to the 74165. The only difference between the two, apart from the pin configurations, is the presence of a CLEAR input on the 74166 chip. You may wish to demonstrate that the 74166 chip behaves in the same manner as does the 74165 chip in the steps above. We give you the pin configuration and the wiring diagram in Figs. 10-37 and 10-38.

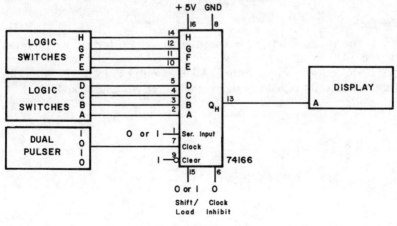

Fig. 10-38.

Questions

1. In the following space, draw a circuit in which you employ several shift registers to create a 24-bit parallel-in serial-out shift register. Label the chips that you use, as well as the pin numbers.

2. In the following space, draw a circuit in which you use several shift registers to create a 24-bit serial-in parallel-out shift register. Label the chips that you employ, as well as the pin numbers.

EXPERIMENT NO. 5

Purpose

The purpose of this experiment is to demonstrate the operation of the 74194 shift register, which can be parallel loaded, shifted right, shifted left, or inhibited. All four outputs from the 4-bit bidirectional shift register can be monitored simultaneously.

Pin Configuration of Integrated Circuit (Fig. 10-39)

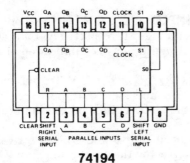

Fig. 10-39.

74194

Schematic Diagram of Circuit (Fig. 10-40)

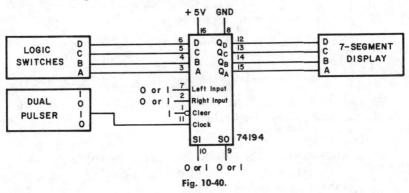

Fig. 10-40.

Step 1

Wire the circuit shown in Fig. 10-40. This 4-bit shift register is more manageable than the 74164 through 74166 8-bit shift registers since you only need four logic switches and four lamp monitors as input/output devices to the 74194 chip.

Step 2

Before you proceed with the experiments, we should describe in greater detail the data and control inputs. They are as follows:

DATA INPUTS:
- Parallel inputs A, B, C, and D at pins 3, 4, 5, and 6, respectively. With the proper settings of the control inputs, data is entered directly into the four flip-flops of the shift register.

CONTROL INPUTS:
- CLEAR input at pin 1. This input clears all four flip-flops and causes the four outputs Q_A through Q_D to go to a logic 0 state.

- CLOCK input at pin 11. This input "clocks" the parallel inputs into the shift register and also "clocks" the shifting of data within the register.
- SHIFT LEFT SERIAL INPUT at pin 7. When the mode inputs S_0 and S_1 are at logic 0 and logic 1, respectively, data at pin 7 will serially enter the shift register on the application of a clock pulse.
- SHIFT RIGHT SERIAL INPUT at pin 2. When the mode inputs S_0 and S_1 are at logic 1 and logic 0, respectively, data at pin 2 will serially enter the shift register on the application of a clock pulse.
- MODE INPUTS S_0 and S_1 at pins 9 and 10, respectively. We can write a brief truth table for these very important inputs:

S_1	S_0	Action
0	0	Clock input is inhibited. Nothing happens.
0	1	Data shifts right synchronously and new data is entered at the shift right serial input.
1	0	Data shifts left synchronously and new data is entered at the shift left serial input.
1	1	Data at inputs ABCD is parallel loaded into shift register in synchronous fashion.

We can summarize the characteristics of the 74194 by indicating that it has four modes of operation, namely,

> Parallel load
> Shift right (in the direction from Q_A toward Q_D)
> Shift left (in the direction from Q_D toward Q_A)
> Inhibit clock and do nothing

You are now ready to perform several experiments using this integrated circuit.

Step 3

To parallel load the shift register, set $S_0 = S_1 = 1$ and CLEAR = 1. Set DCBA = 0111 and press and release the pulser. A decimal 7 should appear on the seven-segment LED display. Set DCBA = 1000 and press and release the pulser a second time. A decimal 8 should now appear on the display. Repeat this procedure for other 4-bit inputs such as 0001, 0011, 0101, etc., and observe that the shift register acquires data on the positive edge of the clock pulse.

Step 4

Set CLEAR = 0 and demonstrate the fact that such a setting clears the shift register and causes a decimal 0 to appear on the seven-segment display.

Step 5

Set $S_0 = 0$ and $S_1 = 1$ and thus prepare the shift reigster for shift left operation. Data will enter at the shift left serial input at pin 7. Clear the register, set pin 7 to a logic 1, and then press and release the pulser four times. You should observe the following numeral and symbols in the order given:

$$8 , \sqcup , \sqsubset , \text{blank}$$

Clear the register and again apply four clock pulses. You should observe the same result. In the following space, explain why you observe such outputs.

These outputs correspond to logic 1 states being shifted in at input Q_D and then propagated to Q_A. When all four flip-flops have logic 1 states, the seven-segment display becomes blank and no further change occurs.

Step 6

Prepare the shift register for shift right operation by setting $S_0 = 1$ and $S_1 = 0$. Set pin 2, the shift right serial input, to a logic 1. Clear the register, then apply four clock pulses. Note that the display changes on the positive edge of the clock pulses. You should observe the following numerals in sequence:

$$1 , 3 , 7 , \text{blank}$$

Clear the register and apply four additional clock pulses. You should observe the same result. Explain why these numbers are different from the shift left experiment above. Use the following space for your answer.

In this case, logic 1 states enter at the Q_A input and propagate to Q_D. When all four flip-flops have logic 1 states, the seven-segment display becomes blank and no further change occurs.

Step 7

The shift left or shift right serial inputs need not remain at the same logic state for all four clock pulses. They can change state after each clock pulse. With the register set up for shift right operation, load a single logic 1 bit into the register and watch it "ripple" across the register with the aid of several clock pulses. You should observe the following outputs on the display in the sequence given:

$$1, \quad 2, \quad 4, \quad 8, \quad 0, \quad 0, \text{ etc.}$$

That is all there is to this chip. You can parallel load information, shift right serial information, shift left serial information, or, if $S_0 = S_1 = 0$, inhibit the register.

Question

1. Can you suggest why it is useful to have shift left and shift right capability in a shift register chip? Do so in the following space.

EXPERIMENT NO. 6

Purpose

The purpose of this experiment is to demonstrate the operation of a 24-pin 8-bit shift register, the 74198, which can be parallel loaded, shifted right, shifted left, and inhibited. All eight outputs from the shift register can be monitored simultaneously. The chip bears considerable resemblance to the 74194 chip, but has four additional bits.

Pin Configuration of Integrated Circuit (Fig. 10-41)

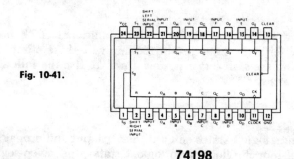

Fig. 10-41.

74198

Schematic Diagram of Circuit (Fig. 10-42)

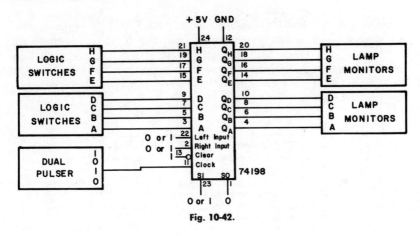

Fig. 10-42.

Step 1

Wire the circuit shown in the schematic diagram in Fig. 10-42. Note that the 74198 chip is almost identical to the 74194 chip; the main difference between the two, as far as function is concerned, is that the 74198 has four additional inputs and four additional outputs, which are required for a full 8-bit shift register.

The two chips can be compared as follows:

	74194	74198
Number of parallel data inputs	4	8
Number of parallel data outputs	4	8
CLEAR input?	yes	yes
CLOCK input?	yes	yes
SHIFT LEFT SERIAL INPUT?	yes	yes
SHIFT RIGHT SERIAL INPUT?	yes	yes
Two MODE inputs, S_0 and S_1?	yes	yes
GROUND and +5-Volts connections?	yes	yes
Number of pins	16	24

On the 74198 chip:

- The CLEAR input is at pin 13. When at a logic 0 state, all eight outputs are cleared to logic 0.
- The CLOCK input is at pin 11. The clock input is inhibited when $S_0 = S_1 = 0$.
- The SHIFT LEFT SERIAL INPUT is at pin 22. When $S_0 = 0$ and $S_1 = 1$, data at this pin will be clocked into the shift register at each clock pulse.

- The SHIFT RIGHT SERIAL INPUT is at pin 2. When $S_0 = 1$ and $S_1 = 0$, data at this pin will be clocked into the shift register at each clock pulse.
- The MODE INPUTS, S_0 and S_1, at pins 1 and 23, respectively, determine whether you parallel load the register (both mode inputs at a logic 1), shift data serially left (in the direction Q_H toward Q_A), shift data serially right (in the direction Q_A toward Q_H), or inhibit the clock. To summarize these two important inputs:

S_1	S_0	Action
0	0	Clock is inhibited. Nothing happens.
0	1	Data shifts right synchronously and new data is entered at the shift serial input.
1	0	Data shifts left synchronously and new data is entered at the shift left serial input.
1	1	Data at inputs ABCDEFGH is parallel loaded synchronously into the shift register.

Step 2

Apply power to the breadboard. The first experiment that you will perform is to parallel load the register and to clear the information that has been loaded. Set $S_0 = S_1 = 1$ and CLEAR = 1. Set HGFEDCBA = 10000001 on the eight logic switches. If any of the lamp monitors are lit, clear the register by touching pin 13, the CLEAR input, to ground for a moment; return the CLEAR input to logic 1 once you have done this.

Apply a single clock pulse to the register. You should observe that outputs A and H go to a logic 1 state, i.e., lamp monitors A and H become lit.

CLEAR the register by applying a negative clock pulse to pin 13. By negative clock pulse, we mean that you should momentarily ground pin 13, then return it to logic 1. Now apply a CLOCK pulse at pin 11. You should again observe that only lamp monitors A and H light up.

If you have correctly followed these procedures, you have demonstrated how to parallel load the 74198 shift register and how to clear the outputs.

Step 3

Now try the shift left operation. Parallel load HGFEDCBA = 10000001 into the shift register. Now set $S_0 = 0$ (leave S_1 at logic 1). If the shift register is wired correctly, and if you have grounded the proper mode input, then you should observe, on clocking the register, that data moves from Q_H toward Q_A. We recommend that you set pins 2 and 22 both at logic 0 so that in this and the following step only a single bit will travel across the register.

Make certain that you have grounded the proper mode input. Apply seven or eight clock pulses to the 74198 shift register and watch a single data bit travel from Q_H to Q_A.

Step 4

Now try the shift right operation. Set pin 2 to logic 0. Set $S_0 = 1$ and $S_1 = 1$ and parallel load HGFEDCBA = 10000001 into the shift register. Now return S_1 to a logic 0 state. Apply eight clock pulses at pin 11. You should observe a single data bit move from Q_A to Q_H and then out of the register.

Step 5

Set $S_0 = S_1 = 0$ and apply clock pulses while changing the parallel load inputs or the serial inputs. You should observe that nothing happens. The CLOCK input is inhibited by an $S_0 = S_1 = 0$ combination of mode input settings.

Step 6

The shift right and shift left serial inputs can be changed after each clock pulse when you are entering serial data into the shift register. Now that you understand how to parallel load, clear, and serial load the shift register, try various operations and demonstrate to yourself that you fully understand how the shift register operates.

Question

1. A radio transmitter transmits radio waves into the air that are received by individual stations called "radios," which are located in homes, offices, cars, etc. A television transmitter functions similarly. A television signal can also be transmitted over wire, as is the case in "cable tv." What would a digital data transmitter do? Could it function both over the air and over wires?

EXPERIMENT NO. 7

Purpose

The purpose of this experiment is to construct a transmitter and receiver that can interchange serial digital data. A pair of 74194 4-bit universal shift registers will be used. This is a simple but extremely interesting experiment, and we encourage you to perform it.

Pin Configuration of Integrated Circuit (Fig. 10-43)

Fig. 10-43.

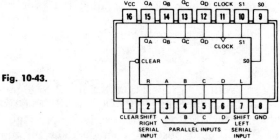

74194

Block Diagram of Integrated Circuit (Fig. 10-44)

We provide you with a block diagram in Fig. 10-44 of the 74194 in order to help you understand the significance of "shift left" and "shift right" operation. Note the shift left serial input at pin 7 and the shift right serial input at pin 2. The D flip-flop is on the far right.

functional block diagrams

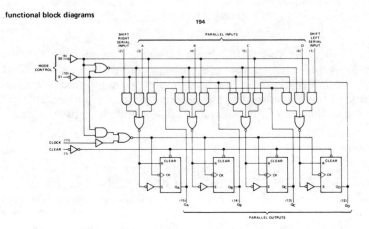

Fig. 10-44.

Schematic Diagram of Circuit (Fig. 10-45)

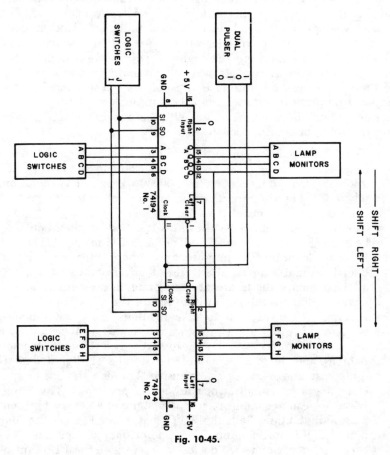

Fig. 10-45.

Discussion of Experiment

In some respects, it is difficult to appreciate the value of digital electronics when you only work with gates and flip-flops. The utility of digital electronic techniques becomes apparent only when you try to do something difficult, such as transmit data from an orbit in the vicinity of Venus, Mars, or Jupiter. It is not feasible to send the information via ultra-thin wires attached to the various space probes, so instead you use the concept of *telemetry* to transmit the data to earth. This same technique, of course, brings you am radio stations, fm radio stations, and television, all of which are transmitted via antennas and high-frequency electromagnetic radiation from a central transmitter to your home. The transmission of data over millions of miles is rather difficult to accomplish, and electrical engineers have found that such data can be transmitted much more reliably if it is sent in digital rather than *analog* form.

Let us consider a typical instrument—a radiation detector, magnetic field analyzer, or particle counter—present in a space probe. The electrical output from the highly expensive and miniaturized instrument frequently consists of a voltage that varies as a function of time and whose magnitude is in some way proportional to the physical property being measured, i.e., an analog electrical signal. Let us now inquire what may happen to this analog voltage in order to prepare it for transmission to earth.

- The voltage may be converted into digital form through the use of an *analog-to-digital converter*. For example, a signal of 257 millivolts may be encoded as 100000001 in binary notation, where it is kept in mind that the number refers to voltage that is measured in terms of mV.

- The instrument reading varies as a function of time, and may be any value between 0 mV and, perhaps, 511 mV, or 111111111 in binary notation. The important point here is that such digital data is available in parallel form at any instant of time, i.e., all nine binary digits are at logic states characteristic of the analog voltage at almost any instant of time.

- Assuming that we wish to take readings every ten minutes, we must have the ability to store the analog voltage until we are ready to transmit such data to earth. The storage of analog data is quite inconvenient, but the storage of digital data is quite easy and relatively inexpensive. Through the use of special integrated circuits, such as *first-in first-out* (FIFO) registers, we can accomplish such data storage. At every ten minutes, a digital pulse tells the FIFO that it should store the nine bits of digital information. This type of data storage may proceed for hours before we decide to interrogate the FIFO memory and ask it to read back the data that it has stored. To the best of our knowledge, FIFO memories are not used in space probes, but they do illustrate the importance of periodic data acquisition and storage.

- Finally, a pulse is transmitted *from* earth that signals the space probe to transmit certain information back to earth. The electronic circuitry on the space probe must convert the stored data into a series of logic 0 and logic 1 states, which are telemetered to earth as a sequence of "boops" and "beeps." In other words, *the data is transmitted serially!*

Our purpose in describing one possible operation of a space probe is to sensitize you to the distinction between *serial* and *parallel* data

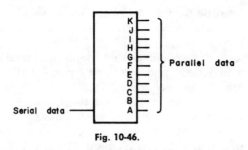

Fig. 10-46.

transmission. According to the Oxford English Dictionary, the term, *transmission*, is defined as conveyance or passage through a medium, as of light, heat, sound, etc. In our case, we are concerned with the "conveyance" of a digital electronic signal from one point to another. As shown in Figs. 10-47 and 10-48, this conveyance can occur either serially or in parallel fashion. For example, if we assume that the logic states at pins A through K on the digital device shown in

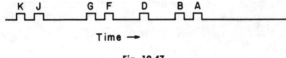

Time →

Fig. 10-47.

Fig. 10-46 are ABCDEFGHIJK = 11010110011, it is possible, by applying a single clock pulse to the digital chip, to transmit all eleven bits of information simultaneously, i.e., in parallel, to some other digital device or perhaps to a computer. The data transmission can occur, in some instances, in less than 1 microsecond.

The same thing cannot be said for the serial data input pin to the device. In order to transmit the 11-bit word ABCDEFGHIJK = 11010110011 serially, it will require eleven clock pulses and a time that is eleven times as long as for parallel data transmission. The

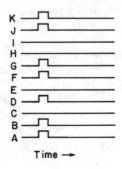

Time →

Fig. 10-48.

serial input into the device would appear as shown in Fig. 4-47 in contrast to the parallel output from the device as represented in Fig. 10-48.

At first glance, it may appear that the use of serial data transmission is rather inefficient and inferior to parallel data transmission. In certain applications, such a conclusion is correct. But in many applications, especially in research laboratories, super-fast data transmission rates are not required and one can easily tolerate the fact that serial data transmission takes 25 to 100 times longer than parallel data transmission. The point here is that copper wire is quite expensive: a 100-conductor wire might cost $1.00 per linear foot, as compared to perhaps $0.03 per linear foot for a shielded twisted-pair cable. If one has to transmit data over a distance of a mile, it would cost $5280 to transmit such data over a 100-conductor cable but only $150 to do the same thing over a two-conductor cable. If super-fast data transmission speeds are not needed, it is rather foolish to spend more money for the cable than for the electronic instrumentation. We could continue this discussion, but suffice to say that there are legitimate reasons why one would want to transmit digital data in serial manner. In this experiment, you will construct a simple circuit that permits you to transmit digital data serially and *synchronously*. By "synchronous," we mean that both the *transmitter* and the *receiver* are clocked by the same clock signal.

Step 1

Carefully study the schematic diagram in Fig. 10-45. You should already be familiar with the 74194 chip from Experiment No. 5. Depending on the settings of logic switches I and J, either 74194 chip can be a "transmitter" or "receiver." In other words, digital data can be transmitted toward the right or toward the left. If this is a classroom experiment, a pair of students may have to team up in order to provide a sufficient number of lamp monitors and logic switches. In a pinch, keep in mind that a wire connected to +5 volts is a convenient logic 1 state and a wire connected to ground is a convenient logic 0 state.

One connection is particularly important, that between the CLOCK pulser and pin 11 on the two 74194 chips. *This connection must be to the "1" output of the pulser, so that the resting state of the pulser when it is not pressed is a logic 1.* Only with a logic state of 1 applied to the two clock inputs will you be able to change the S_0 and S_1 logic switches (I and J) without causing any changes in the two shift registers. If pin 11 is at logic 0, we have observed that changing S_0 and S_1 to logic 0 creates one or more clock pulses that clear or partially clear the registers.

Step 2

Wire the circuit shown. Apply power to the breadboard. Clear the shift registers by pressing and releasing the CLEAR pulser. All eight lamp monitors should be unlit.

Set logic switches I and J to IJ = 11 and logic switches A through H to ABCDEFGH = 11111111. Press and release the CLOCK pulser once. You should observe that all lamp monitors now become lit. You have parallel loaded both shift registers.

Step 3

Clear the shift registers. Note the following:

S_1	S_0	Action
0	0	Clock is inhibited. Nothing happens.
0	1	Data shifts right at each clock pulse.
1	0	Data shifts left at each clock pulse.
1	1	Data is parallel loaded into the shift registers.

Now perform the following procedure:

- Parallel load the binary word ABCDEFGH = 10000000 into the shift registers. Only a single lamp monitor should become lit, that for output Q_A. You will have to set logic switches IJ to 11 to parallel load the word.
- Set logic switches I and J to IJ = 10, corresponding to shift right operation.
- Press and release the clock pulser eight times. You should observe that a single logic 1 bit shifts right through 74194 chip No. 1 and then is transmitted to 74194 chip No. 2, where it shifts right and out of the register. If you observed this result, then you have successfully transmitted data from the "transmitter" (74194 chip No. 1) to the "receiver" (74194 chip No. 2).

Step 4

Clear the registers by setting IJ = 00 and pressing and releasing the CLOCK pulser. Return the logic switches I and J to IJ = 11 and load the word ABCDEFGH = 00000001 into the shift registers. Remember, to load data you must press and release the CLOCK pulser once.

Now set logic switches I and J to IJ = 01, corresponding to shift left operation. Press and release the CLOCK pulser eight times. You should observe that the single logic 1 bit is now transmitted from the 74194 chip No. 2 to the 74194 chip No. 1 and then out of chip No. 1.

You may now wish to "play" with this circuit by transmitting and receiving different 4-bit binary words. Keep in mind that once a

4-bit word is parallel loaded into the transmitter, *four clock pulses are required to transmit the entire word into the receiver. Four additional clock pulses are required to transmit the entire word out of the receiver in a serial manner.*

Question

1. What 4-bit binary word was transmitted in Step 3 above? What 4-bit binary word was transmitted in Step 4 above? You can assume that logic switches D and H represent, respectively, the least significant bits of the 4-bit words in 74194 chips No. 1 and No. 2.

EXPERIMENT NO. 8

Purpose

The purpose of this experiment is to demonstrate the operation of the 74193 synchronous 4-bit up/down counter.

Pin Configuration of Integrated Circuit (Fig. 10-49)

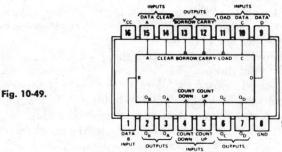

Fig. 10-49.

74192, 74193

Schematic Diagram of Circuit (Fig. 10-50)

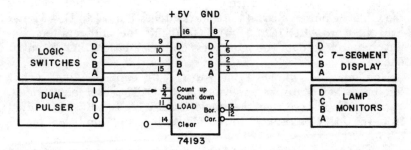

Fig. 10-50.

Step 1

Wire the circuit shown in Fig. 10-50. Apply power to the bread-board. Clear the counter and display by touching the wire at pin 14, the CLEAR input, to a logic 1 state, then return pin 14 to a logic 0 state. The seven-segment LED display should now show a decimal 0. Lamp monitors A and B should both be lit. *When pin 4 is used as the clock input, pin 5 must be disabled by connecting it to a logic 1 state. When pin 5 is used as the clock input, pin 4 must be disabled by connecting it to a logic 1 state.*

Step 2

Set the logic switches to DCBA = 0111. Press and release the LOAD pulser. You should now observe a decimal 7 on the seven-segment display. You have just parallel loaded the counter.

Set the logic switches DCBA to 0011. Press and release the LOAD pulser once more. What decimal numeral appears on the seven-segment display?

Load the following 4-bit words into the counter and write down in the truth table the numeral that appears on the display:

D	C	B	A	Decimal Numeral
0	1	1	1	7
0	0	1	1	
0	0	0	1	
1	0	0	1	
1	0	0	1	
0	1	1	0	
0	1	0	1	
1	1	0	0	
1	1	1	0	
1	1	0	1	
1	1	1	1	
0	1	0	0	
0	0	1	0	

You should convince yourself that you can load any 4-bit binary word between 0000 and 1111 into the 74193 counter.

Step 3

Load DCBA = 0111 into the counter. Connect the CLOCK pulser to pin 5 on the 74193 and a logic 1 to pin 4. You now will be able to count "up" each time you press and release the CLOCK pulser. Press and release the pulser several times and verify that such is the case.

Now connect the CLOCK pulser to pin 4 on the 74193 and a logic 1 to pin 5. Load DCBA = 0111. Press and release the CLOCK pulser several times and observe that you are now counting downwards.

Try loading different binary words into the counter and counting both upwards and downwards. You should observe that the 74193 chip is considerably more powerful than the 7493 binary counter.

Step 4

Your next task is to understand what the BORROW and CARRY outputs at pins 13 and 12, respectively, do. Set the logic switches DCBA to 0000 and load decimal 0 into the counter. Connect the CLOCK pulser to pin 5, corresponding to an upward count. Now repeatedly press and release the CLOCK pulser until you observe that the CARRY output at lamp monitor A goes to logic 0. Between what two readings on the LED display does lamp monitor A go to a logic 0 state?

If you performed this experiment correctly, you should have observed that lamp monitor A becomes a logic 0 during the transition from a blank display to a decimal 0. On the basis of this observation, explain in the following space why we call this output a CARRY output.

A single pulse is generated when there is a "carry" to the next most significant digit. This pulse can be applied to a second 74193 counter in a cascaded counter circuit.

Step 5

Set the logic switches DCBA to 1111 and load the equivalent of decimal 15 (a blank display) into the counter. Connect the CLOCK pulser to pin 4, corresponding to a downward count. Now repeatedly press and release the CLOCK pulser until you observe that the BORROW output at lamp monitor B becomes logic 0. Between what two readings on the LED display does lamp monitor B go to logic 0?

In the following space explain why pin 13 on the 74193 chip is called a BORROW output.

A single pulse is generated when there is a "borrow" from the next least significant digit. This pulse can be applied to a second 74193 counter in a cascaded counter circuit.

Question

1. In Chapter 5, you constructed programmable sequencers using 7490 and 7442 chips. In the following space, draw a circuit for a programmable sequencer using a 74193 chip and one or more suitably chosen 7400-series chip(s).

WHAT HAVE YOU ACCOMPLISHED IN THIS CHAPTER?

Review of Objectives

We have stated in the Introduction to this chapter that when finished you would be able to do the following:

- Define shift register. The definition has been provided early in the chapter.

- List the different types of shift registers that are available and describe their individual characteristics. Static and dynamic shift registers, as well as SIPO, PISO, SISO, PIPO, and universal shift registers have all been discussed in the chapter.

- Define the following terms associated with integrated-circuit counters: modulo, weighting, count direction, synchronism, presettability, and unit cascadability. All of these definitions have been provided in the section on counters.

- Define Schmitt trigger. The definition has been provided in the text.

- List the Boolean algebra symbols for logical addition, logical multiplication, and negation. The symbols have been provided in the text. Examples of their use have been given in Fig. 10-26.

- Describe the functions of an arithmetic/logic unit integrated circuit, such as the 74181. The 74181 has been described in the text; you also performed an experiment using it.

- Test simple arithmetic/logic integrated circuits such as the 7483 and 74181. You have done this in Experiment Nos. 1 and 2.

- Construct a synchronous receiver/transmitter circuit from a pair of 74194 integrated circuits. You have done this in Experiment No. 7 in this chapter.

References

BOOKS

1. Rudolf G. Graf, *Modern Dictionary of Electronics*, Howard W. Sams & Co., Inc., Indianapolis, Indiana 46268, 1972.
2. J. Blukis and M. Baker, *Practical Digital Electronics*, Hewlett-Packard Company, 5301 Stevens Creek Blvd., Santa Clara, California 95050, 1974.
3. M. Bird and R. Schmidt, *Practical Digital Electronics: Laboratory Workbook*, Hewlett-Packard Company, Santa Clara, California 95050, 1974.
4. H. V. Malmstadt and C. G. Enke, *Digital Electronics for Scientists*, W. A. Benjamin, Inc., New York, New York 10022, 1969.
5. H. V. Malmstadt, C. G. Enke, and S. R. Crouch, *Instrumentation for Scientists Series*, W. A. Benjamin, Inc., New York, New York 10022, 1973 and 1974.
6. D. E. Lancaster, *TTL Cookbook*, Howard W. Sams & Co., Inc., Indianapolis, Indiana 46268, 1974.
7. A. James Diefenderfer, *Principles of Electronics Instrumentation*, W. B. Saunders Company, Philadelphia, Pennsylvania, 19105, 1972.
8. J. D. Lenk, *Handbook of Logic Circuits*, Reston Publishing Company, Inc., Reston, Virginia, 22070, 1972.
9. F. M. Mims, III, *LED Circuits & Projects*, Howard W. Sams & Co., Inc., Indianapolis, Indiana 46268, 1973.

PERIODICALS

If you would like to maintain a continuing awareness of new advances in digital electronics, or in the field of electronics in general, you will most likely be interested in one or more of the following periodicals.

Electronics, McGraw-Hill Publishing Co., 1221 Avenue of the Americas, New York, New York 10020.

Electronics Design, 50 Essex Street, Rochelle Park, New York 07662.

Computer Design, Circulation Department, Box A, Winchester, Massachusetts 01890.

Kilobaud, 1001001 Inc., Peterborough, New Hampshire 03458.

Radio-Electronics, Gernsback Publications, Inc., 200 Park Avenue South, New York, New York 10003.

Ham Radio Magazine, Communication Technology, Inc., Greenville, New Hampshire 03048.

THE BASIC L/R OUTBOARDS®

GENERAL INSTRUCTIONS

1. The LR Outboards are designed in such a manner that, when inserted into the SK-10 socket, as shown, the outer terminal strip should be connected to power and the inside terminal strip should be connected to ground.

2. Outboards come packed in bags with the components loose. The pins are premounted due to installation difficulty. Please check that all components are there. Report any shortages to E & L Kit Department with the packing slip.

3. Do not use acid core solder - this voids all warranties; do not use a soldering iron over 35 watts or excessive heat may damage the components. Do not use excess amounts of solder or you will "bridge" the circuits.

4. Always observe the polarity signs when applicable. On L.E.D.'s, the negative (cathode) lead is indicated by a flat or a notch in the flange. On the transistors make certain the lead pattern coincides with the board - do not force them in. When an IC is inserted into a socket, make certain that it is properly oriented. Pin #1 is represented by a dot or the Pin #1 end is notched.

5. Make certain that all solder joints are clipped off cleanly, very close to the circuit board so the Outboard will lay flat on the socket once it is installed.

SPECIAL NOTE: Although the Breadboarding Pins (both BP-25's and BP-26"s) are factory installed, they do require soldering by the kit builder. See below.

BP-26 Breadboarding Pins

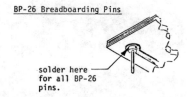

solder here for all BP-26 pins.

BP-25 Breadboarding Pins

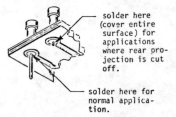

solder here (cover entire surface) for applications where rear projection is cut off.

solder here for normal application.

Courtesy E & L Instruments, Inc.

LR-1 POWER OUTBOARD ®

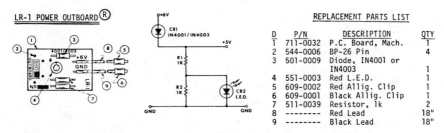

REPLACEMENT PARTS LIST

D	P/N	DESCRIPTION	QTY
1	711-0032	P.C. Board, Mach.	1
2	544-0006	BP-26 Pin	4
3	501-0009	Diode, IN4001 or IN4003	1
4	551-0003	Red L.E.D.	1
5	609-0002	Red Allig. Clip	1
6	609-0001	Black Allig. Clip	1
7	511-0039	Resistor, 1k	2
8	--------	Red Lead	18"
9	--------	Black Lead	18"

The LR-1 is used when operating the SK-10/Outboard System from a 6V battery. It will quickly and easily supply power to a quarter, a half or the whole of the SK-10 socket. The light emitting diode (LED) on the outboard will give a positive indication of power on but will remain unlit if the alligator clips, supplied with the board, are connected to the wrong battery or terminals. The LED will be only dimly lit if the battery voltage is low. CRI insures that if power is connected backwards no damage will occur to the components.

Specifications:
Polarity reversal protected
Indicator Light - LED
Lead Lengths - 18" - Terminated in Alligator Clips

SPECIFIC INSTRUCTIONS

Make certain that the leads going to the battery are put on last and they are "strain relieved" in accordance with the drawing (ie. dressed thru the circuit board before soldering).

LR-2 LOGIC SWITCH OUTBOARD ®

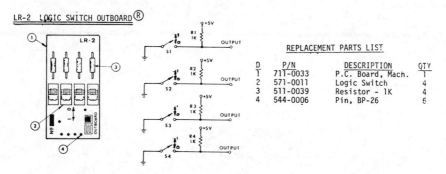

REPLACEMENT PARTS LIST

D	P/N	DESCRIPTION	QTY
1	711-0033	P.C. Board, Mach.	1
2	571-0011	Logic Switch	4
3	511-0039	Resistor - 1K	4
4	544-0006	Pin, BP-26	6

The LR-2 provides four logic switches that switch between GROUND potential (logic 0) and +5 volts (logic 1).

Specifications:
4 Logic Switches - SPDT - rated 1/2 Amp @125V
4 "Pull up" Resistors

Courtesy E & L Instruments, Inc.

LR-4 SEVEN-SEGMENT DISPLAY WITH DECODER/DRIVER ®

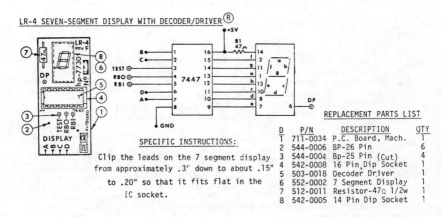

SPECIFIC INSTRUCTIONS:

Clip the leads on the 7 segment display from approximately .3" down to about .15" to .20" so that it fits flat in the IC socket.

REPLACEMENT PARTS LIST

D	P/N	DESCRIPTION	QTY
1	711-0034	P.C. Board, Mach.	1
2	544-0006	BP-26 Pin	6
3	544-0004	Bp-25 Pin (Cut)	4
4	542-0008	16 Pin Dip Socket	1
5	503-0018	Decoder Driver	1
6	552-0002	7 Segment Display	1
7	512-0011	Resistor-47Ω 1/2w	1
8	542-0005	14 Pin Dip Socket	1

The LR-4 contains a seven-segment LED display and a 7447 BCD-to-seven-segment decoder/driver integrated circuit chip. The four inputs A, B, C, D, are used to generate 0 through 9, five symbols, and a blank condition. These are four input jacks (BP-25 Breadboarding Pins); the Blanking Input (RBI), the Blanking Output (RBO) the Lamp Test (TEST) and the decimal point (dp).

Specifications:
Input: BCD, TTL input (5 volts nominal)
Output: LED, 7 Segment display
Current Max: 140 ma.
Miscellaneous: 4 BP-25's - solderless
independent connections to Lamp Test, Blanking Output, Blanking Input and decimal point.
IC and 7 segment display are mounted in IC sockets allowing replacement without soldering.

LR-5 CLOCK OUTBOARD ®

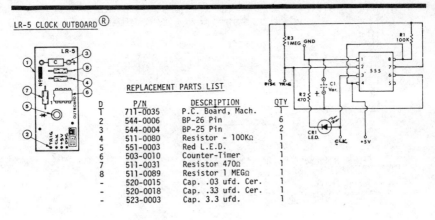

REPLACEMENT PARTS LIST

D	P/N	DESCRIPTION	QTY
1	711-0035	P.C. Board, Mach.	1
2	544-0006	BP-26 Pin	6
3	544-0004	BP-25 Pin	2
4	511-0080	Resistor - 100KΩ	1
5	551-0003	Red L.E.D.	1
6	503-0010	Counter-Timer	1
7	511-0031	Resistor 470Ω	1
8	511-0089	Resistor 1 MEGΩ	1
-	520-0015	Cap. .03 ufd. Cer.	1
-	520-0018	Cap. .33 ufd. Cer.	1
-	523-0003	Cap. 3.3 ufd.	1

Courtesy E & L Instruments, Inc.

The LR-5 generates a sequence of clock pulses, called a "train of clock pulses" whose frequency depends on the value of the timing capacitor. The frequency is generated with the aid of a 555 integrated circuit timer, three resistors, and the timing capacitor. The timing capacitor is connected through solderless terminals (BP-25 Breadboarding Pins) and three values are supplied with the board. An on-board light emitting diode (LED) gives a visual indication that the clock is operating properly. With external components ac   the full range of the outboard is 300 KHz to 1 MHz. The clock output pin is labeled CLK.

Specifications:
Clock: Frequency adjustable from .1 to 20kHz. for a capacitance range of 5 pf to 100 mfd.
Three capacitors are supplied with the LR-5
Miscellaneous: Indicator Light - L.E.D.
Current (Max): 20 ma.

SPECIFIC INSTRUCTIONS:

No IC socket is used here, the NE555 is directly soldered into the circuit board. DO NOT use excessive heat. Note that no "fixed" component goes in the space shown as "C" . . . the various size capacitors plug in here when the circuit is installed on the socket.

LR-6 LED LAMP MONITOR OUTBOARD ®

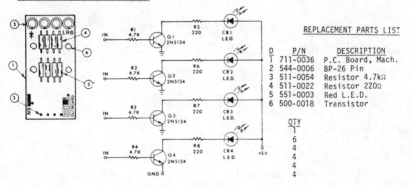

REPLACEMENT PARTS LIST

D	P/N	DESCRIPTION
1	711-0036	P.C. Board, Mach.
2	544-0006	BP-26 Pin
3	511-0054	Resistor 4.7kΩ
4	511-0022	Resistor 220Ω
5	551-0003	Red L.E.D.
6	500-0018	Transistor

QTY
1
6
4
4
4
4

The LR-6 is used for a display for binary digital signals. The light emitting diodes (LEDs) are lit at logic "1" and unlit at logic "0". Transistor lamp drivers are used to reduce current to each LED.

Specifications:
4 logic lights - LED indicators
On at logic state 1 (greater than 2.5 volts)
Off at logic state 0 (less than .5 volts)
Input impedance 4,700 ohms
Current max: 8 ma.

LR-7 DUAL PULSER OUTBOARD ®

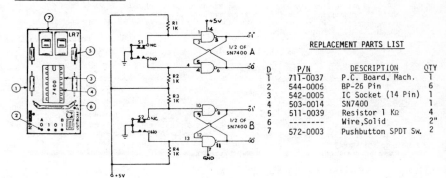

The LR-7 has been designed to eliminate "contact bounce". i.e., the uncontrolled making and breaking of contact when switch contacts are opened or closed. It uses four 2-input NAND gates in a 7400 integrated circuit chip to produce a pair of "debounced" pulsers. This facilitates the LR-7's use in flip-flops, counters, counter circuits, memories, shift registers, and related digital circuits that require clock signals. Complementary "0" and "1" outputs are provided for each pulser by simply pushing the plastic button in, NOT DOWN, using a finernail, small screwdriver, ballpoint pen, etc.

Specifications:
2 minature "spring loaded" switches - electrically debounced
Outputs: 2 each switch: one normally "zero", one normally "one"
Outputs reverse on switching
Current Max: 20 ma.

SPECIFIC INSTRUCTIONS:

Make certain the indicated insulated jumpers are installed: also make sure you solder the switches in completely, including the two tabs on each where they come thru the circuit board.

The preceeding pages include the necessary, information for Outboards LR-1 through LR-7. You will need this information to do the bulk of the experiments contained in these Bugbooks. There are a few experiments that contain the LR-25 through LR-28. The necessary schematics are available through your local representative or direct from the factory. The Outboards themselves may be purchased from your local representative or the nearest computer store in your area.

Courtesy E & L Instruments, Inc.

Index